Speak of the Devil

EDITED BY STERLING NORTH
& C. B. BOUTELL

Speak of the Devil

GARDEN CITY, NEW YORK

DOUBLEDAY, DORAN & COMPANY, INC.   1945

ACKNOWLEDGMENTS

THANKS are due the following authors, agents, and publishers for permission to reprint the selections indicated:

Brandt & Brandt—for "The Litanies of Satan," from *Flowers of Evil,* copyright, 1936, by George Dillon and Edna St. Vincent Millay, published by Harper & Brothers, New York, and Hamish Hamilton, London; "Enoch Soames," from *Seven Men,* by Max Beerbohm, copyright, 1920, published by Alfred A. Knopf, Inc.; and "The Devil and Daniel Webster," by Stephen Vincent Benét, copyright, 1926, published by Farrar & Rinehart, Inc.

Jacques Chambrun, Inc.—for "Satan and Sam Shay," by Robert Arthur, special permission from *The Elks Magazine.*

Constable and Company, Ltd.—for "The Devil in a Nunnery," by Francis Oscar Mann.

Doubleday, Doran & Company, Inc.—for "Ghost Story," from *The Story of Gösta Berling,* by Selma Lagerlöf.

Alfred A. Knopf, Inc.—for a selection from *Faust,* by Johann Wolfgang von Goethe, translated by George Madison Priest, copyright, 1941, by Alfred A. Knopf, Inc.

John Lane the Bodley Head Limited—for a selection from *The Revolt of the Angels,* by Anatole France, translated by Mrs. Wilfrid Jackson; and "The Demon Pope," from *The Twilight of the Gods,* by Richard Garnett.

The Macmillan Company—for selections from *The Screwtape Letters,* by C. S. Lewis, published in England by Geoffrey Bles, Ltd.; and "The Devil and the Old Man," from *A Mainsail Haul,* by John Masefield.

Harold Matson—for "Bottle Party," "Thus I Refute Beelzy," and

"The Devil, George, and Rosie," from *Presenting Moonshine,* by John Collier.

Dr. Chapman J. Milling—for his story "Balaam Foster's Fiddle."

Charles Scribner's Sons—for "The Devil and the Innkeeper," by Robert Louis Stevenson, with special permission from The Society of Authors, Literary Representatives of Mr. Lloyd Osbourne.

FOREWORD

THE PROBLEM of good and evil, of God and the Devil, has as many facets as civilization itself, and the approaches to it are legion.

In this anthology of the appearances of the Devil in the literature of the Western world, the editors have been guided by two major considerations: readability in terms of the current taste and a sociological rather than a theological view of the Devil.

There are many gaps in the career of the anthropomorphic Prince of Evil as he appears here, but the full story would be a virtual history of mankind. The intention has been to include stories which are representative of the Devil in various cultures and to give the reader a taste of his local origins in the sectional introductions, briefly tracing at least some of the threads and symbols which have been woven into the hellish pattern.

It seemed advisable, also, to avoid the various hierarchies of the nether world and to consider all devils, whenever possible, as more or less representative of Satan himself, avoiding the confusion of assigning different personalities and characteristics to such assorted minions as Belphegor, Asmodeus, and Beelzebub.

The history of the Devil has been recorded by numerous scholars, and the editors would be ungrateful not to acknowledge their debt to the research of such men as Albert Reville, Maximilian J. Rudwin, Charles Mackay, Montague Summers, and Paul Carus. They also wish to express their thanks to Edwin Halbmeier for his invaluable assistance in tracking down many an obscure reference and in checking endless dry volumes at the library.

STERLING NORTH
CLIP BOUTELL

New York, December 15, 1944

vii

CONTENTS

Speak of the Devil

THE SMELL OF SULPHUR

Do NOT throw your inkpot at the Devil as Martin Luther did in a moment of ill-considered fury.

He has come to help you with the manuscript. Perhaps you thought it was only the wind rustling the pages. It was in fact the Prince of Literary Critics.

It was no accident that a few of your notes, just now, were blown by a chill gust into the open fire beyond the hearth or that they burned with a brilliant flash of red and yellow. The Diabolical Censor who edits the second most famous Index was offering you a prepublication warning.

The Devil, being a creative fellow, is fascinated by the arts.

He haunts cafés and garrets. Piles the saucers high at the Rotund and the Dome. He is often to be seen in Grub Street, Bloomsbury, or in New York's Greenwich Village, listening with a sly leer to lyric poets reciting their verses with rapt ecstasy.

He is less interested in the poet's couplets, variations of which he has heard since the days of the minor Elizabethans, than in the soul of the artist—the disgruntled, aching, and unfulfilled soul almost ripe for the Satanic Contract.

In this introductory section entitled "The Smell of Sulphur," Max Beerbohm has captured for all time, as an insect in amber, the fatal flaw in character which leads the artist to sell his soul. He knows with William Makepeace Thackeray and Anatole France that not a living artist can resist the Devil's tempting offer of fame and recognition.

And he is well aware that the Devil's nimble fingers can make a canvas gleam with strange luminosity; can run a Devil's trill on the violin as he did for Giuseppe Tartini (circa 1713); can hypnotize a critical world; can charm the savage breast and bolster the waning bank account.

What artist would refuse to pay this Pied Piper his pittance? All that he asks is eternal keeping of the artist's already tortured soul.

That the Devil has always been an accomplished musician is once again proved by Oscar Mann in his haunting story *The Devil in a Nunnery*. Here we have no Balzacian "droll story," no cynical and satirical account of monkish immorality and naughty nuns, but rather the sweet confusion which the Devil's music inspires in the breasts of women who might have walked the earth in spring with mortal lovers but who instead have chosen the veil.

Certainly the Evil One is doubly fascinated by his assignment in such a story. He has an audience for his recital—and that audience is composed of the saintlike ascetics who have always challenged his power. It is curious to discover how often this Fallen Angel seeks the association of hermits and friars, nuns and mothers superior—often at the very moment when they are counting their beads.

There is always the possibility that the Devil has inspired these accounts of his audacity—to further confound an already agnostic world. Certainly he guided the hand of Baudelaire in *The Litanies of Satan* as well as in most of his other poems and stories. Undoubtedly when *Definitive Criticism of the Decadent Movement Volume VII* comes fresh off the presses of Hell we will learn that Satan first introduced Poe's work to Baudelaire, who in turn may have inspired Huysmans to write *La Bas*, thus captivating the sultry imaginations of Oscar Wilde, Aubrey Beardsley, and the Yellow Book Boys.

How much simpler literary criticism becomes when we learn the secret of going to our Satanic sources.

Of the Basque legend in this volume we can only say that Spanish devils before El Greco and Goya were strangely lacking in cultural attributes—filled with fear and superstition, and capable of being tricked by wife, mother-in-law, or mere apothecary. But Spain has always been a backward country.

Bret Harte—far from dissolute European sources—still saw the Devil as an artist with fly rod and cunningly tied lures. While John Collier—whose own imagination is strangely diabolical—makes Beelzy the very antithesis of stolid Philistia.

The moral of this Satanic Sampler is simple to unravel. Taking the modern view, it is obvious that Satan is in league with creative mankind—even anthologists.

ENOCH SOAMES

Max Beerbohm

WHEN a book about the literature of the 1890s was given by Mr. Holbrook Jackson to the world, I looked eagerly in the index for SOAMES, ENOCH. I had feared he would not be there. He was not there. But everybody else was. Many writers whom I had quite forgotten, or remembered but faintly, lived again for me, they and their work, in Mr. Holbrook Jackson's pages. The book was as thorough as it was brilliantly written. And thus the omission found by me was an all the deadlier record of poor Soames's failure to impress himself on his decade.

I dare say I am the only person who noticed the omission. Soames had failed so piteously as all that! Nor is there a counterpoise in the thought that if he had had some measure of success he might have passed, like those others, out of my mind, to return only at the historian's beck. It is true that had his gifts, such as they were, been acknowledged in his lifetime, he would never have made the bargain I saw him make—that strange bargain whose results have kept him always in the foreground of my memory. But it is from those very results that the full piteousness of him glares out.

Not my compassion, however, impels me to write of him. For his sake, poor fellow, I should be inclined to keep my pen out of the ink. It is ill to deride the dead. And how can I write about Enoch Soames without making him ridiculous? Or rather, how am I to hush up the horrid fact that he was ridiculous? I shall not be able to do that. Yet, sooner or later, write about him I must. You will see, in due course, that I have no option. And I may as well get the thing done now.

In the summer term of '93 a bolt from the blue flashed down on Oxford. It drove deep; it hurtlingly embedded itself in the soil. Dons and undergraduates stood around, rather pale, discussing nothing but it. Whence came it, this meteorite? From Paris. Its name? Will Rothenstein. Its aim? To do a series of twenty-four portraits in lithograph. These were to be published from the Bodley Head, London. The matter was urgent. Already the Warden of A, and the Master of B, and the Regius Professor of C had meekly "sat." Dignified and doddering old men, who had never consented to sit to anyone, could not withstand this dynamic little stranger. He did not sue: he invited; he did not invite: he commanded. He was twenty-one years old. He wore spectacles that flashed more than any other pair ever seen. He was a wit. He was brimful of ideas. He knew Whistler. He knew Edmond de Goncourt. He knew everyone in Paris. He knew them all by heart. He was Paris in Oxford. It was whispered about, so soon as he had polished off his selection of dons, he was going to include a few undergraduates. It was a proud day for me when I—I was included. I liked Rothenstein not less than I feared him; and there arose between us a friendship that has grown ever warmer, and been more and more valued by me, with every passing year.

At the end of term he settled in—or, rather meteorically, into—London. It was to him I owed my first knowledge of that forever-enchanting little world-in-itself Chelsea, and my first acquaintance with Walter Sickert and other august elders who dwelt there. It was Rothenstein who took me to see, in Cambridge Street, Pimlico, a young man whose drawings were already famous among the few—Aubrey Beardsley by name. With Rothenstein I paid my first visit to the Bodley Head. By him I was inducted into another haunt of intellect and daring, the domino room of the Café Royal.

There, on that October evening—there, in that exuberant vista of gilding and crimson velvet set amidst all those opposing mirrors and upholding caryatids, with fumes of tobacco ever rising to the painted and pagan ceiling, and with the hum of presumably cynical conversation broken into so sharply now and again by the clatter of dominoes shuffled on marble tables, I drew a deep breath and, "This indeed," said I to myself, "is life."

It was the hour before dinner. We drank vermouth. Those who knew Rothenstein were pointing him out to those who knew him only by name. Men were constantly coming in through the swing doors and wandering slowly up and down in search of vacant tables, or of tables occupied by friends. One of these rovers interested me because I was sure he wanted to catch Rothenstein's eye. He had twice passed our table with a hesitating look, but Rothenstein, in the thick of a disquisition on Puvis de Chavannes, had not seen him. He was a stooping, shambling person, rather tall, very pale, with longish and brownish hair. He had a thin vague beard—or, rather, he had a chin on which a large number of hairs weakly curled and clustered to cover its retreat. He was an odd-looking person, but in the nineties odd apparitions were more frequent, I think, than they are now. The young writers of that era—and I was sure this man was a writer—strove earnestly to be distinct in aspect. This man had striven unsuccessfully. He wore a soft black hat of clerical kind but of bohemian intention and a gray waterproof cape which, perhaps because it was waterproof, failed to be romantic. I decided that "dim" was the *mot juste* for him. I had already essayed to write and was immensely keen on the mot juste, that Holy Grail of the period.

The dim man was now again approaching our table, and this time he made up his mind to pause in front of it. "You don't remember me," he said in a toneless voice.

Rothenstein brightly focused him. "Yes, I do," he replied after a moment, with pride rather than effusion—pride in a retentive memory. "Edwin Soames."

"Enoch Soames," said Enoch.

"Enoch Soames," repeated Rothenstein in a tone implying that it was enough to have hit on the surname. "We met in Paris two or three times when you were living there. We met at the Café Groche."

"And I came to your studio once."

"Oh yes; I was sorry I was out."

"But you were in. You showed me some of your paintings, you know. . . . I hear you're in Chelsea now."

"Yes."

I almost wondered that Mr. Soames did not, after this monosyllable, pass along. He stood patiently there, rather like a dumb animal, rather like a donkey looking over a gate. A sad figure, his. It occurred to me that "hungry" was perhaps the mot juste for him, but—hungry for what? He looked as if he had little appetite for anything. I was sorry for him; and Rothenstein, though he had not invited him to Chelsea, did ask him to sit down and have something to drink.

Seated, he was more self-assertive. He flung back the wings of his cape with a gesture which, had not those wings been waterproof, might have seemed to hurl defiance at things in general. And he ordered an absinthe. *"Je me tiens toujours fidèle,"* he told Rothenstein, *"à la sorcière glauque."*

"It is bad for you," said Rothenstein dryly.

"Nothing is bad for one," answered Soames. *"Dans ce monde il n'y a ni de bien ni de mal."*

"Nothing good and nothing bad? How do you mean?"

"I explained it all in the preface to *Negations*."

"Negations?"

"Yes; I gave you a copy of it."

"Oh yes, of course. But did you explain, for instance, that there was no such thing as bad or good grammar?"

"N-no," said Soames. "Of course in Art there is the good and the evil. But in Life—no." He was rolling a cigarette. He had weak white hands, not well washed, and with finger tips much stained by nicotine. "In Life there are illusions of good and evil, but"—his voice trailed away to a murmur in which the words *"vieux jeu"* and "rococo" were faintly audible. I think he felt he was not doing himself justice and feared that Rothenstein was going to point out fallacies. Anyhow, he cleared his throat and said: *"Parlons d'autre chose."*

It occurs to you that he was a fool? It didn't to me. I was young and had not the clarity of judgment that Rothenstein already had. Soames was quite five or six years older than either of us. Also, he had written a book.

If Rothenstein had not been there I should have revered Soames. Even as it was, I respected him. And I was very near indeed to reverence when he said he had another book coming out soon. I asked if I might ask what kind of book it was to be.

"My poems," he answered. Rothenstein asked if this was to be the title of the book. The poet meditated upon this suggestion but said he rather thought of giving the book no title at all. "If a book is good in itself . . ." he murmured, waving his cigarette.

Rothenstein objected that absence of title might be bad for the sale of a book. "If," he urged, "I went into a bookseller's and said simply: 'Have you got?' or 'Have you a copy of?' how would they know what I wanted?"

"Oh, of course I should have my name on the cover," Soames answered earnestly. "And I rather want," he added, looking hard at Rothenstein, "to have a drawing of myself as frontispiece." Rothenstein admitted that this was a capital idea and mentioned that he was going into the country and would be there for some time. He then looked at his watch, exclaimed at the hour, paid the waiter, and went away with me to dinner. Soames remained at his post of fidelity to the glaucous witch.

"Why were you so determined not to draw him?" I asked.

"Draw him? Him? How can one draw a man who doesn't exist?"

"He is dim," I admitted. But my mot juste fell flat. Rothenstein repeated that Soames was nonexistent.

Still, Soames had written a book. I asked if Rothenstein had read *Negations*. He said he had looked into it. "But," he added crisply, "I don't profess to know anything about writing." A reservation very characteristic of the period! Painters would not then allow that anyone outside their own order had a right to any opinion about painting. This law (graven on the tablets brought down by Whistler from the summit of Fujiyama) imposed certain limitations. If other arts than painting were not utterly unintelligible to all but the men who practiced them, the law tottered—the Monroe Doctrine, as it were, did not hold good. Therefore, no painter would offer an opinion of a book without warning you at any rate that his opinion was worthless. No one is a better judge of literature than Rothenstein, but it wouldn't have done to tell him so in those days, and I knew that I must form an unaided judgment on *Negations*.

Not to buy a book of which I had met the author face to face would have been for me in those days an impossible act of self-denial. When I returned to Oxford for the Christmas term I had duly secured *Negations*. I used to keep it lying carelessly on the table in my room, and whenever a friend took it up and asked what it was about I would say: "Oh, it's rather a remarkable book. It's by a man whom I know." Just "what it was about" I never was able to say. Head or tail was just what I hadn't made of that slim green volume. I found in the preface no clue to the exiguous labyrinth of contents, and in that labyrinth nothing to explain the preface.

"*Lean near to life. Lean very near—nearer.*
"*Life is web, and therein nor warp nor woof is, but web only.*
"*It is for this I am Catholick in church and in thought, yet do let swift Mood weave there what the shuttle of Mood wills.*"

These were the opening phrases of the preface, but those which followed were less easy to understand. Then came "Stark: *A Conte*," about a *midinette* who, so far as I could gather, murdered, or was about to murder, a mannequin. It was rather like a story by Catulle Mendès in which the translator had either skipped or cut out every alternate sentence. Next, a dialogue between Pan and St. Ursula—lacking, I felt, in "snap." Next, some aphorisms (entitled ἀφορίσματα). Throughout, in fact, there was a great variety of form, and the forms had evidently been wrought with much care. It was rather the substance that eluded me. Was there, I wondered, any substance at all? It did not occur to me: suppose Enoch Soames was a fool! Up cropped a rival hypothesis: suppose *I* was! I inclined to give Soames the benefit of the doubt. I had read *L'Après-midi d'un faune* without extracting a glimmer of meaning. Yet Mallarmé, of course, was a Master. How was I to know that Soames wasn't another? There was a sort of music in his prose, not indeed arresting, but perhaps, I thought, haunting, and laden perhaps with meanings as deep as Mallarmé's own. I awaited his poems with an open mind.

And I looked forward to them with positive impatience after I had had a second meeting with him. This was on an evening in January. Going into the aforesaid domino room, I passed a table at which sat a pale man with an open book before him. He looked from his book to me, and I looked back over my shoulder with a vague sense that I ought to have recognized him. I returned to pay my respects. After exchanging a few words I said with a glance to the open book, "I see I am interrupting you," and was about to pass on, but "I prefer," Soames replied in his toneless voice, "to be interrupted," and I obeyed his gesture that I should sit down.

I asked him if he often read here. "Yes, things of this kind I read here," he answered, indicating the title of his book, *The Poems of Shelley*.

"Anything that you really"—and I was going to say "admire?" But I cautiously left my sentence unfinished, and was glad that I had done so, for he said, with unwonted emphasis: "Anything second-rate."

I had read little of Shelley, but "Of course," I murmured, "he's very uneven."

"I should have thought evenness was just what was wrong with him. A deadly evenness. That's why I read him here. The noise of this place breaks the rhythm. He's tolerable here." Soames took up the book and glanced through the pages. He laughed. Soames's laugh was a short, single, and mirthless sound from the throat, unaccompanied by any movement of the face or brightening of the eyes. "What a period!" he uttered, laying the book down. And "What a country!" he added.

I asked rather nervously if he didn't think Keats had more or less held his own against the drawbacks of time and place. He admitted that there were "passages in Keats," but did not specify them. Of "the older men," as he called them, he seemed to like only Milton. "Milton," he said, "wasn't sentimental." Also: "Milton had a dark insight." And again: "I can always read Milton in the reading room."

"The reading room?"

"Of the British Museum. I go there every day."

"You do? I've only been there once. I'm afraid I found it rather a depressing place. It—it seemed to sap one's vitality."

"It does. That's why I go there. The lower one's vitality, the more sensitive one is to great art. I live near the museum. I have rooms in Dyott Street."

"And you go round to the reading room to read Milton?"

"Usually Milton." He looked at me. "It was Milton," he certifically added, "who converted me to Diabolism."

"Diabolism? Oh yes? Really?" said I, with that vague discomfort and that intense desire to be polite which one feels when a man speaks of his own religion. "You—worship the Devil?"

Soames shook his head. "It's not exactly worship," he qualified, sipping his absinthe. "It's more a matter of trusting and encouraging."

"Ah yes. . . . But I had rather gathered from the preface to *Negations* that you were a—a Catholic."

"*Je l'étais à cette époque.* Perhaps I still am. Yes, I'm a Catholic Diabolist."

This profession he made in an almost cursory tone. I could see that what was upmost in his mind was the fact that I had read *Negations*. His pale eyes had for the first time gleamed. I felt as one who is about to be examined, viva voce, on the very subject in which he is shakiest. I hastily asked him how soon his poems were to be published. "Next week," he told me.

"And are they to be published without a title?"

"No. I found a title at last. But I shan't tell you what it is," as though I had been so impertinent as to inquire. "I am not sure that it wholly satisfies me. But it is the best I can find. It suggests something of the quality of the poems. . . . Strange growths, natural and wild, yet exquisite," he added, "and many-hued, and full of poisons."

I asked him what he thought of Baudelaire. He uttered the snort that was his laugh, and "Baudelaire," he said, "was a *bourgeois malgré lui.*" France had only one poet, Villon, "and two thirds of Villon were sheer journalism." Verlaine was "an *épicier malgré lui.*" Altogether, rather to my surprise, he rated French literature lower than English. There were "passages" in Villiers de l'Isle-Adam. But "I," he summed up, "owe nothing to France." He nodded at me. "You'll see," he predicted.

I did not, when the time came, quite see that. I thought the author of *Fungoids* did—unconsciously, of course—owe something to the young Parisian decadents or to the young English ones who owed something to *them*. I still think so. The little book, bought by me in Oxford, lies before me as I write. Its pale gray buckram cover and silver lettering have not worn well. Nor have its contents. Through these, with a melancholy interest, I have again been looking. They are not much. But at the time of their publication I had a vague suspicion that they *might* be. I suppose it is my capacity for faith, not poor Soames's work, that is weaker than it once was. . . .

To a Young Woman

Thou art, who hast not been!
Pale tunes irresolute
And traceries of old sounds
Blown from a rotted flute

Mingle with noise of cymbals rouged with rust,
Nor not strange forms and epicene
Lie bleeding in the dust,
Being wounded with wounds.

For this it is
That in thy counterpart
Of age-long mockeries
Thou hast not been nor art!

There seemed to me a certain inconsistency as between the first and last lines of this. I tried, with bent brows, to resolve the discord. But I did not take my failure as wholly incompatible with a meaning in Soames's mind. Might it not rather indicate the depth of his meaning? As for the craftsmanship, "rouged with rust" seemed to me a fine stroke, and "nor not" instead of "and" had a curious felicity. I wondered who the Young Woman was, and what she had made of it all. I sadly suspect that Soames could not have made more of it than she. Yet, even now, if one doesn't try to make any sense at all of the poem, and reads it just for the sound, there is a certain grace of cadence. Soames was an artist—in so far as he was anything, poor fellow!

It seemed to me, when first I read *Fungoids*, that, oddly enough, the Diabolistic side of him was the best. Diabolism seemed to be a cheerful, even a wholesome, influence in his life.

NOCTURNE

Round and round the shutter'd Square
I stroll'd with the Devil's arm in mine.
No sound but the scrape of his hoofs was there
And the ring of his laughter and mine.
We had drunk black wine.

I scream'd: "I will race you, Master!"
"What matter," he shriek'd, "tonight
Which of us runs the faster?
There is nothing to fear tonight
In the foul moon's light!"

Then I look'd him in the eyes,
And I laugh'd full shrill at the lie he told
And the gnawing fear he would fain disguise.
It was true, what I'd time and again been told:
He was old—old.

There was, I felt, quite a swing about that first stanza—a joyous and rollicking note of comradeship. The second was slightly hysterical perhaps. But I liked the third: it was so bracingly unorthodox, even according to the tenets of Soames's peculiar sect in the faith. Not much "trusting and encouraging" here! Soames triumphantly exposing the Devil as a liar, and laughing "full shrill," cut a quite heartening figure, I thought—then! Now, in the light of what befell, none of his poems depresses me so much as *Nocturne*.

I looked out for what the metropolitan reviewers would have to say. They seemed to fall into two classes: those who had little to say and those who had nothing. The second class was the larger, and the words of the first were cold; insomuch that

Strikes a note of modernity throughout. . . . These tripping numbers.
—Preston *Telegraph*.

was the only lure offered in advertisements by Soames's publisher. I had hopes that when next I met the poet I could congratulate him on having made a stir, for I fancied he was not so sure of his intrinsic greatness as he seemed. I was but able to say, rather coarsely, when next I did see him, that I hoped *Fungoids* was "selling splendidly." He looked at me across his glass of absinthe and asked if I had bought a copy. His publisher had told him that three had been sold. I laughed, as at a jest.

"You don't suppose I *care*, do you?" he said, with something like a snarl. I disclaimed the notion. He added that he was not a tradesman. I said mildly that I wasn't, either, and murmured that an artist who gave truly new and great things to the world had always to wait long for recognition. He said he cared not a sou for recognition. I agreed that the act of creation was its own reward.

His moroseness might have alienated me if I had regarded myself as a nobody. But ah! hadn't both John Lane and Aubrey Beardsley suggested that I should write an essay for the great new venture that was afoot—*The Yellow Book?* And hadn't Henry Harland, as editor, accepted my essay? And wasn't it to be in the very first number? At Oxford I was still in *statu pupillari*. In London I regarded myself as very much indeed a graduate now—one whom no Soames could ruffle. Partly to show off, partly in sheer good will, I told Soames he ought to contribute to *The Yellow Book*. He uttered from the throat a sound of scorn for that publication.

Nevertheless, I did, a day or two later, tentatively ask Harland if he knew anything of the work of a man called Enoch Soames. Harland paused in the midst of his characteristic stride around the room, threw up his hands toward the ceiling, and groaned aloud: he had often met "that absurd creature" in Paris, and this very morning had received some poems in manuscript from him.

"Has he *no* talent?" I asked.

"He has an income. He's all right." Harland was the most joyous of men and most generous of critics, and he hated to talk of anything about which he couldn't be enthusiastic. So I dropped the subject of Soames. The news that Soames had an income did take the edge off solicitude. I learned afterward that he was the son of an unsuccessful and deceased bookseller in Preston but had inherited an annuity of three hundred pounds from a married aunt and had no surviving relatives of any kind. Materially, then, he was "all right." But there was still a spiritual pathos about him, sharpened for me now by the possibility that even the praises of the Preston *Telegraph* might not have been forthcoming had he not been the son of a Preston man. He had a sort of weak doggedness which I could not but admire. Neither he nor his work received the slightest encouragement, but he persisted in behaving as a personage; always he kept his dingy little flag flying. Wherever congregated the *jeunes féroces* of the arts, in whatever Soho restaurant they had just discovered, in whatever music hall they were most frequenting, there was Soames in the midst of them, or, rather, on the fringe of them, a dim but inevitable figure. He never sought to propitiate his fellow writers, never bated a jot of his arrogance about his own work or of his contempt for theirs. To the painters he was respectful, even humble; but for the poets and prosaists of *The Yellow Book,* and later of *The Savoy,* he had never a word but of scorn. He wasn't resented. It didn't occur to anybody that he or his Catholic Diabolism mattered. When, in the autumn of '96, he brought out (at his own expense, this time) a third book, his last book, nobody said a word for or against it. I meant, but forgot, to buy it. I never saw it and am ashamed to say I don't even remember what it was called. But I did, at the time of its publication, say to Rothenstein that I thought poor old Soames was really a rather tragic figure and that I believed he would literally die for want of recognition. Rothenstein scoffed. He said I was trying to get credit for a kind heart which I didn't possess, and perhaps this was so. But at the private view of the New English Art Club, a few weeks later, I beheld a pastel portrait of "Enoch Soames, Esq." It was very like him, and very like Rothenstein to have done it. Soames was standing near it, in his soft hat and his waterproof cape, all through the afternoon. Anybody who knew him would have recognized the portrait at a glance, but nobody who didn't know him would have recognized the portrait from its bystander: it "existed" so much more than he; it was bound to. Also, it had not that expression of faint happiness which on this day was discernible, yes, in Soames's countenance. Fame had breathed on him. Twice again in the course of the month I went to the New English, and on both occasions Soames himself was on view there. Looking back, I regard the close of that exhibition as having been virtually the close of his career. He had felt the breath of Fame against his cheek—so late, for such a little while; and at its withdrawal he gave in, gave up, gave out. He, who had never looked strong or well, looked ghastly now—a shadow of the shade he had once been. He still frequented the domino room, but having lost all wish to excite curiosity, he no longer read books there. "You read only at the museum now?" asked I, with attempted cheerfulness. He said he never went there now. "No absinthe there," he muttered. It was the sort of thing that in the old days he would have said for effect, but it carried conviction now. Absinthe, erst but a point in the "personality" he had striven so hard to build up, was solace and necessity now. He no longer called it "*la sorcière glauque.*" He had shed away all his French phrases. He had become a plain, unvarnished Preston man.

Failure, if it be a plain, unvarnished, complete failure, and even though it be a squalid failure, has always a certain dignity. I avoided Soames because he made me feel rather vulgar. John Lane had published, by this time, two little books of mine, and they had had a pleasant little success of esteem. I was a—slight but definite—"personality." Frank Harris had engaged me to kick up my heels in *The Saturday Review;* Alfred Harmsworth was letting me do likewise in *The Daily Mail.* I was just what Soames wasn't. And he shamed my gloss. Had I known that he really and firmly believed in the greatness of what he as an artist had achieved, I might not have shunned him. No man who hasn't lost his vanity can be held to have altogether failed. Soames's dignity was an illusion of mine. One day in the first week of June 1897 that illusion went. But on the evening of that day Soames went too.

I had been out most of the morning, and, as it was too late to reach home in time for luncheon, I sought the Vingtième. This little place— Restaurant du Vingtième Siècle, to give it its full title—had been discovered in '96 by the poets and prosaists but had now been more or less abandoned in favor of some later find. I don't think it lived long enough to justify its name, but at that time there it still was, in Greek Street, a few doors from Soho Square, and almost opposite to that house where, in the first years of the century, a little girl, and with her a boy named De Quincey, made nightly encampment in darkness and hunger among dust and rats and old legal parchments. The Ving-tième was but a small whitewashed room, leading out into the street at one end and into a kitchen at the other. The proprietor and cook was a Frenchman, known to us as Monsieur Vingtième; the waiters were his two daughters, Rose and Berthe; and the food, according to faith, was good. The tables were so narrow and were set so close to-gether that there was space for twelve of them, six jutting from either wall.

Only the two nearest to the door, as I went in, were occupied. On one side sat a tall, flashy, rather Mephistophelean man whom I had seen from time to time in the domino room and elsewhere. On the other side sat Soames. They made a queer contrast in that sunlit room —Soames sitting haggard in that hat and cape which nowhere at any season had I seen him doff, and this other, this keenly vital man, at sight of whom I more than ever wondered whether he were a diamond merchant, a conjurer, or the head of a private-detective agency. I was sure Soames didn't want any company, but I asked, as it would have seemed brutal not to, whether I might join him, and took the chair opposite to his. He was smoking a cigarette, with an untasted salmi of something on his plate and a half-empty bottle of sauterne before him, and he was quite silent. I said that the preparations for the Jubilee made London impossible. (I rather liked them, really.) I professed a wish to go right away till the whole thing was over. In vain did I at-tune myself to his gloom. He seemed not to hear me, nor even to see me. I felt that his behavior made me ridiculous in the eyes of the other man. The gangway between the two rows of tables at the Vingtième was hardly more than two feet wide (Rose and Berthe, in their minis-trations, had always to edge past each other, quarreling in whispers as they did so), and anyone at the table abreast of yours was practically at yours. I thought our neighbor was amused at my failure to interest Soames, and so, as I could not explain to him that my insistence was merely charitable, I became silent. Without turning my head I had him well within my range of vision. I hoped I looked less vulgar than he in contrast with Soames. I was sure he was not an Englishman, but what was his nationality? Though his jet-black hair was *enbrosse*, I did not think he was French. To Berthe, who waited on him, he spoke French fluently, but with a hardly native idiom and accent. I gathered that this was his first visit to the Vingtième, but Berthe was offhand in her manner to him: he had not made a good impression. His eyes were handsome, but—like the Vingtième's tables—too narrow and set too close together. His nose was predatory, and the points of his mustache, waxed up beyond his nostrils, gave a fixity to his smile. Decidedly he

was sinister. And my sense of discomfort in his presence was intensi-
fied by the scarlet waistcoat which tightly, and so unseasonably in June,
sheathed his ample chest. This waistcoat wasn't wrong merely because
of the heat, either. It was somehow all wrong in itself. It wouldn't have
done on Christmas morning. It would have struck a jarring note at the
first night of *Hernani*. I was trying to account for its wrongness when
Soames suddenly and strangely broke silence. "A hundred years
hence!" he murmured, as in a trance.

"We shall not be here!" I briskly but fatuously added.

"We shall not be here. No," he droned, "but the museum will still
be just where it is. And the reading room, just where it is. And people
will be able to go and read there." He inhaled sharply, and a spasm as
of actual pain contorted his features.

I wondered what train of thought poor Soames had been following.
He did not enlighten me when he said, after a long pause: "You think
I haven't minded."

"Minded what, Soames?"

"Neglect. Failure."

"*Failure?*" I said heartily. "Failure?" I repeated vaguely. "Neglect
—yes, perhaps; but that's quite another matter. Of course you haven't
been—appreciated. But what then? Any artist who—who gives——"
What I wanted to say was: "Any artist who gives truly new and great
things to the world has always to wait long for recognition," but the
flattery would not out: in the face of his misery, a misery so genuine
and so unmasked, my lips would not say the words.

And then—he said them for me. I flushed. "That's what you were
going to say, isn't it?" he asked.

"How did you know?"

"It's what you said to me three years ago, when *Fungoids* was published." I flushed the more. I need not have done so at all, for "It's the
only important thing I ever heard you say," he continued. "And I've
never forgotten it. It's a true thing. It's a horrible truth. But—d'you
remember what I answered? I said: 'I don't care a sou for recognition.' And you believed me. You've gone on believing I'm above that
sort of thing. You're shallow. What should you know of the feelings
of a man like me? You imagine that a great artist's faith in himself and
in the verdict of posterity is enough to keep him happy. . . . You've
never guessed at the bitterness and loneliness, the——" His voice
broke, but presently he resumed, speaking with a force that I had
never known in him. "Posterity! What use is it to *me?* A dead man
doesn't know that people are visiting his grave—visiting his birth-
place—putting up tablets to him—unveiling statues of him. A dead

man can't read the books that are written about him. A hundred years hence! Think of it! If I could come back to life *then*—just for a few hours—and go to the reading room and *read!* Or better still: if I could be projected, now, at this moment, into that future, into that reading room, just for this one afternoon! I'd sell myself body and soul to the Devil for that! Think of the pages and pages in the catalogue: 'Soames, Enoch,' endlessly—endless editions, commentaries, prolegomena, biographies———" But here he was interrupted by a sudden loud creak of the chair at the next table. Our neighbor had half risen from his place. He was leaning toward us, apologetically intrusive.

"Excuse—permit me," he said softly. "I have been unable not to hear. Might I take a liberty? In this little restaurant-sans-façon"—he spread wide his hands—"might I, as the phrase is, 'cut in'?"

I could but signify our acquiescence. Berthe had appeared at the kitchen door, thinking the stranger wanted his bill. He waved her away with his cigar and in another moment had seated himself beside me, commanding a full view of Soames.

"Though not an Englishman," he explained, "I know my London well, Mr. Soames. Your name and fame—Mr. Beerbohm's too—very known to me. Your point is: who am I?" He glanced quickly over his shoulder and in a lowered voice said: "I am the Devil."

I couldn't help it: I laughed. I tried not to; I knew there was nothing to laugh at; my rudeness shamed me, but I laughed with increasing volume. The Devil's quiet dignity, the surprise and disgust of his raised eyebrows did but the more dissolve me. I rocked to and fro; I lay back aching. I behaved deplorably.

"I am a gentleman, and," he said with intense emphasis, "I thought I was in the company of *gentlemen*."

"Don't!" I gasped faintly. "Oh, don't!"

"Curious, *nicht wahr?*" I heard him say to Soames. "There is a type of person to whom the very mention of my name is—oh-so-awfully-funny! In your theaters the dullest *comédien* needs only to say: 'The Devil!' and right away they give him 'the loud laugh that speaks the vacant mind.' Is it not so?"

I had now just breath enough to offer my apologies. He accepted them, but coldly, and readdressed himself to Soames.

"I am a man of business," he said, "and always I would put things through 'right now,' as they say in the States. You are a poet. *Les affaires*—you detest them. So be it. But with me you will deal, eh? What you have said just now gives me furiously to hope."

Soames had not moved, except to light a fresh cigarette. He sat crouched forward, with his elbows squared on the table, and his head just above the level of his hands, staring up at the Devil. "Go on." He nodded. I had no remnant of laughter in me now.

"It will be the more pleasant, our little deal," the Devil went on, "because you are—I mistake not?—a Diabolist."

"A Catholic Diabolist," said Soames.

The Devil accepted the reservation genially. "You wish," he resumed, "to visit now—this afternoon as-ever-is—the reading room of the British Museum, yes? But of a hundred years hence, yes? *Parfaitement*. Time—an illusion. Past and future—they are as ever present as the present, or at any rate only what you call 'just-round-the-corner.' I switch you on to any date. I project you—pouf! You wish to be in the reading room just as it will be on the afternoon of June 3, 1997? You wish to find yourself standing in that room, just past the swing doors, this very minute, yes? And to stay there till closing time? Am I right?"

Soames nodded.

The Devil looked at his watch. "Ten past two," he said. "Closing time in summer same then as now: seven o'clock. That will give you almost five hours. At seven o'clock—pouf—you find yourself again here, sitting at this table. I am dining tonight *dans le monde—dans le higlif*. That concludes my present visit to your great city. I come and fetch you here, Mr. Soames, on my way home."

"Home?" I echoed.

"Be it never so humble!" said the Devil lightly.

"All right," said Soames.

"Soames!" I entreated. But my friend moved not a muscle.

The Devil had made as though to stretch forth his hand across the table and touch Soames's forearm, but he paused in his gesture.

"A hundred years hence, as now"—he smiled—"no smoking allowed in the reading room. You would better, therefore——"

Soames removed the cigarette from his mouth and dropped it into his glass of sauterne.

"Soames!" again I cried. "Can't you——?" But the Devil had now stretched forth his hand across the table. He brought it slowly down on—the tablecloth. Soames's chair was empty. His cigarette floated sodden in his wineglass. There was no other trace of him.

For a few moments the Devil let his hand rest where it lay, gazing at me out of the corners of his eyes, vulgarly triumphant.

A shudder shook me. With an effort I controlled myself and rose from my chair. "Very clever," I said condescendingly. "But—*The*

Time Machine is a delightful book, don't you think? So entirely original!"

"You are pleased to sneer," said the Devil, who had also risen, "but it is one thing to write about an impossible machine; it is a quite other thing to be a Supernatural Power." All the same, I had scored.

Berthe had come forth at the sound of our rising. I explained to her that Mr. Soames had been called away and that both he and I would be dining here. It was not until I was out in the open air that I began to feel giddy. I have but the haziest recollection of what I did, where I wandered, in the glaring sunshine of that endless afternoon. I remember the sound of carpenters' hammers all along Piccadilly and the bare chaotic look of the half-erected "stands." Was it in the Green Park, or in Kensington Gardens, or where was it that I sat on a chair beneath a tree, trying to read an evening paper? There was a phrase in the leading article that went on repeating itself in my fagged mind —"Little is hidden from this august Lady full of the garnered wisdom of sixty years of Sovereignity." I remember wildly conceiving a letter (to reach Windsor by express messenger told to await answer):

MADAM: Well knowing that Your Majesty is full of the garnered wisdom of sixty years of Sovereignity, I venture to ask your advice in the following delicate matter. Mr. Enoch Soames, whose poems you may or may not know . . .

Was there no way of helping him—saving him? A bargain was a bargain, and I was the last man to aid or abet anyone in wriggling out of a reasonable obligation. I wouldn't have lifted a little finger to save Faust. But poor Soames!—doomed to pay without respite an eternal price for nothing but a fruitless search and a bitter disillusioning. . . .

Odd and uncanny it seemed to me that he, Soames, in the flesh, in the waterproof cape, was at this moment living in the last decade of the next century, poring over books not yet written, and seeing and seen by men not yet born. Uncannier and odder still, that tonight and evermore he would be in Hell. Assuredly, truth was stranger than fiction.

Endless that afternoon was. Almost I wished I had gone with Soames—not indeed to stay in the reading room, but to sally forth for a brisk sight-seeing walk around a new London. I wandered restlessly out of the park I had sat in. Vainly I tried to imagine myself an ardent tourist from the eighteenth century. Intolerable was the strain of the slow-passing and empty minutes. Long before seven o'clock I was back at the Vingtième.

I sat there just where I had sat for luncheon. Air came in listlessly through the open door behind me. Now and again Rose or Berthe appeared for a moment. I had told them I would not order any dinner till Mr. Soames came. A hurdy-gurdy began to play, abruptly drowning the noise of a quarrel between some Frenchmen farther up the street. Whenever the tune was changed I heard the quarrel still raging. I had bought another evening paper on my way. I unfolded it. My eyes gazed ever away from it to the clock over the kitchen door. . . .

Five minutes, now, to the hour! I remembered that clocks in restaurants are kept five minutes fast. I concentrated my eyes on the paper. I vowed I would not look away from it again. I held it upright, at its full width, close to my face, so that I had no view of anything but it. . . . Rather a tremulous sheet? Only because of the draft, I told myself.

My arms gradually became stiff; they ached, but I could not drop them—now. I had a suspicion; I had a certainty. Well, what then? . . . What else had I come for? Yet I held tight that barrier of newspaper. Only the sound of Berthe's brisk footstep from the kitchen enabled me, forced me, to drop it and to utter:

"What shall we have to eat, Soames?"

"*Il est souffrant, ce pauvre Monsieur Soames?*" asked Berthe.

"He's only—tired." I asked her to get some wine—burgundy—and whatever food might be ready. Soames sat crouched forward against the table, exactly as when last I had seen him. It was as though he had never moved—he who had moved so unimaginably far. Once or twice in the afternoon it had for an instant occurred to me that perhaps his journey was not to be fruitless—that perhaps we had all been wrong in our estimate of the works of Enoch Soames. That we had been horribly right was horribly clear from the look of him. But "Don't be discouraged," I falteringly said. "Perhaps it's only that you—didn't leave enough time. Two, three centuries hence, perhaps——"

"Yes," his voice came. "I've thought of that."

"And now—now for the more immediate future! Where are you going to hide? How would it be if you caught the Paris express from Charing Cross? Almost an hour to spare. Don't go on to Paris. Stop at Calais. Live in Calais. He'd never think of looking for you in Calais."

"It's like my luck," he said, "to spend my last hours on earth with an ass." But I was not offended. "And a treacherous ass," he strangely added, tossing across to me a crumpled bit of paper which he had been holding in his hand. I glanced at the writing on it—some sort of gibberish, apparently. I laid it impatiently aside.

"Come, Soames! Pull yourself together! This isn't a mere matter of life and death. It's a question of eternal torment, mind you! You don't mean to say you're going to wait limply here till the Devil comes to fetch you?"

"I can't do anything else. I've no choice."

"Come! This is 'trusting and encouraging' with a vengeance! This is Diabolism run mad!" I filled his glass with wine. "Surely, now that you've *seen* the brute——"

"It's no good abusing him."

"You must admit there's nothing Miltonic about him, Soames."

"I don't say he's not rather different from what I expected."

"He's a vulgarian; he's a swellmobsman; he's the sort of man who hangs about the corridors of trains going to the Riviera and steals ladies' jewel cases. Imagine eternal torment presided over by *him!*"

"You don't suppose I look forward to it, do you?"

"Then why not slip quietly out of the way?"

Again and again I filled his glass, and always, mechanically, he emptied it; but the wine kindled no spark of enterprise in him. He did not eat, and I myself ate hardly at all. I did not in my heart believe that any dash for freedom could save him. The chase would be swift, the capture certain. But better anything than this passive, meek, miserable waiting. I told Soames that for the honor of the human race he ought to make some show of resistance. He asked what the human race had ever done for him. "Besides," he said, "can't you understand that I'm in his power? You saw him touch me, didn't you? There's an end of it. I've no will. I'm sealed."

I made a gesture of despair. He went on repeating the word "sealed." I began to realize that the wine had clouded his brain. No wonder! Foodless he had gone into futurity; foodless he still was. I urged him to eat, at any rate, some bread. It was maddening to think that he, who had so much to tell, might tell nothing. "How was it all," I asked, "yonder? Come! Tell me your adventures."

"They'd make first-rate 'copy,' wouldn't they?"

"I'm awfully sorry for you, Soames, and I make all possible allowances, but what earthly right have you to insinuate that I should make 'copy,' as you call it, out of you?"

The poor fellow pressed his hands to his forehead. "I don't know," he said. "I had some reason, I know. . . . I'll try to remember."

"That's right. Try to remember everything. Eat a little more bread. What did the reading room look like?"

"Much as usual," he at length muttered.

"Many people there?"

"Usual sort of number."

"What did they look like?"

Soames tried to visualize them. "They all," he presently remembered, "looked very like one another."

My mind took a fearsome leap. "All dressed in jäger?"

"Yes, I think so. Grayish-yellowish stuff."

"A sort of uniform?" He nodded. "With a number on it, perhaps? —a number on a large disk of metal sewn onto the left sleeve? DKF 78,910—that sort of thing?" It was even so. "And all of them—men and women alike—looking very well cared for? Very Utopian? And smelling rather strongly of carbolic? And all of them quite hairless?" I was right every time. Soames was only not sure whether the men and women were hairless or shorn. "I hadn't time to look at them very closely," he explained.

"No, of course not. But——"

"They stared at *me,* I can tell you. I attracted a great deal of attention." At last he had done that! "I think I rather scared them. They moved away whenever I came near. They followed me about at a distance wherever I went. The men at the round desk in the middle seemed to have a sort of panic whenever I went to make inquiries."

"What did you do when you arrived?"

Well, he had gone straight to the catalogue, of course—to the S volumes—and had stood long before SN-SOF, unable to take this volume out of the shelf because his heart was beating so. . . . At first, he said, he wasn't disappointed—he only thought there was some new arrangement. He went to the middle desk and asked where the catalogue of *twentieth*-century books was kept. He gathered that there was still only one catalogue. Again he looked up his name, stared at the three little pasted slips he had known so well. Then he went and sat down for a long time. . . .

"And then," he droned, "I looked up the *Dictionary of National Biography* and some encyclopedias. . . . I went back to the middle desk and asked what was the best modern book on late-nineteenth-century literature. They told me Mr. T. K. Nupton's book was considered the best. I looked it up in the catalogue and filled in a form for it. It was brought to me. My name wasn't in the index, but—yes!" he said with a sudden change of tone. "That's what I'd forgotten. Where's that bit of paper? Give it me back."

I, too, had forgotten that cryptic screed. I found it fallen on the floor and handed it to him.

He smoothed it out, nodding and smiling at me disagreeably. "I found myself glancing through Nupton's book," he resumed. "Not very easy reading. Some sort of phonetic spelling. . . . All the modern books I saw were phonetic."

"Then I don't want to hear any more, Soames, please."

"The proper names seemed all to be spelled in the old way. But for that, I mightn't have noticed my own name."

"Your own name? Really? Soames, I'm very glad."

"And yours."

"No!"

"I thought I should find you waiting here tonight. So I took the trouble to copy out the passage. Read it."

I snatched the paper. Soames's handwriting was characteristically dim. It, and the noisome spelling, and my excitement, made me all the slower to grasp what T. K. Nupton was driving at.

The document lies before me at this moment. Strange that the words I here copy out for you were copied out for me by poor Soames just seventy-eight years hence. . . .

From p. 234 of *Inglish Littracher* 1890–1900 bi T. K. Nupton, publishd bi th Stait, 1992:

"Fr egzarmpl, a riter ov th time, naimd Max Beerbohm, hoo woz stil alive in th twentieth cenchri, rote a stauri in wich e pautraid an immajnari karrakter kauld 'Enoch Soames'—a thurd-rait poit hoo beleevz imself a grate jeneus an maix a bargin with th Devvl in auder ter no wot posterriti thinx ov im! It iz a sumwot labud sattire but not without vallu az showing hou seriusli the yung men ov th aiteen-ninetiz took themselvz. Nou that the littreri profeshn haz bin auganized az a departmnt of publik servis, our riters hav found their levvl an hav lernt ter doo their duti without thort ov the morro. 'Th laibrer iz werthi ov hiz hire,' an that iz aul. Thank hevvn we hav no Enoch Soameses amung us todai!"

I found that by murmuring the words aloud (a device which I commend to my reader) I was able to master them, little by little. The clearer they became, the greater was my bewilderment, my distress and horror. The whole thing was a nightmare. Afar, the great grisly background of what was in store for the poor dear art of letters; here, at the table, fixing on me a gaze that made me hot all over, the poor fellow whom—whom evidently . . . But no: whatever downgrade my character might take in coming years, I should never be such a brute as to . . .

Again I examined the screed. "Immajnari"—but here Soames was, no more imaginary, alas! than I. And "labud"—what on earth was that? (To this day I have never made out that word.) "It's all very— baffling," I at length stammered.

Soames said nothing but cruelly did not cease to look at me.

"Are you sure," I temporized, "quite sure you copied the thing out correctly?"

"Quite."

"Well, then it's this wretched Nupton who must have made—must be going to make—some idiotic mistake. . . . After all, the name 'Max Beerbohm' is not at all an uncommon one, and there must be several Enoch Soameses running around—or rather, 'Enoch Soames' is a name that might occur to anyone writing a story. And I don't write stories: I'm an essayist, an observer, a recorder. . . . I admit that it's an extraordinary coincidence. But you must see——"

"I see the whole thing," said Soames quietly. And he added, with a touch of his old manner but with more dignity than I had ever known in him: *"Parlons d'autre chose."*

I accepted that suggestion very promptly. I returned straight to the more immediate future. I spent most of the long evening in renewed appeals to Soames to slip away and seek refuge somewhere. I remember saying at last that if indeed I was destined to write about him, the supposed "stauri" had better have at least a happy ending. Soames repeated those last three words in a tone of intense scorn. "In Life and in Art," he said, "all that matters is an *inevitable* ending."

"But," I urged, more hopeful than I felt, "an ending that can be avoided *isn't* inevitable."

"You aren't an artist," he rasped. "And you're so hopelessly not an artist that, so far from being able to imagine a thing and make it seem true, you're going to make even a true thing seem as if you'd made it up. You're a miserable bungler. And it's like my luck."

I protested that the miserable bungler was not I—was not going to be I—but T. K. Nupton; and we had a rather heated argument, in the thick of which it suddenly seemed to me that Soames saw he was in the wrong; he had quite physically cowered. But I wondered why—and now I guessed with a cold throb just why—he stared so, past me. The bringer of that "inevitable ending" filled the doorway.

I managed to turn in my chair and to say, not without a semblance of lightness: "Aha, come in!" Dread was indeed rather blunted in me by his looking so absurdly like a villain in a melodrama. The sheen of his tilted hat and of his shirt front, the repeated twists he was giving to his mustache, and most of all the magnificence of his sneer gave token that he was there only to be foiled.

He was at our table in a stride. "I am sorry," he sneered witheringly, "to break up your pleasant party, but——"

"You don't: you complete it," I assured him. "Mr. Soames and I want to have a little talk with you. Won't you sit? Mr. Soames got nothing—frankly nothing—by his journey this afternoon. We don't wish to say that the whole thing was a swindle—a common swindle.

On the contrary, we believe you meant well. But of course the bargain, such as it was, is off."

The Devil gave no verbal answer. He merely looked at Soames and pointed with rigid forefinger to the door. Soames was wretchedly rising from his chair when, with a desperate quick gesture, I swept together two dinner knives that were on the table and laid their blades across each other. The Devil stepped sharp back against the table behind him, averting his face and shuddering.

"You are not superstitious!" he hissed.

"Not at all." I smiled.

"Soames," he said as to an underling, but without turning his face, "put those knives straight!"

With an inhibitive gesture to my friend, "Mr. Soames," I said emphatically to the Devil, "is a *Catholic Diabolist*"; but my poor friend did the Devil's bidding, not mine; and now, with his master's eyes again fixed on him, he arose; he shuffled past me. I tried to speak. It was he that spoke. "Try," was the prayer he threw back at me as the Devil pushed him roughly out through the door, "try to make them know that I did exist!"

In another instant I, too, was through that door. I stood staring all ways—up the street, across it, down it. There was moonlight and lamplight, but there was not Soames nor that other.

Dazed, I stood there. Dazed, I turned back, at length, into the little room, and I suppose I paid Berthe or Rose for my dinner and luncheon, and for Soames's; I hope so, for I never went to the Vingtième again. Ever since that night I have avoided Greek Street altogether. And for years I did not set foot even in Soho Square, because on that same night it was there that I paced and loitered long and long, with some such dull sense of hope as a man has in not straying far from the place where he has lost something. . . . "Round and round the shutter'd Square"—that line came back to me on my lonely beat, and with it the whole stanza, ringing in my brain and bearing in on me how tragically different from the happy scene imagined by him was the poet's actual experience of that prince in whom of all princes we should put not our trust.

But—strange how the mind of an essayist, be it never so stricken, roves and ranges!—I remember pausing before a wide doorstep and wondering if perchance it was on this very one that the young De Quincey lay ill and faint while poor Ann flew as fast as her feet would carry her to Oxford Street, the "stonyhearted stepmother" of them both, and came back bearing that "glass of port wine and spices" but for which he might, so he thought, actually have died. Was this the very doorstep that the old De Quincey used to revisit in homage? I pondered Ann's fate, the cause of her sudden vanishing from the ken of her boy friend, and presently I blamed myself for letting the past override the present. Poor vanished Soames!

And for myself, too, I began to be troubled. What had I better do? Would there be a hue and cry—Mysterious Disappearance of an Author, and all that? He had last been seen lunching and dining in my company. Hadn't I better get a hansom and drive straight to Scotland Yard? . . . They would think I was a lunatic. After all, I reassured myself, London was a very large place, and one very dim figure might easily drop out of it unobserved—now, especially, in the blinding glare of the near Jubilee. Better say nothing at all, I thought.

And I was right. Soames's disappearance made no stir at all. He was utterly forgotten before anyone, so far as I am aware, noticed that he was no longer hanging around. Now and again some poet or prosaist may have said to another: "What has become of that man Soames?" but I never heard any such question asked. The solicitor through whom he was paid his annuity may be presumed to have made inquiries, but no echo of these resounded. There was something rather ghastly to me in the general unconsciousness that Soames had existed, and more than once I caught myself wondering whether Nupton, that babe unborn, were going to be right in thinking him a figment of my brain.

In that extract from Nupton's repulsive book there is one point which perhaps puzzles you. How is it that the author, though I have here mentioned him by name and have quoted the exact words he is going to write, is not going to grasp the obvious corollary that I have invented nothing? The answer can be only this: Nupton will not have read the later passages of this memoir. Such lack of thoroughness is a serious fault in anyone who undertakes to do scholar's work. And I hope these words will meet the eye of some contemporary rival to Nupton and be the undoing of Nupton.

I like to think that sometime between 1992 and 1997 somebody will have looked up this memoir and will have forced on the world his inevitable and startling conclusions. And I have reasons for believing that this will be so. You realize that the reading room into which Soames was projected by the Devil was in all respects precisely as it will be on the afternoon of June 3, 1997. You realize, therefore, that on that afternoon, when it comes round, there the selfsame crowd will be, and there Soames, too, will be, punctually, he and they doing precisely what they did before. You may say that the mere difference of his costume was enough to make him sensational in that uniformed crowd. You wouldn't say so if you had ever seen him. I assure you that in no period could Soames be anything but dim. The fact that people are going to stare at him and follow him around and seem afraid of him can be explained only on the hypothesis that they will somehow have been prepared for his ghostly visitation. They will have been awfully waiting to see whether he really would come. And when he does come the effect will of course be—awful.

An authentic, guaranteed, proven ghost, but—only a ghost, alas! Only that. In his first visit Soames was a creature of flesh and blood, whereas the creatures into whose midst he was projected were but ghosts, I take it—solid, palpable, vocal, but unconscious and automatic ghosts, in a building that was itself an illusion. Next time that building and those creatures will be real. It is of Soames that there will be but the semblance. I wish I could think him destined to revisit the world actually, physically, consciously. I wish he had this one brief escape, this one small treat, to look forward to. I never forget him for long. He is where he is, and forever. The more rigid moralists among you may say he has only himself to blame. For my part, I think he has been very hardly used. It is well that vanity should be chastened, and Enoch Soames's vanity was, I admit, above the average and called for special treatment. But there was no need for vindictiveness. You say he contracted to pay the price he is paying; yes, but I maintain that he was induced to do so by fraud. Well informed in all things, the Devil must have known that my friend would gain nothing by his visit to futurity. The whole thing was a very shabby trick. The more I think of it, the more detestable the Devil seems to me.

Of him I have caught sight several times, here and there, since that day at the Vingtième. Only once, however, have I seen him at close quarters. This was in Paris. I was walking one afternoon along the Rue d'Antin, when I saw him advancing from the opposite direction —overdressed as ever, and swinging an ebony cane, and altogether behaving as though the whole pavement belonged to him. At thought of Enoch Soames and the myriads of other sufferers eternally in this brute's dominion, a great cold wrath filled me, and I drew myself up to my full height. But—well, one is so used to nodding and smiling in the street to anybody whom one knows that the action becomes almost independent of oneself: to prevent it requires a very sharp effort and great presence of mind. I was miserably aware, as I passed the Devil, that I nodded and smiled to him. And my shame was the deeper and hotter because he, if you please, stared straight at me with the utmost haughtiness.

To be cut—deliberately cut—by *him!* I was—I still am—furious at having had that happen to me.

THE DEVIL IN A NUNNERY

Francis Oscar Mann

BUCKINGHAM is as pleasant a shire as a man shall see on a seven days' journey. Neither was it any less pleasant in the days of our Lord King Edward, the third of that name, he who fought and put the French to shameful discomfiture at Crécy and Poitiers and at many another hard-fought field. May God rest his soul, for he now sleeps in the great church at Westminster.

Buckinghamshire is full of smooth round hills and woodlands of hawthorn and beech, and it is a famous country for its brooks and shaded waterways running through the low hay meadows. Upon its hills feed a thousand sheep, scattered like the remnants of the spring snow, and it was from these that the merchants made themselves fat purses, sending the wool into Flanders in exchange for silver crowns. There were many strong castles there, too, and rich abbeys, and the King's Highway ran through it from north to south, upon which the pilgrims went in crowds to worship at the Shrine of the Blessed St. Alban. Thereon also rode noble knights and stout men-at-arms, and these you could follow with the eye by their glistening armor as they wound over hill and dale, mile after mile, with shining spears and shields and fluttering pennons, and anon a trumpet or two sounding the same keen note as that which rang out dreadfully on those bloody fields of France. The girls used to come to the cottage doors or run to hide themselves in the wayside woods to see them go trampling by, for Buckinghamshire girls love a soldier above all men. Nor, I warrant you, were jolly friars lacking in the highways and the byways and under the hedges, good men of religion, comfortable of penance and easy of life, who could tip a wink to a housewife and drink and crack a joke with the good man, going on their several ways with tight paunches, skins full of ale and a merry salutation for everyone. A fat pleasant land was this Buckinghamshire; always plenty to eat and drink therein, and pretty girls and lusty fellows; and God knows what more a man can expect in a world where all is vanity, as the Preacher truly says.

There was a nunnery at Maids Moreton, two miles out from Buckingham Borough, on the road to Stony Stratford, and the place was called Maids Moreton because of the nunnery. Very devout creatures were the nuns, being holy ladies out of families of gentle blood. They punctually fulfilled to the letter all the commands of the pious founder, just as they were blazoned on the great parchment Regula, which the Lady Mother kept on her reading desk in her little cell. If ever any of the nuns, by any chance or subtle machination of the Evil One, was guilty of the smallest backsliding from the conduct that beseemed them, they made full and devout confession thereof to the holy father who visited them for this purpose. This good man loved swan's meat and galingale, and the charitable nuns never failed to provide of their best for him on his visiting days; and whatsoever penance he laid upon them they performed to the utmost, and with due contrition of heart.

From Matins to Complin they regularly and decently carried out the services of Holy Mother Church. After dinner, one read aloud to them from the Rule, and again after supper there was reading from the life of some notable saint or virgin, that thereby they might find ensample for themselves on their own earthly pilgrimage. For the rest, they tended their herb garden, reared their chickens, which were famous for miles around, and kept strict watch over their haywards and swineherds. If time was when they had nothing more important on hand, they set to and made the prettiest blood bandages imaginable for the bishop, the bishop's chaplain, the archdeacon, the neighboring abbot, and other godly men of religion round about, who were forced often to bleed themselves for their health's sake and their eternal salvation, so that these venerable men in process of time came to have by them great chests full of these useful articles. If little tongues wagged now and then as the sisters sat at their sewing in the great hall, who shall blame them, *Eva peccatrice?* Not I; besides, some of them were something stricken in years, and old women are garrulous and hard to be constrained from chattering and gossiping. But, being devout women, they could have spoken no evil.

One evening after Vespers all these good nuns sat at supper, the abbess on her high dais and the nuns ranged up and down the hall at the long trestled tables. The abbess had just said *"Gratias,"* and the sisters had sung *"Qui vivit et regnat per omnia saecula saeculorum. Amen,"* when in came the manciple mysteriously, and, with many deprecating bows and outstretchings of the hands, sidled himself up upon the dais, and, permission having been given him, spoke to the Lady Mother thus:

"Madam, there is a certain pilgrim at the gate who asks refreshment and a night's lodging." It is true he spoke softly, but little pink ears are sharp of hearing, and nuns, from their secluded way of life, love to hear news of the great world.

"Send him away," said the abbess. "It is not fit that a man should lie within this house."

"Madam, he asks food and a bed of straw lest he should starve of hunger and exhaustion on his way to do penance and worship at the Holy Shrine of the Blessed St. Alban."

"What kind of pilgrim is he?"

"Madam, to speak truly, I know not; but he appears of a reverend and gracious aspect, a young man well spoken and well disposed. Madam knows it waxeth late, and the ways are dark and foul."

"I would not have a young man, who is given to pilgrimages and good works, to faint and starve by the wayside. Let him sleep with the haywards."

"But, madam, he is a young man of goodly appearance and conversation; saving your reverence, I would not wish to ask him to eat and sleep with churls."

"He must sleep without. Let him, however, enter and eat of our poor table."

"Madam, I will strictly enjoin him what you command. He hath with him, however, an instrument of music and would fain cheer you with spiritual songs."

A little shiver of anticipation ran down the benches of the great hall, and the nuns fell to whispering.

"Take care, Sir Manciple, that he be not some light juggler, a singer of vain songs, a mocker. I would not have these quiet halls disturbed by wanton music and unholy words. God forbid." And she crossed herself.

"Madam, I will answer for it."

The manciple bowed himself from the dais and went down the middle of the hall, his keys rattling at his belt. A little buzz of conversation rose from the sisters and went up to the oak roof trees, like the singing of bees. The abbess told her beads.

The hall door opened, and in came the pilgrim. God knows what manner of man he was; I cannot tell you. He certainly was lean and lithe like a cat; his eyes danced in his head like the very Devil, but his cheeks and jaws were as bare of flesh as any hermit's that lives on roots and ditchwater. His yellow-hosed legs went like the tune of a May game, and he screwed and twisted his scarlet-jerkined body in time with them. In his left hand he held a cittern, on which he twanged with his right, making a cunning noise that titillated the backbones of those who heard it and teased every delicate nerve in the body. Such a tune would have tickled the ribs of Death himself. A queer fellow to go pilgrimaging certainly, but why, when they saw him, all the young nuns tittered and the old nuns grinned, until they showed their red gums, it is hard to tell. Even the Lady Mother on the dais smiled, though she tried to frown a moment later.

The pilgrim stepped lightly up to the dais, the infernal Devil in his legs making the nuns think of the games the village folk play all night in the churchyard on St. John's Eve.

"Gracious Mother," he cried, bowing deeply and in comely wise, "allow a poor pilgrim on his way to confess and do penance at the Shrine of St. Alban to take food in your hall and to rest with the haywards this night, and let me thereof make some small recompense with a few sacred numbers, such as your pious founder would not have disdained to hear."

"Young man," returned the abbess, "right glad am I to hear that God has moved thy heart to godly works and to go on pilgrimages, and verily I wish it may be to thy soul's health and to the respite of thy pains hereafter. I am right willing that thou shouldst refresh thyself with meat and rest at this holy place."

"Madam, I thank thee from my heart, but as some slight token of gratitude for so large a favor, let me, I pray thee, sing one or two of my divine songs, to the uplifting of these holy sisters' hearts."

Another burst of chatter, louder than before, from the benches in the hall. One or two of the younger sisters clapped their plump white hands and cried, "Oh!" The Lady Abbess held up her hand for silence.

"Verily, I should be glad to hear some sweet songs of religion, and I think it would be to the uplifting of these sisters' hearts. But, young man, take warning against singing any wanton lines of vain imagination, such as the ribalds use on the highways, and the idlers and haunters of taverns. I have heard them in my youth, although my ears tingle to think of them now, and I should think it shame that any such light words should echo among these sacred rafters or disturb the slumber of our pious founder, who now sleeps in Christ. Let me remind you of what saith St. Jeremie, '*Onager solitarius, in desiderio animae suae, attraxit ventum amoris* [the wild ass of the wilderness, in the desire of his heart, snuffeth up the wind of love]'; whereby that holy man signifies that vain earthly love, which is but wind and air, and shall avail nothing at all, when this weak, impure flesh is sloughed away."

"Madam, such songs as I shall sing, I learned at the mouth of our holy parish priest, Sir Thomas, a man of all good learning and purity of heart."

"In that case," said the abbess, "sing in God's name, but stand at the end of the hall, for it suits not the dignity of my office a man should stand so near this dais."

Whereon the pilgrim, making obeisance, went to the end of the hall, and the eyes of all the nuns danced after his dancing legs, and their ears hung on the clear, sweet notes he struck out of his cittern as he walked. He took his place with his back against the great hall door, in such attitude as men use when they play the cittern. A little trembling ran through the nuns, and some rose from their seats and knelt on the benches, leaning over the table, the better to see and hear him. Their eyes sparkled like dew on meadowsweet on a fair morning.

Certainly his fingers were bewitched or else the Devil was in his cittern, for such sweet sounds had never been heard in the hall since the day when it was built and consecrated to the service of the servants of God. The shrill notes fell like a tinkling rain from the high roof in mad, fantastic trills and dying falls that brought all one's soul to one's lips to suck them in. What he sang about, God only knows; not one of the nuns or even the holy abbess herself could have told you, although you had offered her a piece of the True Cross or a hair of the Blessed Virgin for a single word. But a divine yearning filled all their hearts; they seemed to hear ten thousand thousand angels singing in choruses, "Alleluia, Alleluia, Alleluia"; they floated up on impalpable clouds of azure and silver, up through the blissful paradises of the uppermost Heaven; their nostrils were filled with the odors of exquisite spices and herbs and smoke of incense; their eyes dazzled at splendors and lights and glories; their ears were full of gorgeous harmonies and all created concords of sweet sounds; the very fibers of being were loosened within them, as though their souls would leap forth from their bodies in exquisite dissolution. The eyes of the younger nuns grew round and large and tender, and their breath almost died upon their velvet lips. As for the old nuns, the great, salt tears coursed down their withered cheeks and fell like rain on their gnarled hands. The abbess sat on her dais with her lips apart, looking into space, ten thousand thousand miles away. But no one saw her, and she saw no one; everyone had forgotten everyone else in that delicious intoxication.

Then with a shrill cry, full of human yearnings and desire, the minstrel came to a sudden stop. . . .

> "Western wind, when wilt thou blow,
> And the small rain will down rain?
> Christ, if my love were in my arms,
> And I in my bed again."

Silence! Not one of the holy sisters spoke, but some sighed; some put their hands over their hearts, and one put her hand in her hood, but when she felt her hair shorn close to her scalp drew it out again sharply, as though she had touched red-hot iron, and cried, "O Jesu."

Sister Peronelle, a toothless old woman, began to speak in a cracked, high voice, quickly and monotonously, as though she spoke in a dream. Her eyes were wet and red, and her thin lips trembled. "God knows," she said, "I loved him; God knows it. But I bid all those who be maids here to be mindful of the woods. For they are green, but they are deep and dark, and it is merry in the springtime with the thick turf below and the good boughs above, all alone with your heart's darling—all alone in the green wood. But God help me, he would not stay any more than snow at Easter. I thought just now that I was back with him in the woods. God keep all those that be maids from the green woods."

The pretty Sister Ursula, who had only just finished her novitiate, was as white as a sheet. Her breath came thickly and quickly, as though she bore a great burden uphill. A great sigh made her comely shoulders rise and fall. "Blessed Virgin," she cried. "Ah, ye ask too much; I did not know; God help me, I did not know," and her gray eyes filled with sudden tears, and she dropped her head on her arms on the table and sobbed aloud.

Then cried out Sister Katherine, who looked as old and dead as a twig dropped from a tree of last autumn, and at whom the younger sisters privily mocked, "It is the wars, the wars, the cursed wars. I have held his head in this lap, I tell you; I have kissed his soul into mine. But now he lies dead, and his pretty limbs all dropped away into earth. Holy Mother, have pity on me. I shall never kiss his sweet lips again or look into his jolly eyes. My heart is broken long since. Holy Mother! Holy Mother!"

"He must come oftener," said a plump sister of thirty, with a little nose turned up at the end, eyes black as sloes and lips round as a plum. "I go to the orchard day after day and gather my lap full of apples. He is my darling. Why does he not come? I look for him every time that I gather the ripe apples. He used to come, but that was in the spring, and Our Lady knows that is long ago. Will it not be spring again soon? I have gathered many ripe apples."

Sister Margarita rocked herself to and fro in her seat and crossed her arms on her breast. She was singing quietly to herself:

> *"Lulla, lullay, thou tiny little child,*
> *Lulla, lullay, lullay;*
> *Suck at my breast that am thereat beguiled,*
> *Lulla, lullay, lullay."*

She moaned to herself, "I have seen the village women go to the well, carrying their babies with them, and they laugh as they go by on the way. Their babies hold them tight round the neck, and their mothers comfort them, saying, 'Hey, hey, my little son; hey, hey, my sweeting.' Christ and the blessed saints know that I have never felt a baby's little hand in my bosom—and now I shall die without it, for I am old and past the age of bearing children.

> *"Lulla, lullay, thou tiny little boy,*
>   *Lulla, lullay, lullay;*
> *To feel thee suck doth soothe my great annoy,*
>   *Lulla, lullay, lullay."*

"I have heard them on a May morning with their pipes and tabors and jolly, jolly music," cried Sister Helen; "I have seen them, too, and my heart has gone with them to bring back the white hawthorn from the woods. 'A man and a maid to a hawthorn bough,' as it says in the song. They sing outside my window all St. John's Eve so that I cannot say my prayers for the wild thoughts they put into my brain, as they go dancing up and down in the churchyard; I cannot forget the pretty words they say to each other, 'Sweet love, a kiss'; 'Kiss me, my love, nor let me go'; 'As I went through the garden gate'; 'A bonny black knight, a bonny black knight, and what will you give to me? A kiss, and a kiss, and no more than a kiss, under the wild rose tree.' Oh, Mary Mother, have pity on a poor girl's heart; I shall die, if no one love me, I shall die."

"In faith, I am truly sorry, William," said Sister Agnes, who was gaunt and hollow-eyed with long vigils and overfasting, for which the good father had rebuked her time after time, saying that she over-tasked the poor weak flesh. "I am truly sorry that I could not wait. But the neighbors made such a clamor, and my father and mother buffeted me too sorely. It is under the oak tree, no more than a foot deep, and covered with the red and brown leaves. It was a pretty sight to see the red blood on its neck, as white as whalebone, and it neither cried nor wept, so I put it down among the leaves, the pretty poppet, and it was like thee, William; it was like thee. I am sorry I did not wait, and now I'm worn and wan for thy sake, this many a long year, and all in vain, for thou never comest. I am an old woman now, and I shall soon be quiet and not complain any more."

Some of the sisters were sobbing as if their hearts would break; some sat quiet and still and let the tears fall from their eyes unchecked; some smiled and cried together; some sighed a little and trembled like aspen leaves in a southern wind. The great candles in the hall were burning down to their sockets. One by one they spluttered out. A ghostly, flickering light fell upon the legend over the broad dais, *"Con-*

nubium mundum sed virginitas paradisum complet [Marriage replen-
isheth the world, but virginity Paradise]."

"Dong, dong, dong." Suddenly the great bell of the nunnery began
to toll. With a cry the abbess sprang to her feet; there were tearstains
on her white cheeks, and her hand shook as she pointed fiercely to the
door.

"Away, false pilgrim," she cried. "Silence, foul blasphemer! *Retro
me, Satanas.*" She crossed herself again and again, saying, *"Pater
Noster."*

The nuns screamed and trembled with terror. A little cloud of blue
smoke arose from where the minstrel had stood. There was a little
tongue of flame, and he had disappeared. It was almost dark in the
hall. A few sobs broke the silence. The dying light of a single candle
fell on the form of the Lady Mother.

"Tomorrow," she said, "we shall fast and sing 'Placebo and Dirige'
and the seven penitential psalms. May the Holy God have mercy upon
us for all we have done and said and thought amiss this night. Amen."

THE LITANIES OF SATAN

Charles Pierre Baudelaire

TRANSLATED BY EDNA ST. VINCENT MILLAY

O THOU, of all the Angels loveliest and most learned,
To whom no praise is chanted and no incense burned,

Satan, have pity upon me in my deep distress!

O Prince of exile, god betrayed by foulest wrong,
Thou that in vain art vanquished, rising up more strong,

Satan, have pity upon me in my deep distress!

O thou who knowest all, each weak and shameful thing,
Kind minister to man in anguish, mighty king,

Satan, have pity upon me in my deep distress!

Thou that dost teach the leper, the pariah we despise,
To love like other men, and taste sweet Paradise,

Satan, have pity upon me in my deep distress!

O thou, that in the womb of Death, thy fecund mate,
Engenderest Hope, with her sweet eyes and her mad gait,

Satan, have pity upon me in my deep distress!

Thou who upon the scaffold dost give that calm and proud
Demeanour to the felon, which condemns the crowd,

Satan, have pity upon me in my deep distress!

Thou that hast seen in darkness and canst bring to light
The gems a jealous God has hidden from our sight,

Satan, have pity upon me in my deep distress!

Thou to whom all the secret arsenals are known
Where iron, where gold and silver, slumber, locked in stone,

Satan, have pity upon me in my deep distress!

Thou whose broad hand dost hide the precipice from him
Who, barefoot, in his sleep, walks on the building's rim,

Satan, have pity upon me in my deep distress!

O thou who makest supple between the horses' feet
The old bones of the drunkard fallen in the street,

Satan, have pity upon me in my deep distress!

Thou who hast taught the frail and over-burdened mind
How easily saltpeter and sulphur are combined,

Satan, have pity upon me in my deep distress!

Thou that hast burned thy brand beyond all help secure,
Into the rich man's brow, who tramples on the poor,

Satan, have pity upon me in my deep distress!

O thou, who makest gentle the eyes and hearts of whores
With kindness for the wretched, homage for rags and sores,

Satan, have pity upon me in my deep distress!

Staff of the exile, lamp of the inventor, last
Priest of the man about whose neck the rope is passed,

Satan, have pity upon me in my deep distress!

O thou, adopted father of those fatherless
Whom God from Eden thrust in terror and nakedness,

Satan, have pity upon me in my deep distress!

PRAYER

Glory and praise to thee, Satan, in the most high,
Where thou didst reign; and in deep hell's obscurity,
Where, manacled, thou broodest long! O silent power,
Grant that my soul be near to thee in thy great hour,
When, like a living Temple, victorious bough on bough,
Shall rise the Tree of Knowledge, whose roots are in thy brow!

THE DEVIL AND THE BROKER

Bret Harte

A MEDIEVAL LEGEND

THE CHURCH CLOCKS in San Francisco were striking ten. The Devil, who had been flying over the city that evening, just then alighted on the roof of a church near the corner of Bush and Montgomery streets. It will be perceived that the popular belief that the Devil avoids holy edifices and vanishes at the sound of a credo or paternoster is long since exploded. Indeed, modern skepticism asserts that he is not averse to these orthodox discourses, which particularly bear reference to himself and in a measure recognize his power and importance.

I am inclined to think, however, that his choice of a resting place was a good deal influenced by its contiguity to a populous thoroughfare. When he was comfortably seated he began pulling out the joints of a small rod which he held in his hand and which presently proved to be an extraordinary fishing pole with a telescopic adjustment that permitted its protraction to a marvelous extent. Affixing a line thereto, he selected a fly of a particular pattern from a small box which he carried with him and, making a skillful cast, threw his line into the very center of that living stream which ebbed and flowed through Montgomery Street.

Either the people were very virtuous that evening or the bait was not a taking one. In vain the Devil whipped the stream at an eddy in front of the Occidental, or trolled his line into the shadows of the Cosmopolitan; five minutes passed without even a nibble. "Dear me!" quoth the Devil. "That's very singular; one of my most popular flies, too! Why, they'd have risen by shoals in Broadway or Beacon Street for that. Well, here goes another." And, fitting a new fly from his well-filled box, he gracefully recast his line.

For a few moments there was every prospect of sport. The line was continually bobbing, and the nibbles were distinct and gratifying. Once or twice the bait was apparently gorged and carried off in the upper stories of the hotels to be digested at leisure. At such times the professional manner in which the Devil played out his line would have thrilled the heart of Izaak Walton. But his efforts were unsuccessful; the bait was invariably carried off without hooking the victim, and the Devil finally lost his temper. "I've heard of these San Franciscans before," he muttered. "Wait till I get hold of one—that's all!" he added malevolently as he rebaited his hook. A sharp tug and a wriggle foiled his next trial, and finally, with considerable effort, he landed a portly two-hundred-pound broker upon the church roof.

As the victim lay there gasping it was evident that the Devil was in no hurry to remove the hook from his gills; nor did he exhibit in this delicate operation that courtesy of manner and graceful manipulation which usually distinguished him.

"Come," he said gruffly as he grasped the broker by the waistband, "quit that whining and grunting. Don't flatter yourself that you're a prize, either. I was certain to have had you. It was only a question of time."

"It is not that, my lord, which troubles me," whined the unfortunate wretch as he painfully wriggled his head, "but that I should have been fooled by such a paltry bait. What will they say of me down there? To have let 'bigger things' go by, and to be taken in by this cheap trick," he added as he groaned and glanced at the fly which the Devil was carefully rearranging, "is what—pardon me, my lord—is what gets me!"

"Yes," said the Devil philosophically, "I never caught anybody yet who didn't say that; but tell me, ain't you getting somewhat fastidious down there? Here is one of my most popular flies, the greenback," he continued, exhibiting an emerald-looking insect which he drew from his box. "This, so generally considered excellent in election season, has not even been nibbled at. Perhaps your sagacity, which, in spite of this unfortunate contretemps, no one can doubt," added the Devil with a graceful return to his usual courtesy, "may explain the reason or suggest a substitute."

The broker glanced at the contents of the box with a supercilious smile. "Too old-fashioned, my lord—long ago played out. Yet," he added with a gleam of interest, "for a consideration I might offer something—ahem!—that would make a taking substitute for these trifles. Give me," he continued in a brisk, businesslike way, "a slight percentage and a bonus down, and I'm your man."

"Name your terms," said the Devil earnestly.

"My liberty and a percentage on all you take, and the thing's done."

The Devil caressed his tail thoughtfully for a few moments. He was certain of the broker anyway, and the risk was slight. "Done!" he said.

"Stay a moment," said the artful broker. "There are certain contingencies. Give me your fishing rod and let me apply the bait myself. It requires a skillful hand, my lord; even your well-known experience might fail. Leave me alone for half an hour, and if you have reason to complain of my success I will forfeit my deposit—I mean my liberty."

The Devil acceded to his request, bowed, and withdrew. Alighting gracefully in Montgomery Street, he dropped into Meade & Co.'s clothing store, where, having completely equipped himself *à la mode,* he sallied forth intent on his personal enjoyment. Determining to sink his professional character, he mingled with the current of human life and enjoyed, with that immense capacity for excitement peculiar to his nature, the whirl, bustle, and feverishness of the people, as a purely aesthetic gratification unalloyed by the cares of business. What he did that evening does not belong to our story. We return to the broker, whom we left on the roof.

When he made sure that the Devil had retired he carefully drew from his pocketbook a slip of paper and affixed it on the hook. The line had scarcely reached the current before he felt a bite. The hook was swallowed. To bring up his victim rapidly, disengage him from the hook, and reset his line was the work of a moment. Another bite and the same result. Another, and another. In a very few minutes the roof was covered with his panting spoil. The broker could himself distinguish that many of them were personal friends; nay, some of them were familiar frequenters of the building on which they were now miserably stranded. That the broker felt a certain satisfaction in being instrumental in thus misleading his fellow brokers no one acquainted with human nature will for a moment doubt. But a stronger pull on his line caused him to put forth all his strength and skill. The magic pole bent like a coachwhip. The broker held firm, assisted by the battlements of the church. Again and again it was almost wrested from his hand, and again and again he slowly reeled in a portion of the tightening line. At last, with one mighty effort, he lifted to the level of the roof a struggling object. A howl like Pandemonium rang through the air as the broker successfully landed at his feet—the Devil himself!

The two glared fiercely at each other. The broker, perhaps mindful of his former treatment, evinced no haste to remove the hook from his antagonist's jaw. When it was finally accomplished he asked quietly if the Devil was satisfied. That gentleman seemed absorbed in the contemplation of the bait which he had just taken from his mouth. "I am," he said finally, "and forgive you, but what do you call this?"

"Bend low," replied the broker as he buttoned up his coat, ready to depart. The Devil inclined his ear. "I call it WILD CAT!"

THE DEVIL'S AGE

Franchun Beltzarri

THERE WERE a gentleman and lady who were very poor. This man used to sit sadly at a crossroads. There came to him a gentleman who asked, "Why are you so sad?"

"Because I have not wherewith to live."

The gentleman said to him, "I will give you as much money as you like, if at such and such a time you tell the age of the Devil."

Our man went off happy. He led a merry life with his wife, for they wanted for nothing. They lived at a great rate. But time went on, and *the* time was approaching. This man recollected that he had not busied himself at all about the Devil's age. He became pensive. His wife asked him what was the matter with him then? Why was he not happy? They wanted for nothing; why was he so sad? He told her how it was that he got rich and what compact he had made with the gentleman. His wife said to him:

"If you have nothing but that, it is nothing at all. Get into a barrel of honey, and when you come out of it get into another barrel of feathers and, dressed like that, go to the crossroads and wait for the Devil there. You will put yourself on all fours and walk backward and forward and go between his legs and walk all round him."

The man did as his wife told him. The Devil came and drew back when he saw him, and our man went up quite close to the Devil. The Devil, being frightened, said to him:

"I am 7,777 years old and I have never seen any animal like that, and such a frightful one."

Our man had heard enough. He went off home at full speed and told his wife that they would want for nothing, that he had done as she had told him, just as if she had been a witch, and that he was no longer afraid of the Devil. They lived rich and happily, and if they lived well, they died well too.

THUS I REFUTE BEELZY

John Collier

"THERE GOES THE TEA BELL," said Mrs. Carter. "I hope Simon hears it."

They looked out from the window of the drawing room. The long garden, agreeably neglected, ended in a waste plot. Here a little summerhouse was passing close by beauty on its way to complete decay. This was Simon's retreat: it was almost completely screened by the tangled branches of the apple tree and the pear tree, planted too close together, as they always are in suburban gardens. They caught a glimpse of him now and then as he strutted up and down, mouthing and gesticulating, performing all the solemn mumbo-jumbo of small boys who spend long afternoons at the forgotten ends of long gardens.

"There he is, bless him," said Betty.

"Playing his game," said Mrs. Carter. "He won't play with the other children any more. And if I go down there—the temper! And comes in tired out."

"He doesn't have his sleep in the afternoons?" asked Betty.

"You know what Big Simon's ideas are," said Mrs. Carter. " 'Let him choose for himself,' he says. That's what he chooses, and he comes in as white as a sheet."

"Look. He's heard the bell," said Betty. The expression was justified, though the bell had ceased ringing a full minute ago. Small Simon stopped in his parade exactly as if its tinny dingle had at that moment reached his ear. They watched him perform ritual sweeps and scratchings with his little stick and come lagging over the hot and flaggy grass toward the house.

Mrs. Carter led the way down to the playroom, or garden room, which was also the tearoom for hot days. It had been the huge scullery of this tall Georgian house. Now the walls were cream-washed; there was coarse blue net in the windows, canvas-covered armchairs on the stone floor, and a reproduction of Van Gogh's Sunflowers over the mantelpiece.

Small Simon came drifting in and accorded Betty a perfunctory greeting. His face was an almost perfect triangle, pointed at the chin, and he was paler than he should have been. "The little elf child!" cried Betty.

Simon looked at her. "No," he said.

At that moment the door opened, and Mr. Carter came in, rubbing his hands. He was a dentist and washed them before and after everything he did. "You!" said his wife. "Home already!"

"Not unwelcome, I hope," said Mr. Carter, nodding to Betty. "Two people canceled their appointments; I decided to come home. I said, I hope I am not unwelcome."

"Silly!" said his wife. "Of course not."

"Small Simon seems doubtful," continued Mr. Carter. "Small Simon, are you sorry to see me at tea with you?"

"No, Daddy."

"No, what?"

"No, Big Simon."

"That's right. Big Simon and Small Simon. That sounds more like friends, doesn't it? At one time little boys had to call their father 'sir.' If they forgot—a good spanking. On the bottom, Small Simon! On the bottom!" said Mr. Carter, washing his hands once more with his invisible soap and water.

The little boy turned crimson with shame or rage.

"But now, you see," said Betty, to help, "you can call your father whatever you like."

"And what," asked Mr. Carter, "has Small Simon been doing this afternoon? While Big Simon has been at work."

"Nothing," muttered his son.

"Then you have been bored," said Mr. Carter. "Learn from experience, Small Simon. Tomorrow do something amusing and you will not be bored. I want him to learn from experience, Betty. That is my way, the new way."

"I have learned," said the boy, speaking like an old, tired man, as little boys so often do.

"It would hardly seem so," said Mr. Carter, "if you sit on your behind all the afternoon, doing nothing. Had *my* father caught me doing nothing I should not have sat very comfortably."

"He played," said Mrs. Carter.

"A bit," said the boy, shifting on his chair.

"Too much," said Mrs. Carter. "He comes in all nervy and dazed. He ought to have his rest."

"He is six," said her husband. "He is a reasonable being. He must choose for himself. But what game is this, Small Simon, that is worth getting nervy and dazed over? There are very few games as good as all that."

"It's nothing," said the boy.

"Oh, come," said his father. "We are friends, are we not? You can tell me. I was a Small Simon once, just like you, and played the same games you play. Of course there were no airplanes in those days. With whom do you play this fine game? Come on, we must all answer civil questions, or the world would never go round. With whom do you play?"

"Mr. Beelzy," said the boy, unable to resist.

"Mr. Beelzy?" said his father, raising his eyebrows inquiringly at his wife.

"It's a game he makes up," she said.

"Not makes up!" cried the boy. "Fool!"

"That is telling stories," said his mother. "And rude as well. We had better talk of something different."

"No wonder he is rude," said Mr. Carter, "if you say he tells lies and then insist on changing the subject. He tells you his fantasy; you implant a guilt feeling. What can you expect? A defense mechanism. Then you get a real lie."

"Like in *These Three*," said Betty. "Only different, of course. *She* was an unblushing little liar."

"I would have made her blush," said Mr. Carter, "in the proper part of her anatomy. But Small Simon is in the fantasy stage. Are you not, Small Simon? You just make things up."

"No, I don't," said the boy.

"You do," said his father. "And because you do, it is not too late to reason with you. There is no harm in a fantasy, old chap. There is no harm in a bit of make-believe.Only you have to know the difference between daydreams and real things, or your brain will never grow. It will never be the brain of a Big Simon. So come on. Let us hear about this Mr. Beelzy of yours. Come on. What is he like?"

"He isn't like anything," said the boy.

"Like nothing on earth?" said his father. "That's a terrible fellow."

"I'm not frightened of him," said the child, smiling. "Not a bit."

"I should hope not," said his father. "If you were, you would be frightening yourself. I am always telling people, older people than you are, that they are just frightening themselves. Is he a funny man? Is he a giant?"

"Sometimes he is," said the little boy.

"Sometimes one thing, sometimes another," said his father. "Sounds pretty vague. Why can't you tell us just what he's like?"

"I love him," said the small boy. "He loves me."

"That's a big word," said Mr. Carter. "That might be better kept for real things, like Big Simon and Small Simon."

"He is real," said the boy passionately. "He's not a fool. He's real."

"Listen," said his father. "When you go down the garden there's nobody there. Is there?"

"No," said the boy.

"Then you think of him, inside your head, and he comes."

"No," said Small Simon. "I have to do something with my stick."

"That doesn't matter."

"Yes, it does."

"Small Simon, you are being obstinate," said Mr. Carter. "I am trying to explain something to you. I have been longer in the world than you have, so naturally I am older and wiser. I am explaining that Mr. Beelzy is a fantasy of yours. Do you hear? Do you understand?"

"Yes, Daddy."

"He is a game. He is a let's-pretend."

The little boy looked down at his plate, smiling resignedly.

"I hope you are listening to me," said his father. "All you have to do is to say, 'I have been playing a game of let's-pretend. With someone I make up, called Mr. Beelzy.' Then no one will say you tell lies, and you will know the difference between dreams and reality. Mr. Beelzy is a daydream."

The little boy still stared at his plate.

"He is sometimes there and sometimes not there," pursued Mr. Carter. "Sometimes he's like one thing, sometimes another. You can't really see him. Not as you see me. I am real. You can't touch him. You can touch me. I can touch you." Mr. Carter stretched out his big white dentist's hand and took his little son by the shoulder. He stopped speaking for a moment and tightened his hand. The little boy sank his head still lower.

"Now you know the difference," said Mr. Carter, "between a pretend and a real thing. You and I are one thing; he is another. Which is the pretend? Come on. Answer me. Which is the pretend?"

"Big Simon and Small Simon," said the little boy.

"Don't!" cried Betty, and at once put her hand over her mouth, for why should a visitor cry "Don't!" when a father is explaining things in a scientific and modern way?

"Well, my boy," said Mr. Carter, "I have said you must be allowed to learn from experience. Go upstairs. Right up to your room. You shall learn whether it is better to reason or to be perverse and obstinate. Go up. I shall follow you."

"You are not going to beat the child?" cried Mrs. Carter.

"No," said the little boy. "Mr. Beelzy won't let him."

"Go on up with you!" shouted his father.

Small Simon stopped at the door. "He said he wouldn't let anyone hurt me," he whimpered. "He said he'd come like a lion, with wings on, and eat them up."

"You'll learn how real he is!" shouted his father after him. "If you can't learn it at one end, you shall learn it at the other. I'll have your breeches down. I shall finish my cup of tea first, however," he said to the two women.

Neither of them spoke. Mr. Carter finished his tea and unhurriedly left the room, washing his hands with his invisible soap and water.

Mrs. Carter said nothing. Betty could think of nothing to say. She wanted to be talking; she was afraid of what they might hear.

Suddenly it came. It seemed to tear the air apart. "Good God!" she cried. "What was that? He's hurt him." She sprang out of her chair, her silly eyes flashing behind her glasses. "I'm going up there!" she cried, trembling.

"Yes, let us go up," said Mrs. Carter. "Let us go up. That was not Small Simon."

It was on the second-floor landing that they found the shoe, with the man's foot still in it, like that last morsel of a mouse which sometimes fall from the jaws of a hasty cat.

FOREIGN DEVILS

WHETHER or not you agree that nationalism is the work of the Devil, it is obvious to all students of Diabolism that the Devil is a nationalist.

In old Russia he was a bloodthirsty Slav full of vodka and borsch, bitter as Gorki, dour as Dostoevski; in Poland he has had every attribute of a colonel when not emulating a barefooted peasant beating his wife; his Walpurgis Night antics in Germany anticipated the mountaintop orgies of Julius Streicher. Hell itself is a Teutonic word—from "Hel," daughter of Loki and queen of the underworld.

Bon vivant of the demimonde, his French alter ego celebrated the black Mass with Huysmans and always welcomed Aubrey Beardsley at Calais.

Only in England has the Devil been a world citizen not noticeably Anglo-Saxon. First cousin of the Saxon's nefarious Nifelheim, he undoubtedly danced beneath the mistletoe and celebrated the winter solstice with Druids. Later he drank wassail and played bloodybones—taking in vain the Mass of our Saviour. By the time he was completely disassociated with Stonehenge he had begun to assume a Levantine complexion and bore a remote resemblance to Disraeli.

Never out of the top drawer in later years, the Devil needed a stronger bond than his old school tie to seduce Etonians. His work for the British Foreign Office in the Middle East is seldom mentioned at the better clubs.

But those who feel that Satan is the empire's chief collaborator should remember that he plays few favorites among international connivers. He stood at Machiavelli's shoulder as that Florentine wrote *The Prince,* and his cloven hoof was later seen on a little propaganda minister in Berlin.

Internationalists who wish a federated world forget that the most polished delegate at any conference will be a gentleman who has been making war his profession since time immemorial. Master of protocol and balance of power politics, he understands the irony of "peace in our time."

French

SATAN'S ADAPTABILITY is not the least of his charms, as Eve discovered when she passed the time of day with a certain wily serpent who had twined himself about the tree of knowledge in the Garden of Eden.

In medieval Paris we can safely assume that the tortured, hungry student found the Devil of great assistance in arguing the minute details of the latest heresy. It might be reasonable to suppose that Villon drained many a tankard in his company at Fat Margot's, and to Villon the Devil would have been another adept at roistering as well as rhyme. Surely Satan daintily embraced many an aristocrat in the Bastille while the tumbrel waited for its cargo, making a mental tally of his progress while readjusting the perfumed lace on his satin sleeve.

Of recent years, in Paris, he has been *boulevardier* with an acquired taste for vermouth-cassis and the less respectable products of the daily press. He has played the sophisticated lover and gambler, the gourmet who knows each *spécialité de la maison*. He has learned the whereabouts of the best wine and he has had a roving eye for a trim feminine figure and an empty purse.

Baudelaire welcomed this Satan into his decadent circle. In *The Generous Gambler* we find a certain admiration for the Devil's talents. Guy de Maupassant's Devil is medieval—a Norman landowner, but lazy, and no match for St. Michael's trickery and deceit. But this Devil, too, is very French.

As a mere footnote to history, it might be added in passing that Satan cheerfully carried the first bundle of fagots to the feet of the Maid of Orléans, that he tied Laval's white tie on occasion, that he hooded many a *Cagoulard,* and often discussed the return of the monarchy at a certain Parisian café. But in no case was his cloven hoof noticeable in the company present at the time.

THE GENEROUS GAMBLER

Charles Pierre Baudelaire

YESTERDAY, across the crowd of the boulevard, I found myself touched by a mysterious Being I had always desired to know, and whom I recognized immediately, in spite of the fact that I had never seen him. He had, I imagined, in himself, relatively as to me, a similar desire, for he gave me, in passing, so significant a sign in his eyes that I hastened to obey him. I followed him attentively, and soon I descended behind him into a subterranean dwelling, astonishing to me as a vision, where shone a luxury of which none of the actual houses in Paris could give me an approximate example. It seemed to me singular that I had passed so often that prodigious retreat without having discovered the entrance. There reigned an exquisite, an almost stifling atmosphere, which made one forget almost instantaneously all the fastidious horrors of life; there I breathed a somber sensuality, like that of opium smokers when, set on the shore of an enchanted island over which shone an eternal afternoon, they felt born in them, to the soothing sounds of melodious cascades, the desire of never again seeing their households, their women, their children, and of never again being tossed on the decks of ships by storms.

There were there strange faces of men and women, gifted with so fatal a beauty that I seemed to have seen them years ago and in countries which I failed to remember and which inspired in me that curious sympathy and that equally curious sense of fear that I usually discover in unknown aspects. If I wanted to define in some fashion or other the singular expression of their eyes, I would say that never had I seen such magic radiance more energetically expressing the horror of ennui and of desire—of the immortal desire of feeling themselves alive.

As for mine host and myself, we were already, as we sat down, as perfect friends as if we had always known each other. We drank immeasurably of all sorts of extraordinary wines, and—a thing not less bizarre—it seemed to me, after several hours, that I was no more intoxicated than he was.

However, gambling, this superhuman pleasure, had cut, at various intervals, our copious libations, and I ought to say that I had gained and lost my soul, as we were playing, with a heroic carelessness and lightheartedness. The soul is so invisible a thing, often useless and sometimes so troublesome, that I did not experience, as to this loss, more than that kind of emotion I might have, had I lost my visiting card in the street.

We spent hours in smoking cigars, whose incomparable savor and perfume give to the soul the nostalgia of unknown delights and sights, and, intoxicated by all these spiced sauces, I dared, in an access of familiarity which did not seem to displease him, to cry, as I lifted a glass filled to the brim with wine: "To your immortal health, old he-goat!"

We talked of the universe, of its creation and of its future destruction; of the leading ideas of the century—that is to say, of progress and perfectibility—and, in general, of all kinds of human infatuations. On this subject His Highness was inexhaustible in his irrefutable jests, and he expressed himself with a splendor of diction and with a magnificence in drollery such as I have never found in any of the most famous conversationalists of our age. He explained to me the absurdity of different philosophies that had so far taken possession of men's brains, and deigned even to take me in confidence in regard to certain fundamental principles, which I am not inclined to share with anyone.

He complained in no way of the evil reputation under which he lived, indeed, all over the world, and he assured me that he himself was of all living beings the most interested in the destruction of *Superstition,* and he avowed to me that he had been afraid, relatively as to his proper power, once only, and that was on the day when he had heard a preacher, more subtle than the rest of the human herd, cry in his pulpit: "My dear brethren, do not ever forget, when you hear the progress of lights praised, that the loveliest trick of the Devil is to persuade you that he does not exist!"

The memory of this famous orator brought us naturally on the subject of academies, and my strange host declared to me that he didn't disdain, in many cases, to inspire the pens, the words, and the consciences of pedagogues, and that he almost always assisted in person, in spite of being invisible, at all the scientific meetings.

Encouraged by so much kindness, I asked him if he had any news of God—who has not his hours of impiety?—especially as the old friend of the Devil. He said to me, with a shade of unconcern united with a deeper shade of sadness: "We salute each other when we meet." But, for the rest, he spoke in Hebrew.

It is uncertain if His Highness has ever given so long an audience to a simple mortal, and I feared to abuse it.

Finally, as the dark approached shivering, this famous personage, sung by so many poets and served by so many philosophers who work for his glory's sake without being aware of it, said to me: "I want you to remember me always, and to prove to you that I—of whom one says so much evil—am often enough *bon diable,* to make use of one of your vulgar locutions. So as to make up for the irremediable loss that you have made of your soul, I shall give you back the stake you ought to have gained, if your fate had been fortunate—that is to say, the possibility of solacing and of conquering, during your whole life, this bizarre affection of ennui, which is the source of all your maladies and of all your miseries. Never a desire shall be formed by you that I will not aid you to realize; you will reign over your vulgar equals; money and gold and diamonds, fairy palaces, shall come to seek you and shall ask you to accept them without your having made the least effort to obtain them; you can change your abode as often as you like; you shall have in your power all sensualities without lassitude, in lands where the climate is always hot and where the women are as scented as the flowers." With this he rose and said good-by to me with a charming smile.

If it had not been for the shame of humiliating myself before so immense an assembly, I might have voluntarily fallen at the feet of this generous gambler, to thank him for his unheard-of munificence. But little by little, after I had left him, an incurable defiance entered into me; I dared no longer believe in so prodigious a happiness, and as I went to bed, making over again my nightly prayer by means of all that remained in me in the matter of faith, I repeated in my slumber: "My God, my Lord, my God! Do let the Devil keep his word with me!"

THE LEGEND OF MONT ST.-MICHEL

Guy de Maupassant

I HAD FIRST SEEN IT from Cancale, this fairy castle in the sea. I got an indistinct impression of it as of a gray shadow outlined against the misty sky. I saw it again from Avranches at sunset. The immense stretch of sand was red; the horizon was red; the whole boundless bay was red. The rocky castle rising out there in the distance like a weird, seignorial residence, like a dream palace, strange and beautiful—this alone remained black in the crimson light of the dying day.

The following morning at dawn I went toward it across the sands, my eyes fastened on this gigantic jewel, as big as a mountain, cut like a cameo, and as dainty as lace. The nearer I approached, the greater my admiration grew, for nothing in the world could be more wonderful or more perfect.

As surprised as if I had discovered the habitation of a god, I wandered through those halls supported by frail or massive columns, raising my eyes in wonder to those spires which looked like rockets starting for the sky, and to that marvelous assemblage of towers, of gargoyles, of slender and charming ornaments, a regular fireworks of stone, granite lace, a masterpiece of colossal and delicate architecture.

As I was looking up in ecstasy a Lower Normandy peasant came up to me and told me the story of the great quarrel between St. Michael and the Devil.

A skeptical genius has said: "God made man in his image and man has returned the compliment."

This saying is an eternal truth, and it would be very curious to write the history of the local divinity of every continent, as well as the history of the patron saints in each one of our provinces. The Negro has his ferocious man-eating idols; the polygamous Mohammedan fills his paradise with women; the Greeks, like a practical people, deified all the passions.

Every village in France is under the influence of some protecting saint, modeled according to the characteristics of the inhabitants.

St. Michael watches over Lower Normandy, St. Michael, the radiant and victorious angel, the sword carrier, the hero of Heaven, the victorious, the conqueror of Satan.

But this is how the Lower Normandy peasant, cunning, deceitful, and tricky, understands and tells of the struggle between the great saint and the Devil.

To escape from the malice of his neighbor, the Devil, St. Michael built himself, in the open ocean, this habitation worthy of an archangel, and only such a saint could build a residence of such magnificence.

But, as he still feared the approaches of the wicked one, he surrounded his domains by quicksands, more treacherous even than the sea.

The Devil lived in a humble cottage on the hill, but he owned all the salt marshes, the rich lands where grow the finest crops, the wooded valleys, and all the fertile hills of the country, while the saint ruled only over the sands. Therefore, Satan was rich, whereas St. Michael was as poor as a church mouse.

After a few years of fasting the saint grew tired of this state of affairs and began to think of some compromise with the Devil, but the matter was by no means easy, as Satan kept a good hold on his crops.

He thought the thing over for about six months; then one morning he walked across to the shore. The demon was eating his soup in front of his door when he saw the saint. He immediately rushed toward him, kissed the hem of his sleeve, invited him in, and offered him refreshments.

St. Michael drank a bowl of milk and then began: "I have come here to propose to you a good bargain."

The Devil, candid and trustful, answered: "That will suit me."

"Here it is. Give me all your lands."

Satan, growing alarmed, wished to speak. "But——"

The saint continued: "Listen first. Give me all your lands. I will take care of all the work, the plowing, the sowing, the fertilizing, everything, and we will share the crops equally. How does that suit you?"

The Devil, who was naturally lazy, accepted. He only demanded in addition a few of those delicious gray mullet which are caught around the solitary mount. St. Michael promised the fish.

They grasped hands and spat on the ground to show that it was a bargain, and the saint continued: "See here, so that you will have nothing to complain of, choose that part of the crops which you prefer: the part that grows aboveground or the part that stays in the ground."

Satan cried out: "I will take all that will be aboveground."

"It's a bargain!" said the saint. And he went away.

Six months later, all over the immense domain of the Devil, one could see nothing but carrots, turnips, onions, salsify, all the plants whose juicy roots are good and savory and whose useless leaves are good for nothing but for feeding animals.

Satan wished to break the contract, calling St. Michael a swindler. But the saint, who had developed quite a taste for agriculture, went back to see the Devil and said: "Really, I hadn't thought of that at all; it was just an accident, no fault of mine. And to make things fair with you, this year I'll let you take everything that is under the ground."

"Very well," answered Satan.

The following spring all the evil spirit's lands were covered with golden wheat, oats as big as beans, flax, magnificent colza, red clover, peas, cabbage, artichokes, everything that develops into grains or fruit in the sunlight.

Once more Satan received nothing, and this time he completely lost his temper. He took back his fields and remained deaf to all the fresh propositions of his neighbor.

A whole year rolled by. From the top of his lonely manor St. Michael looked at the distant and fertile lands and watched the Devil direct the work, take in his crops, and thresh the wheat. And he grew angry, exasperated at his powerlessness. As he was no longer able to deceive Satan, he decided to wreak vengeance on him, and he went out to invite him to dinner for the following Monday.

"You have been very unfortunate in your dealings with me," he said; "I know it, but I don't want any ill feeling between us, and I expect you to dine with me. I'll give you some good things to eat."

Satan, who was as greedy as he was lazy, accepted eagerly. On the day appointed he donned his finest clothes and set out for the castle.

St. Michael sat him down to a magnificent meal. First there was a *vol-au-vent*, full of cocks' crests and kidneys, with meat balls, then two big gray mullet with cream sauce, a turkey stuffed with chestnuts soaked in wine, some salt-marsh lamb as tender as cake, vegetables which melted in the mouth, and a nice hot pancake which was brought on smoking and spreading a delicious odor of butter.

They drank new, sweet, sparkling cider and heady red wine, and after each course they whetted their appetites with some old apple brandy.

The Devil drank and ate to his heart's content; in fact, he took so much that he was very uncomfortable and began to retch.

Then St. Michael arose in anger and cried in a voice like thunder: "What! Before me, rascal! You dare—before me——"

Satan, terrified, ran away, and the saint, seizing a stick, pursued him. They ran through the halls, turning round the pillars, running up the staircases, galloping along the cornices, jumping from gargoyle to gargoyle. The poor Devil, who was woefully ill, was running about madly and trying hard to escape. At last he found himself at the top of the last terrace, right at the top, from which could be seen the immense bay, with its distant towns, sands, and pastures. He could no longer escape, and the saint came up behind him and gave him a furious kick, which shot him through space like a cannon ball.

He shot through the air like a javelin and fell heavily before the town of Mortain. His horns and claws stuck deep into the rock, which keeps through eternity the traces of this fall of Satan.

He stood up again, limping, crippled until the end of time, and as he looked at this fatal castle in the distance, standing out against the setting sun, he understood well that he would always be vanquished in this unequal struggle, and he went away limping, heading for distant countries, leaving to his enemy his fields, his hills, his valleys, and his marshes.

And this is how St. Michael, the patron saint of Normandy, vanquished the Devil.

Another people would have dreamed of this battle in an entirely different manner.

Irish

St. patrick may have driven the snakes out of Ireland, but "The Old Serpent" in several of his Protean changes has been back for a nip of John Jameson on several occasions.

In Ireland he speaks with a brogue as soft and easy as peat smoke on a misty morning, attends the Irish Sweepstakes, and often confers with Oliver St. John Gogarty. In a land of leprechauns and little people and Irish Republicans he easily passes as a logical and three-dimensional fellow—not in the least a figment of the imagination.

The following tale by W. Carleton makes use of a diabolical basic— the three wishes. In other forms, and with different local color, this story is found in German, Russian, and American folklore. It would be unfair to state that Billy Dawson was the only rogue who has ever outwitted the Devil or has been refused a comfortable and familiar eternity in Hell.

Dawson's shocking experience is not to be construed as evidence of an Irish Exclusion Act in the Nether Regions.

THE THREE WISHES

W. Carleton

In ancient times there lived a man called Billy Dawson, and he was known to be a great rogue. They say he was descended from the family of the Dawsons, which was the reason, I suppose, of his carrying their name upon him.

Billy, in his youthful days, was the best hand at doing nothing in all Europe; devil a mortal could come next or near him at idleness; and, in consequence of his great practice that way, you may be sure that if any man could make a fortune by it he would have done it.

Billy was the only son of his father, barring two daughters, but they have nothing to do with the story I'm telling you. Indeed it was kind father and grandfather for Billy to be handy at the knavery as well as at the idleness, for it was well known that not one of their blood ever did an honest act, except with a roguish intention. In short, they were altogether a *dacent* connection and a credit to the name. As for Billy, all the villainy of the family, both plain and ornamental, came down to him by way of legacy, for it so happened that the father, in spite of all his cleverness, had nothing but his roguery to *lave* him.

Billy, to do him justice, improved the fortune he got. Every day advanced him farther into dishonesty and poverty, until, at the long run, he was acknowledged on all hands to be the completest swindler and the poorest vagabond in the whole parish.

Billy's father, in his young days, had often been forced to acknowledge the inconvenience of not having a trade, in consequence of some nice point in law, called the "Vagrant Act," that sometimes troubled him. On this account he made up his mind to give Bill an occupation, and he accordingly bound him to a blacksmith; but whether Bill was to *live* or *die* by *forgery* was a puzzle to his father—though the neighbors said that *both* was most likely. At all events, he was put apprentice to a smith for seven years, and a hard card his master had to play in managing him. He took the proper method, however, for Bill was so lazy and roguish that it would vex a saint to keep him in order.

"Bill," says his master to him one day that he had been sunning himself about the ditches, instead of minding his business, "Bill, my boy, I'm vexed to the heart to see you in such a bad state of health. You're very ill with that complaint called an *all-overness;* however," says he, "I think I can cure you. Nothing will bring you about but three or four sound doses every day of a medicine called 'the oil o' the hazel.' Take the first dose now," says he, and he immediately banged him with a hazel cudgel until Bill's bones ached for a week afterward.

"If you were my son," said his master, "I tell you that, as long as I could get a piece of advice growing convenient in the hedges, I'd have you a different youth from what you are. If working was a sin, Bill, not an innocenter boy ever broke bread than you would be. Good people's scarce, you think; but however that may be, I throw it out as a hint, that you must take your medicine till you're cured, whenever you happen to get unwell in the same way."

From this out he kept Bill's nose to the grinding stone, and whenever his complaint returned he never failed to give him a hearty dose for his improvement.

In the course of time, however, Bill was his own man and his own master, but it would puzzle a saint to know whether the master or the man was the more precious youth in the eyes of the world.

He immediately married a wife, and devil a doubt of it, but if *he* kept *her* in whisky and sugar, *she* kept *him* in hot water. Bill drank and she drank; Bill fought and she fought; Bill was idle and she was idle; Bill whacked her and she whacked Bill. If Bill gave her one black eye, she gave him another, *just to keep herself in countenance*. Never was there a blessed pair so well met, and a beautiful sight it was to see them both at breakfast time, blinking at each other across the potato basket, Bill with his right eye black, and she with her left.

In short, they were the talk of the whole town; and to see Bill of a morning staggering home drunk, his shirt sleeves rolled up on his smutted arms, his breast open, and an old tattered leather apron, with one corner tucked up under his belt, singing one minute and fighting with his wife the next—she, reeling beside him with a discolored eye, as aforesaid, a dirty ragged cap on one side of her head, a pair of Bill's old slippers on her feet, a squalling child on her arm—now cuffing and dragging Bill, and again kissing and hugging him! Yes, it was a pleasant picture to see this loving pair in such a state!

This might do for a while, but it could not last. They were idle, drunken, and ill conducted; and it was not to be supposed that they would get a farthing candle on their words. They were, of course, *dhruv* to great straits; and faith, they soon found that their fighting and drinking and idleness made them the laughing sport of the neighbors; but neither brought food to their *childhre,* put a coat upon their backs, nor satisfied their landlord when he came to look for his own. Still, the never a one of Bill but was a funny fellow with strangers, though, as we said, the greatest rogue unhanged.

One day he was standing against his own anvil, completely in a brown study—being brought to his wit's end how to make out a breakfast for the family. The wife was scolding and cursing in the house, and the naked creatures of childhre squalling about her knees for food. Bill was fairly at an amplush, and knew not where or how to turn himself, when a poor, withered old beggar came into the forge, tottering on his staff. A long white beard fell from his chin, and he looked as thin and hungry that you might blow him, one would think, over the house. Bill at this moment had been brought to his senses by distress, and his heart had a touch of pity toward the old man, for, on looking at him a second time, he clearly saw starvation and sorrow in his face.

"God save you, honest man!" said Bill.

The old man gave a sigh, and raising himself with great pain on his staff, he looked at Bill in a very beseeching way.

"Musha, God save you kindly!" says he. "Maybe you could give a poor, hungry, helpless ould man a mouthful of something to ait? You see yourself I'm not able to work; if I was, I'd scorn to be beholding to anyone."

"Faith, honest man," said Bill, "if you knew who you're speaking to, you'd as soon ask a monkey for a churnstaff as me for either mate or money. There's not a blackguard in the three kingdoms so fairly on the *shaughran* as I am for both the one and the other. The wife within is sending the curses thick and heavy on me, and the childhre's playing the cat's melody to keep her in comfort. Take my word for it, poor man, if I had either mate or money I'd help you, for I know particularly well what it is to want them at the present speaking; an empty sack won't stand, neighbor."

So far Bill told him truth. The good thought was in his heart, because he found himself on a footing with the beggar; and nothing brings down pride, or softens the heart, like feeling what it is to want.

"Why, you are in a worse state than I am," said the old man; "you have a family to provide for, and I have only myself to support."

"You may kiss the book on that, my old worthy," replied Bill; "but come, what I can do for you I will; plant yourself up here beside the fire, and I'll give it a blast or two of my bellows that will warm the old blood in your body. It's a cold, miserable, snowy day, and a good heat will be of service."

"Thank you kindly," said the old man; "I *am* cold, and a warming at your fire will do me good, sure enough. Oh, but it *is* a bitter, bitter day; God bless it!"

He then sat down, and Bill blew a rousing blast that soon made the stranger edge back from the heat. In a short time he felt quite comfortable, and when the numbness was taken out of his joints, he buttoned himself up and prepared to depart.

"Now," says he to Bill, "you hadn't the food to give me, but *what you could you did*. Ask any three wishes you choose, and be they what they may, take my word for it, they shall be granted."

Now, the truth is, that Bill, though he believed himself a great man in point of 'cuteness, wanted, after all, a full quarter of being square, for there is always a great difference between a wise man and a knave. Bill was so much of a rogue that he could not, for the blood of him, ask an honest wish, but stood scratching his head in a puzzle.

"Three wishes!" said he. "Why, let me see—did you say *three?*"

"Ay," replied the stranger, "three wishes—that was what I said."

"Well," said Bill, "here goes—aha!—let me alone, my old worthy! —faith I'll overreach the parish, if what you say is true. I'll cheat them in dozens, rich and poor, old and young; let me alone, man—I have it here," and he tapped his forehead with great glee. "Faith, you're the sort to meet of a frosty morning, when a man wants his breakfast; and I'm sorry that I have neither money nor credit to get a bottle of whisky, that we might take our *morning* together."

"Well, but let us hear the wishes," said the old man; "my time is short, and I cannot stay much longer."

"Do you see this sledge hammer?" said Bill. "I wish, in the first place, that whoever takes it up in their hands may never be able to lay it down till I give them lave; and that whoever begins to sledge with it may never stop sledging till it's my pleasure to release him.

"Secondly—I have an armchair, and I wish that whoever sits down in it may never rise out of it till they have my consent.

"And, thirdly—that whatever money I put into my purse, nobody may have power to take it out of it but myself!"

"You Devil's rip!" says the old man in a passion, shaking his staff across Bill's nose. "Why did you not ask something that would sarve you both here and hereafter? Sure it's as common as the market cross, that there's not a vagabone in His Majesty's dominions stands more in need of both."

"Oh! By the elevens," said Bill, "I forgot that altogether! Maybe you'd be civil enough to let me change one of them? The sorra purtier wish ever was made than I'll make, if only you'll give me another chance at it."

"Get out, you reprobate," said the old fellow, still in a passion. "Your day of grace is past. Little you knew who was speaking to you all this time. I'm St. Moroky, you blackguard, and I gave you an opportunity of doing something for yourself and your family; but you neglected it, and now your fate is cast, you dirty, bog-trotting profligate. Sure, it's well known what you are! Aren't you a byword in everybody's mouth, you and your scold of a wife? By this and by that, if ever you happen to come across me again, I'll send you to where you won't freeze, you villain!"

He then gave Bill a rap of his cudgel over the head and laid him at his length beside the bellows, kicked a broken coal scuttle out of his way, and left the forge in a fury.

When Billy recovered himself from the effects of the blow and began to think on what had happened, he could have quartered himself with vexation for not asking great wealth as one of the wishes at least; but now the die was cast on him, and he could only make the most of the three he pitched upon.

He now bethought him how he might turn them to the best account, and here his cunning came to his aid. He began by sending for his wealthiest neighbors on pretense of business, and when he got them under his roof he offered them the armchair to sit down in. He now had them safe, nor could all the art of man relieve them except worthy Bill was willing. Bill's plan was to make the best bargain he could before he released his prisoners; and let him alone for knowing how to make their purses bleed. There wasn't a wealthy man in the country he did not fleece. The parson of the parish bled heavily; so did the lawyer; and a rich attorney, who had retired from practice, swore that the Court of Chancery itself was paradise compared to Bill's chair.

This was all very good for a time. The fame of his chair, however, soon spread; so did that of his sledge. In a short time neither man, woman, nor child would darken his door; all avoided him and his fixtures as they would a spring gun or mantrap. Bill, so long as he fleeced his neighbors, never wrought a hand's turn; so that when his money was out he found himself as badly off as ever. In addition to all this, his character was fifty times worse than before, for it was the general belief that he had dealings with the old boy. Nothing now could exceed his misery, distress, and ill temper. The wife and he and their children all fought among one another. Everybody hated them, cursed them, and avoided them. The people thought they were acquainted with more than Christian people ought to know. This, of course, came to Bill's ears, and it vexed him very much.

One day he was walking about the fields, thinking of how he could raise the wind once more; the day was dark, and he found himself, before he stopped, in the bottom of a lonely glen covered by great bushes that grew on each side. "Well," thought he, when every other means of raising money failed him, "it's reported that I'm in league with the old boy, and as it's a folly to have the name of the connection without the profit, I'm ready to make a bargain with him any day—so," said he, raising his voice, "Nick, you sinner, if you be convanient and willing, why stand out here; show your best leg—here's your man."

The words were hardly out of his mouth when a dark, sober-looking old gentleman, not unlike a lawyer, walked up to him. Bill looked at the foot and saw the hoof. "Morrow, Nick," says Bill.

"Morrow, Bill," says Nick. "Well, Bill, what's the news?"

"Devil a much myself hears of late," says Bill; "is there anything *fresh* below?"

"I can't exactly say, Bill; I spend little of my time down now; the Tories are in office, and my hands are consequently too full of business here to pay much attention to anything else."

"A fine place this, sir," says Bill, "to take a constitutional walk in; when I want an appetite I often come this way myself—hem! *High* feeding is very bad without exercise."

"High feeding! Come, come, Bill, you know you didn't taste a morsel these four-and-twenty hours."

"You know that's a bounce, Nick. I eat a breakfast this morning that would put a stone of flesh on you, if you only smelt at it."

"No matter; this is not to the purpose. What's that you were muttering to yourself a while ago? If you want to come to the brunt, here I'm for you."

"Nick," said Bill, "you're complate; you want nothing barring a pair of Brian O'Lynn's breeches."

Bill, in fact, was bent on making his companion open the bargain, because he had often heard that, in that case, with proper care on his own part, he might defeat him in the long run. The other, however, was his match.

"What was the nature of Brian's garment?" inquired Nick.

"Why, you know the song," said Bill:

> *"Brian O'Lynn had no breeches to wear,*
> *So he got a sheep's skin for to make him a pair;*
> *With the fleshy side out and the woolly side in,*
> *'They'll be pleasant and cool,' says Brian O'Lynn.*

"A *cool* pare would sarve you, Nick."

"You're mighty waggish today, Misther Dawson."

"And good right I have," said Bill; "I'm a man snug and well to do in the world; have lots of money, plenty of good eating and drinking, and what more need a man wish for?"

"True," said the other; "in the meantime it's rather odd that so respectable a man should not have six inches of unbroken cloth in his apparel. You're as naked a tatterdemalion as I ever laid my eyes on; in full dress for a party of scarecrows, William?"

"That's my own fancy, Nick; I don't work at my trade like a gentleman. This is my forge dress, you know."

"Well, but what did you summon me here for?" said the other; "you may as well speak out, I tell you, for, my good friend, unless *you* do, *I* shan't. Smell that."

"I smell more than that," said Bill; "and by the way, I'll thank you to give me the windy side of you—curse all sulphur, I say. There, that's what I call an improvement in my condition. But as you *are* so stiff," says Bill, "why, the short and long of it is—that—ahem—you see I'm—tut—sure you know I have a thriving trade of my own, and that if I like I needn't be at a loss; but in the meantime I'm rather in a kind of a so—so—don't you *take?*"

And Bill winked knowingly, hoping to trick him into the first proposal.

"You must speak aboveboard, my friend," says the other. "I'm a man of few words, blunt and honest. If you have anything to say, be plain. Don't think I can be losing my time with such a pitiful rascal as you are."

"Well," says Bill. "I want money, then, and am ready to come into terms. What have you to say to that, Nick?"

"Let me see—let me look at you," says his companion, turning him about. "Now, Bill, in the first place, are you not as finished a scarecrow as ever stood upon two legs?"

"I play second fiddle to you there again," says Bill.

"There you stand, with the blackguards' coat of arms quartered under your eye, and——"

"Don't make little of *black*guards," said Bill, "nor spake disparagingly of *your own* crest."

"Why, what would you bring, you brazen rascal, if you were fairly put up at auction?"

"Faith, I'd bring more bidders than you would," said Bill, "if you were to go off at auction tomorrow. I tell you they should bid *downward* to come to your value, Nicholas. We have no coin *small* enough to purchase you."

"Well, no matter," said Nick. "If you are willing to be mine at the expiration of seven years, I will give you more money than ever the rascally breed of you was worth."

"Done!" said Bill. "But no disparagement to my family, in the meantime; so down with the hard cash, and don't be a *neger*."

The money was accordingly paid down; but as nobody was present, except the giver and receiver, the amount of what Bill got was never known.

"Won't you give me a luck penny?" said the old gentleman.

"Tut," said Billy, "so prosperous an old fellow as you cannot want it; however, bad luck to you, with all my heart! and it's rubbing grease to a fat pig to say so. Be off now, or I'll commit suicide on you. Your absence is a cordial to most people, you infernal old profligate. You have injured my morals even for the short time you have been with me, for I don't find myself so virtuous as I was."

"Is that your gratitude, Billy?"

"Is it gratitude *you* speak of, man? I wonder you don't blush when you name it. However, when you come again, if you bring a third eye in your head you will see what I mane, Nicholas, ahagur."

The old gentleman, as Bill spoke, hopped across the ditch on his way to *Downing* Street, where of late 'tis thought he possesses much influence.

Bill now began by degrees to show off, but still wrought a little at his trade to blindfold the neighbors. In a very short time, however, he became a great man. So long indeed as he was a *poor* rascal, no decent person would speak to him; even the proud servingmen at the "Big House" would turn up their noses at him. And he well deserved to be made little of by others, because he was mean enough to make little of himself. But when it was seen and known that he had oceans of money, it was wonderful to think, although he was *now* a greater blackguard than ever, how those who despised him before began to come round him and court his company. Bill, however, had neither sense nor spirit to make those sunshiny friends know their distance; not he—instead of that he was proud to be seen in decent company, and so long as the money lasted, it was "hail fellow well met" between himself and every fair-faced *spunger* who had a horse under him, a decent coat to his back, and a good appetite to eat his dinners. With riches and all, Bill was the same man still; but, somehow or other, there is a great difference between a rich profligate and a poor one, and Bill found it so to his cost in *both* cases.

Before half the seven years was passed, Bill had his carriage and his equipages; was hand and glove with my Lord This, and my Lord That; kept hounds and hunters; was the first sportsman at the Curragh; patronized every boxing ruffian he could pick up; and betted night and day on cards, dice, and horses. Bill, in short, *should* be a blood, and except he did all this, he could not presume to mingle with the fashionable bloods of his time.

It's an old proverb, however, that "what is got over the Devil's back is sure to go off under it," and in Bill's case this proved true. In short, the old boy himself could not supply him with money so fast as he made it fly; it was "come easy, go easy," with Bill, and so sign was on it, before he came within two years of his time he found his purse empty.

And now came the value of his summer friends to be known. When it was discovered that the cash was no longer flush with him—that stud, and carriage, and hounds were going to the hammer—whish! off they went, friends, relations, pot companions, dinner eaters, black-legs, and all, like a flock of crows that had smelt gunpowder. Down Bill soon went, week after week and day after day, until at last he was obliged to put on the leather apron and take to the hammer again; and not only that, for as no experience could make him wise, he once more began his taproom brawls, his quarrels with Judy, and took to his "high feeding" at the dry potatoes and salt. Now, too, came the cutting tongues of all who knew him, like razors upon him. Those that he scorned because they were poor and himself rich now paid him back his own with interest; and those that he had measured himself with, because they were rich, and who only countenanced him in consequence of his wealth, gave him the hardest word in their cheeks. The Devil mend him! He deserved it all, and more if he had got it.

Bill, however, who was a hardened sinner, never fretted himself down an ounce of flesh by what was said to him or of him. Not he; he cursed, and fought, and swore, and schemed away as usual, taking in everyone he could; and surely none could match him at villainy of all sorts and sizes.

At last the seven years became expired, and Bill was one morning sitting in his forge, sober and hungry, the wife cursing him, and the childhre squalling as before; he was thinking how he might defraud some honest neighbor out of a breakfast to stop their mouths and his own, too, when who walks in to him but old Nick to demand his bargain.

"Morrow, Bill!" says he with a sneer.

"The Devil welcome you!" says Bill. "But you have a fresh memory."

"A bargain's a bargain between two *honest* men, any day," says Satan; "when I speak of *honest* men, I mean *yourself* and *me,* Bill"; and he put his tongue in his cheek to make game of the unfortunate rogue he had come for.

"Nick, my worthy fellow," said Bill, "have bowels; you wouldn't do a shabby thing; you wouldn't disgrace your own character by putting more weight upon a falling man. You know what it is to get a *comedown* yourself, my worthy; so just keep your toe in your pump, and walk off with yourself somewhere else. A *cool* walk will sarve you better than my company, Nicholas."

"Bill, it's no use in shirking," said his friend; "your swindling tricks may enable you to cheat others, but you won't cheat *me,* I guess. You want nothing to make you perfect in your way but to travel; and travel you shall under my guidance, Billy. No, no—*I'm* not to be swindled, my good fellow. I have rather a—a—better opinion of myself, Mr. D., than to think that you could outwit one Nicholas Clutie, Esq.— ahem!"

"You may sneer, you sinner," replied Bill, "but I tell you that I have outwitted men who could buy and sell you to your face. Despair, you villain, when I tell you that *no attorney* could stand before me."

Satan's countenance got blank when he heard this; he wriggled and fidgeted about and appeared to be not quite comfortable.

"In that case, then," says he, "the sooner I *deceive* you the better; so turn out for the *Low Countries.*"

"Is it come to that in earnest?" said Bill. "And are you going to act the rascal at the long run?"

" 'Pon honor, Bill."

"Have patience, then, you sinner, till I finish this horseshoe—it's the last of a set I'm finishing for one of your friend the attorney's horses. And here, Nick, I hate idleness; you know it's the mother of mischief; take this sledge hammer and give a dozen strokes or so, till I get it out of hands, and then here's with you, since it must be so."

He then gave the bellows a puff that blew half a peck of dust in Club-foot's face, whipped out the red-hot iron, and set Satan sledging away for bare life.

"Faith," says Bill to him, when the shoe was finished, "it's a thousand pities ever the sledge should be out of your hand; the great *Parra Gow* was a child to you at sledging, you're such an able tyke. Now just exercise yourself till I bid the wife and childhre good-by, and then I'm off."

Out went Bill, of course, without the slightest notion of coming back; no more than Nick had that he could not give up the sledging, and indeed neither could he, but was forced to work away as if he was sledging for a wager. This was just what Bill wanted. He was now compelled to sledge on until it was Bill's pleasure to release him; and so we leave him very industriously employed, while we look after the worthy who outwitted him.

In the meantime Bill broke cover and took to the country at large; wrought a little journey work wherever he could get it, and in this way went from one place to another, till, in the course of a month, he walked back very coolly into his own forge to see how things went on in his absence. There he found Satan in a rage, the perspiration pouring from him in torrents, hammering with might and main upon the naked anvil. Bill calmly leaned back against the wall, placed his hat upon the side of his head, put his hands into his breeches pockets, and began to whistle *Shaun Gow's* hornpipe. At length he says, in a very quiet and good-humored way:

"Morrow, Nick!"

"Oh!" says Nick, still hammering away. "Oh! you double-distilled villain (hech!), may the most refined, ornamental (hech!) collection of curses that ever was gathered (hech!) into a single nosegay of ill fortune (hech!) shine in the buttonhole of your conscience (hech!) while your name is Bill Dawson! I denounce you (hech!) as a double-milled villain, a finished, hot-pressed knave (hech!), in comparison of whom all the other knaves I ever knew (hech!), attorneys included, are honest men. I brand you (hech!) as the pearl of cheats, a tiptop take-in (hech!). I denounce you, I say again, for the villainous treatment (hech!) I have received at your hands in this most untoward (hech!) and unfortunate transaction between us; for (hech!) unfortunate, in every sense, is he that has anything to do with (hech!) such a prime and finished impostor."

"You're very warm, Nicky," says Bill; "what puts you into a passion, you old sinner? Sure if it's your own will and pleasure to take exercise at my anvil, *I'm* not to be abused for it. Upon my credit, Nicky, you ought to blush for using such blackguard language, so unbecoming your grave character. You cannot say that it was I set you a-hammering at the empty anvil, you profligate.

"However, as you are so very industrious, I simply say it would be a thousand pities to take you from it. Nick, I love industry in my heart, and I always encourage it, so work away; it's not often you spend your time so creditably. I'm afraid if you weren't at that you'd be worse employed."

"Bill, have bowels," said the operative; "you wouldn't go to lay more weight on a falling man, you know; you wouldn't disgrace your character by such a piece of iniquity as keeping an inoffensive gentleman advanced in years, at such an unbecoming and rascally job as this. Generosity's your top virtue, Bill; not but that you have many other excellent ones, as well as that, among which, as you say yourself, I reckon industry; but still it is in generosity you *shine*. Come, Bill, honor bright, and release me."

"Name the terms, you profligate."

"You're above terms, William; a generous fellow like you never thinks of terms."

"Good-by, old gentleman!" said Bill very coolly. "I'll drop in to see you once a month."

"No, no, Bill, you infern—a—a—— You excellent, worthy, delightful fellow, not so fast; not so fast. Come, name your terms, you sland—— My dear Bill, name your terms."

"Seven years more."

"I agree; but——"

"And the same supply of cash as before, down on the nail here."

"Very good; very good. You're rather simple, Bill; rather soft, I must confess. Well, no matter. I shall yet turn the tab—a—hem! You are an exceedingly simple fellow, Bill; still there will come a day, my *dear* Bill—there will come——"

"Do you grumble, you vagrant? Another word, and I double the terms."

"Mum, William—mum; *tace* is Latin for a candle."

"Seven years more of grace, and the same measure of the needful that I got before. Ay or no?"

"Of grace, Bill! Ay! Ay! Ay! There's the cash. I accept the terms. Oh, blood! The rascal—of grace!! Bill!"

"Well, now drop the hammer and vanish," says Billy; "but what would you think to take this sledge, while you stay, and give me a—— Eh! Why in such a hurry?" he added, seeing that Satan withdrew in double-quick time.

"Hollo! Nicholas!" he shouted. "Come back; you forgot something!" And when the old gentleman looked behind him, Billy shook the hammer at him, on which he vanished altogether.

Billy now got into his old courses; and what shows the kind of people the world is made of, he also took up with his old company. When they saw that he had the money once more and was sowing it about him in all directions, they immediately began to find excuses for his former extravagance.

"Say what you will," said one, "Bill Dawson's a spirited fellow that bleeds like a prince."

"He's a hospitable man in his own house, or out of it, as ever lived," said another.

"His only fault is," observed a third, "that he is, if anything, too generous and doesn't know the value of money; his fault's on the right side, however."

"He has the spunk in him," said a fourth; "keeps a capital table, prime wines, and a standing welcome for his friends."

"Why," said a fifth, "if he doesn't enjoy his money while he lives, he won't when he's dead; so more power to him, and a wider throat to his purse."

Indeed, the very persons who were cramming themselves at his expense despised him at heart. They knew very well, however, how to take him on the weak side. Praise his generosity, and he would do anything; call him a man of spirit, and you might fleece him to his face. Sometimes he would toss a purse of guineas to this knave, another to that flatterer, a third to a bully, and a fourth to some broken-down rake—and all to convince them that *he* was a sterling friend—a man of mettle and liberality. But never was he known to help a virtuous and struggling family—to assist the widow or the fatherless, or to do any other act that was *truly* useful. It is to be supposed the reason of this was that as he spent it, as most of the world do, in the service of the Devil, by whose aid he got it, he was prevented from turning it to a good account. Between you and me, dear reader, there are more persons acting after Bill's fashion in the same world than you dream about.

When his money was out again, his friends played him the same rascally game once more. No sooner did his poverty become plain than the knaves began to be troubled with small fits of modesty, such as an unwillingness to come to his place when there was no longer anything to be got there. A kind of virgin bashfulness prevented them from speaking to him when they saw him getting out on the wrong side of his clothes. Many of them would turn away from him in the prettiest and most delicate manner when they thought he wanted to borrow money from them—all for fear of putting him to the blush for asking it. Others again, when they saw him coming toward their houses about dinner hour, would become so confused, from mere gratitude, as to think themselves in another place; and their servants, seized, as it were, with the same feeling, would tell Bill that their masters were "not at home."

At length, after traveling the same villainous round as before, Bill was compelled to betake himself, as the last remedy, to the forge; in other words, he found that there is, after all, nothing in this world that a man can rely on so firmly and surely as his own industry. Bill, however, wanted the organ of common sense, for his experience—and it was sharp enough to leave an impression—ran off him like water off a duck.

He took to his employment sorely against his grain, but he had now no choice. He must either work or starve, and starvation is like a great doctor—nobody tries it till every other remedy fails them. Bill had been twice rich; twice a gentleman among blackguards, but always a blackguard among gentlemen, for no wealth or acquaintance with decent society could rub the rust of his native vulgarity off him. He was now a common blinking sot in his forge; a drunken bully in the taproom, cursing and browbeating everyone as well as his wife; boasting of how much money he had spent in his day; swaggering about the high doings he carried on; telling stories about himself and Lord This at the Curragh; the dinners he gave—how much they cost him—and attempting to extort credit upon the strength of his former wealth. He was too ignorant, however, to know that he was publishing his own disgrace and that it was a mean-spirited thing to be proud of what ought to make him blush through a deal board nine inches thick.

He was one morning industriously engaged in a quarrel with his wife, who, with a three-legged stool in her hand, appeared to mistake his head for his own anvil; he, in the meantime, paid his addresses to her with his leather apron, when who steps in to jog his memory about the little agreement that was between them but old Nick. The wife, it seems, in spite of all her exertions to the contrary, was getting the worst of it; and Sir Nicholas, willing to appear a gentleman of great gallantry, thought he could not do less than take up the lady's quarrel, particularly as Bill had laid her in a sleeping posture. Now Satan thought this too bad, and as he felt himself under many obligations to the sex, he determined to defend one of them on the present occasion; so as Judy rose, he turned upon her husband and floored him by a clever facer.

"You unmanly villain," said he, "is this the way you treat your wife? 'Pon honor, Bill, I'll chastise you on the spot. I could not stand by, a spectator of such ungentlemanly conduct, without giving you all claim to gallant——" Whack! The word was divided in his mouth by the blow of a churnstaff from Judy, who no sooner saw Bill struck than she nailed Satan, who "fell" once more.

"What, you villain! That's for striking my husband like a murderer behind his back," said Judy, and she suited the action to the word. "That's for interfering between man and wife. Would you murder the poor man before my face, eh? If *he* bates me, you shabby dog you, who has a better right? I'm sure it's nothing out of your pocket. Must you have your finger in every pie?"

This was anything but *idle* talk, for at every word she gave him a remembrance, hot and heavy. Nicholas backed, danced, and hopped; she advanced, still drubbing him with great perseverance, till at length he fell into the redoubtable armchair, which stood exactly behind him. Bill, who had been putting in two blows for Judy's one, seeing that his enemy was safe, now got between the Devil and his wife, *a situation that few will be disposed to envy him.*

"Tenderness, Judy," said the husband; "I hate cruelty. Go put the tongs in the fire, and make them red-hot. Nicholas, you have a nose," said he.

Satan began to rise but was rather surprised to find that he could not budge.

"Nicholas," says Bill, "how is your pulse? You don't look well; that is to say, you look worse than usual."

The other attempted to rise but found it a mistake.

"I'll thank you to come along," said Bill. "I have a fancy to travel under your guidance, and we'll take the *Low Countries* in our way, won't we? Get to your legs, you sinner; you know a bargain's a bargain between two *honest* men, Nicholas, meaning *yourself* and *me*. Judy, are the tongs hot?"

Satan's face was worth looking at as he turned his eyes from the husband to the wife and then fastened them on the tongs, now nearly at a furnace heat in the fire, conscious at the same time that he could not move out of the chair.

"Billy," said he, "you won't forget that I rewarded you generously the last time I saw you, in the way of business."

"Faith, Nicholas, it fails me to remember any generosity I ever showed you. Don't be womanish. I simply want to see what kind of stuff your nose is made of and whether it will stretch like a rogue's conscience. If it does we will flatter it up the *chimly* with red-hot tongs, and when this old hat is fixed on the top of it, let us alone for a weathercock."

"Have a *fellow feeling*, Mr. Dawson; you know *we* ought not to dispute. Drop the matter, and I give you the next seven years."

"We know all that," says Billy, opening the red-hot tongs very coolly.

"Mr. Dawson," said Satan, "if you cannot remember my friendship to yourself, don't forget how often I stood your father's friend, your grandfather's friend, and the friend of all your relations up to the tenth generation. I intended, also, to stand by your children after you, so long as the name of Dawson—and a respectable one it is—might last."

"Don't be blushing, Nick," says Bill; "you are too modest; that was ever your failing; hould up your head, there's money bid for you. I'll give you such a nose, my good friend, that you will have to keep an outrider before you, to carry the end of it on his shoulder."

"Mr. Dawson, I pledge my honor to raise your children in the world as high as they can go, no matter whether they desire it or not."

"That's very kind of you," says the other, "and I'll do as much for your nose."

He gripped it as he spoke, and the old boy immediately sung out; Bill pulled, and the nose went with him like a piece of warm wax. He then transferred the tongs to Judy, got a ladder, resumed the tongs, ascended the chimney, and tugged stoutly at the nose until he got it five feet above the roof. He then fixed the hat upon the top of it and came down.

"There's a weathercock," said Billy; "I defy Ireland to show such a beauty. Faith, Nick, it would make the purtiest steeple for a church in all Europe, and the old hat fits it to a shaving."

In this state, with his nose twisted up the chimney, Satan sat for some time, experiencing the novelty of what might be termed a peculiar sensation. At last the worthy husband and wife began to relent.

"I think," said Bill, "that we have made the most of the nose, as well as the joke; I believe, Judy, it's long enough."

"What is?" says Judy.

"Why, the joke," said the husband.

"Faith, and I think so is the nose," said Judy.

"What do you say yourself, Satan?" said Bill.

"Nothing at all, William," said the other; "but that—ha! ha!—it's a good joke—an excellent joke, and a goodly nose, too, as it *stands*. You were always a gentlemanly man, Bill, and did things with a grace; still, if I might give an opinion on such a trifle——"

"It's no trifle at all," says Bill, "if you spake of the nose."

"Very well, it is not," says the other; "still, I am decidedly of opinion that if you could shorten both the joke and the nose without further violence, you would lay me under very heavy obligations, which I shall be ready to acknowledge and *repay* as I ought."

"Come," said Bill, "shell out once more, and be off for seven years. As much as you came down with the last time, and vanish."

The words were scarcely spoken, when the money was at his feet and Satan invisible. Nothing could surpass the mirth of Bill and his wife at the result of this adventure. They laughed till they fell down on the floor.

It is useless to go over the same ground again. Bill was still incorrigible. The money went as the Devil's money always goes. Bill caroused and squandered but could never turn a penny of it to a good purpose. In this way year after year went, till the seventh was closed and Bill's hour come. He was now, and had been for some time past, as miserable a knave as ever. Not a shilling had he, nor a shilling's worth, with the exception of his forge, his cabin, and a few articles of crazy furniture. In this state he was standing in his forge as before, straining his ingenuity how to make out a breakfast, when Satan came to look after him. The old gentleman was sorely puzzled how to get at him. He kept skulking and sneaking about the forge for some time, till he saw that Bill hadn't a cross to bless himself with. He immediately changed himself into a guinea and lay in an open place where he knew Bill would see him. "If," said he, "I once get into his possession, I can manage him." The honest smith took the bait, for it was well gilded; he clutched the guinea, put it into his purse, and closed it up. "Ho! Ho!" shouted the Devil out of the purse. "You're caught, Bill; I've secured you at last, you knave you. Why don't you despair, you villain, when you think of what's before you?"

"Why, you unlucky ould dog," said Bill, "is it there you are? Will you always drive your head into every loophole that's set for you? Faith, Nick achora, I never had you bagged till now."

Satan then began to tug and struggle with a view of getting out of the purse, but in vain.

"Mr. Dawson," said he, "we understand each other. I'll give the seven years additional and the cash on the nail."

"Be aisey, Nicholas. You know the weight of the hammer, that's enough. It's not a whipping with feathers you're going to get, anyhow. Just be aisey."

"Mr. Dawson, I grant I'm not your match. Release me, and I double the case. I was merely trying your temper when I took the shape of a guinea."

"Faith and I'll try yours before I lave it, I've a notion." He immediately commenced with the sledge, and Satan sang out with a considerable want of firmness. "Am I heavy enough?" said Bill.

"Lighter, lighter, William, if you love me. I haven't been well latterly, Mr. Dawson—I have been delicate—my health, in short, is in a very precarious state, Mr. Dawson."

"I can believe *that*," said Bill, "and it will be more so before I have done with you. Am I doing it right?"

"Bill," said Nick, "is this gentlemanly treatment in your own respectable shop? Do you think, if you dropped into my little place, that I'd act this rascally part toward you? Have you no compunction?"

"I know," replied Bill, sledging away with vehemence, "that you're notorious for giving your friends a *warm* welcome. Divil an ould youth more so; but you must be daling in bad coin, must you? However, good or bad, you're in for a sweat now, you sinner. Am I doin' it purty?"

"Lovely, William—but, if possible, a little more delicate."

"Oh, how delicate you are! Maybe a cup o' tay would sarve you, or a little small gruel to compose your stomach?"

"Mr. Dawson," said the gentleman in the purse, "hold your hand and let us understand one another. I have a proposal to make."

"Hear the sinner anyhow," said the wife.

"Name your own sum," said Satan, "only set me free."

"No, the sorra may take the toe you'll budge till you let Bill off," said the wife; "hould him hard, Bill, barrin' he sets *you* clear of your engagement."

"There it is, my posy," said Bill; "that's the condition. If you don't give *me up,* here's at you once more—and you must double the cash you gave the last time, too. So, if you're of that opinion, say *ay*—leave the cash and be off."

The money appeared in a glittering heap before Bill, upon which he exclaimed, "The *ay* has it, you dog. Take to your pumps now, and fair weather after you, you vagrant; but, Nicholas—Nick—here, here ——" The other looked back and saw Bill, with a broad grin upon him, shaking the purse at him. "Nicholas, come back," said he. "I'm short a guinea." Nick shook his fist and disappeared.

It would be useless to stop now, merely to inform our readers that Bill was beyond improvement. In short, he once more took to his old habits and lived on exactly in the same manner as before. He had two sons—one as great a blackguard as himself, and who was also named after him; the other was a well-conducted, virtuous young man called James, who left his father and, having relied upon his own industry and honest perseverance in life, arrived afterward to great wealth and built the town called Castle Dawson, which is so called from its founder until this day.

Bill, at length, in spite of all his wealth, was obliged, as he himself said, "to travel"—in other words, he fell asleep one day and forgot to awaken; or, in still plainer terms, he died.

Now, it is usual, when a man dies, to close the history of his life and adventures at once; but with our hero this cannot be the case. The moment Bill departed he very naturally bent his steps toward the residence of St. Moroky, as being, in his opinion, likely to lead him toward the snuggest berth he could readily make out. On arriving, he gave a very humble kind of knock, and St. Moroky appeared.

"God save your Reverence!" said Bill, very submissively.

"Be off; there's no admittance here for so poor a youth as you are," said St. Moroky.

He was now so cold and fatigued that he cared little where he went, provided only, as he said himself, "he could rest his bones and get an air of the fire." Accordingly, after arriving at a large black gate, he knocked, as before, and was told he would get *instant* admittance the moment he gave his name.

"Billy Dawson," he replied.

"Off, instantly," said the porter to his companions, "and let His Majesty know that the rascal he dreads so much is here at the gate."

Such a racket and tumult were never heard as the very mention of Billy Dawson created.

In the meantime, his old acquaintance came running toward the gate with such haste and consternation that his tail was several times nearly tripping up his heels.

"Don't admit that rascal," he shouted; "bar the gate—make every chain and lock and bolt fast—I won't be safe—and I won't stay here, nor none of us need stay here, if he gets in—my bones are sore yet after him. No, no—begone, you villain—you'll get no entrance here—I know you too well."

Bill could not help giving a broad, malicious grin at Satan, and, putting his nose through the bars, he exclaimed, "Ha! You ould dog, I have you afraid of me at last, have I?"

He had scarcely uttered the words, when his foe, who stood inside, instantly tweaked him by the nose, and Bill felt as if he had been gripped by the same red-hot tongs with which he himself had formerly tweaked the nose of Nicholas.

Bill then departed but soon found that in consequence of the inflammable materials which strong drink had thrown into his nose, that organ immediately took fire, and, indeed, to tell the truth, kept burning night and day, winter and summer, without ever once going out from that hour to this.

Such was the sad fate of Billy Dawson, who has been walking without stop or stay, from place to place, ever since; and in consequence of the flame on his nose, and his beard being tangled like a wisp of hay, he has been christened by the country folk Will-O'-the-Wisp, while, as it were, to show the mischief of his disposition, the circulating knave, knowing that he must seek the coldest bogs and quagmires in order to cool his nose, seizes upon that opportunity of misleading the unthinking and tipsy night travelers from their way, just that he may have the satisfaction of still taking in as many as possible.

Scotch

THE DEVIL once claimed with an awesome oath at a midnight revel in the kirk of North Berwick that James I was the greatest enemy he ever had.

This flattering testament was revealed at the trial of the infamous Dr. Fian and Gellie (or Geillis) Duncan(e), by Agnes Sampson, one of their forty-odd accomplices in the plot to drown James at sea in May 1590. James was returning at that time from Copenhagen with his bride, the Princess of Denmark, and the Deil's good offices had been enlisted to raise such a storm that the royal party would be wrecked. Strangely enough, history records that James almost *had* wet his cork-heeled shoon.

The case of Dr. Fian may have been partly responsible, as Charles Mackay suggests, for James's lifelong interest in the Devil and for the publication of his famous *Demonologie*. But the Devil was very much in evidence in Scotland during James's entire life. Between 1563, three years before his birth, when the death penalty was first instituted against witches, and 1603, when James ascended the throne of England, there were some 17,000 executions for witchcraft in Scotland —or approximately seventeen times the number of Scots who were later to die on the field at Culloden.

There is a documentary literature as profuse as it is bloody which covers this incredible period. Of more recent date there are Stevenson's succinct little fable (included here); *Witch Wood,* an excellent novel by John Buchan, the late Lord Tweedsmuir, and Robert Burns's poem, *Tam O'Shanter,* of gelid dialect:

> *There sat auld Nick, in shape o' beast;*
> *A towzie tyke, black, grim, and large,*
> *To gie them music was his charge;*
> *He screwed the pipes and gart them skirl*
> *Till roof an' rafters a' did dirl.*

At which point it is logical to introduce Sir Walter Scott's Devil from *Redgauntlet*—a devil so very much a Scot, himself, that he was willing to do a favor for a piper. This yarn, a complete story introduced to pass the time in the course of an otherwise indifferent work, manages to combine several threads common to Satanic literature.

Note the emphasis put upon the danger of accepting any gift, or any food or drink, while under the Deil's aegis. Note the white-hot chanter on the pipes offered to Steenie and the efficacy of the mention of God when the going gets tough.

Yes, the Deil has worn a tartan with the best of them.

THE DEVIL AND THE INNKEEPER

Robert Louis Stevenson

ONCE UPON A TIME the Devil stayed at an inn, where no one knew him, for they were people whose education had been neglected. He was bent on mischief and for a time kept everybody by the ears. But at last the innkeeper set a watch upon the Devil and took him in the fact.

The innkeeper got a rope's end.

"Now I am going to thrash you," said the innkeeper.

"You have no right to be angry with me," said the Devil. "I am only the Devil, and it is my nature to do wrong."

"Is that so?" asked the innkeeper.

"Fact, I assure you," said the Devil.

"You really cannot help doing ill?" asked the innkeeper.

"Not in the smallest," said the Devil. "It would be useless cruelty to thrash a thing like me."

"It would indeed," said the innkeeper.

And he made a noose and hanged the Devil.

"There!" said the innkeeper.

WANDERING WILLIE'S TALE

Sir Walter Scott

YE MAUN HAVE HEARD of Sir Robert Redgauntlet of that Ilk, who lived in these parts before the dear years. The country will lang mind him; and our fathers used to draw breath thick if ever they heard him named. He was out wi' the Hielandmen in Montrose's time; and again he was in the hills wi' Glencairn in the saxteen hundred and fifty-twa; and sae when King Charles the Second came in, wha was in sic favour as the Laird of Redgauntlet? He was knighted at Lonon court, wi' the King's ain sword; and being a red-hot prelatist, he came down here, rampauging like a lion, with commissions of lieutenancy (and of lunacy, for what I ken), to put down a' the Whigs and Covenanters in the country. Wild wark they made of it; for the Whigs were as dour as the Cavaliers were fierce, and it was which should first tire the other. Redgauntlet was aye for the strong hand; and his name is kend as wide in the country as Claverhouse's or Tam Dalyell's. Glen, nor dargle, nor mountain, nor cave could hide the puir Hill-folk when Redgauntlet was out with bugle and bloodhound after them, as if they had been sae mony deer. And troth when they fand them, they didna mak muckle mair ceremony than a Hielandman wi' a roebuck. It was just, "Will ye tak the test?" If not, "Make ready—present— fire!" and there lay the recusant.

Far and wide was Sir Robert hated and feared. Men thought he had a durect compact with Satan; that he was proof against steel, and that bullets happed aff his buff-coat like hailstanes from a hearth; that he had a mear that would turn a hare on the side of Carrifra Gauns—and muckle to the same purpose, of whilk mair anon. The best blessing they wared on was, "Deil scowp wi' Redgauntlet!" He wasna a bad maister to his ain folk though, and was weel aneugh liked by his tenants; and as for the lackies and troopers that raid out wi' him to the persecutions, as the Whigs ca'd those killing times, they wad hae drunken themsells blind to his health at ony time.

Now you are to ken that my gudesire lived on Redgauntlet's grund; they ca' the place Primrose Knowe. We had lived on the grund, and under the Redgauntlets, since the riding days, and lang before. It was a pleasant bit; and I think the air is callerer and fresher there than onywhere else in the country. It's a' deserted now; and I sat on the broken door-cheek three days since, and was glad I couldna see the plight the place was in; but that's a' wide o' the mark. There dwelt my gudesire, Steenie Steenson, a rambling, rattling chiel, he had been in his young days, and could play weel on the pipes; he was famous at "hoopers and Girders," a' Cumberland couldna touch him at "Jockie Lattin," and he had the finest finger for the backlilt between Berwick and Carlisle. The like o' Steenie wasna the sort that they made Whigs o'. And so he became a Tory, as they ca' it, which we now ca' Jacobites, just out of a kind of needcessity, that he might belang to some side or other. He had nae ill-will to the Whig bodies, and liked little to see the blude rin, though, being obliged to follow Sir Robert in hunting and hoisting, watching and warding, he saw muckle mischief, and maybe did some, that he couldna avoid.

Now Steenie was a kind of favourite with his master, and kend a' the folks about the castle, and was often sent for to play the pipes when they were at their merriment. Auld Dougal MacCallum, the butler, that had followed Sir Robert through gude and ill, thick and thin, pool and stream, was specially fond of the pipes, and aye gae my gudesire his gude word wi' the laird; for Dougal could turn his master round his finger.

Weel, round came the Revolution, and it had like to have broken the hearts baith of Dougal and his master. But the change was not a'thegither sae great as they feared, and other folk thought for. The Whigs made an unco crawing what they wad do with their auld enemies, and in special wi' Sir Robert Redgauntlet. But there were ower mony great folks dipped in the same doings to mak a spick and span new warld. So Parliament passed it a' ower easy; and Sir Robert, bating that he was held to hunting foxes instead of Covenanters, remained just the man he was. His revel was as loud, and his hall as weel lighted, as ever it had been, though maybe he lacked the fines of the Noncomformists, that used to come to stock his larder and cellar; for it is certain he began to be keener about the rents than his tenants used to find him before, and they behoved to be prompt to the rent-day, or else the laird wasna pleased. And he was sic an awsome body that naebody cared to anger him; for the oaths he swore, and the rages that he used to get into, and the looks that he put on, made men sometimes think him a devil incarnate.

Weel, my gudesire was nae manager—no that he was a very great misguider—but he hadna the saving gift, and he got twa terms' rent in arrear. He got the first brash at Whitsunday put ower wi' fair word and piping; but when Martinmas came, there was a summons from the grund-officer to come wi' the rent on a day preceese, or else Steenie behoved to flit. Sair wark he had to get the siller; but he was weel-freended, and at last he got the haill scraped thegither—a thousand merkes; the maist of it was from a neighbour they ca'd Laurie Lapraik —a sly tod. Laurie had walth o'gear—could hunt wi' the hound and rin wi' the hare—and be Whig or Tory, saunt or sinner, as the wind stood. He was a professor in this Revolution warld; but he liked an orra sough of this warld, and a tune on the pipes weel aneugh at a bye-time; and abune a', he thought he had gude security for the siller he lent my gudesire ower the stocking at Primrose Knowe.

Away trots my gudesire to Redgauntlet Castle, wi' a heavy purse and a light heart, glad to be out of the laird's danger. Weel, the first thing he learned at the castle was that Sir Robert had fretted himsell into a fit of the gout, because he did not appear before twelve o'clock. It wasna a'thegither for sake of the money, Dougal thought; but be-cause he didna like to part wi' my gudesire aff the grund. Dougal was glad to see Steenie, and brought him into the great oak parlour, and there sat the laird his leesome lane, excepting that he had beside him a great ill-favoured jackanape, that was a special pet of his—a can-kered beast it was, and mony an ill-natured trick it played; ill to please it was, and easily angered—ran about the haill castle, chattering and yowling, and pinching and biting folk, especially before ill weather, or disturbances in the state. Sir Robert ca'd it Major Weir, after the war-lock that was burnt; and few folk liked either the name or the condi-tions of the creature—they thought there was something in it by ordi-nar—and my gudesire was not just easy in mind when the door shut on him, and he saw himself in the room wi' naebody but the laird, Dougal MacCallum, and the major, a thing that hadna chanced to him before.

Sir Robert sat, or, I should say, lay, in a great armed chair, wi' his grand velvet gown, and his feet on a cradle; for he had baith gout and gravel, and his face looked as gash and ghastly as Satan's. Major Weir sat opposite to him, in a red laced coat, and the laird's wig on his head; and aye as Sir Robert girned wi' pain, the jackanape girned too, like a sheep's-head between a pair of tangs—an ill-faured, fearsome couple they were. The laird's buff-coat was hung on a pin behind him, and his broadsword and his pistols within reach; for he keepit up the auld fashion of having the weapons ready, and a horse saddled day and night, just as he used to do when he was able to loup on horse-back, and away after ony of the Hill-folk he could get speerings of.

Some said it was for fear of the Whigs taking vengeance, but I judge it was just his auld custom—he wasna gien to fear onything. The rental-book, wi' its black cover and brass clasps, was lying beside him; and a book of sculduddry sangs was put betwixt the leaves, to keep it open at the place where it bore evidence against the goodman of Primrose Knowe, as behind the hand with his mails and duties. Sir Robert gave my gudesire a look as if he would have withered his heart in his bosom. Ye maun ken he had a way of bending his brows that men saw the visible mark of a horse-shoe in his forehead, deep-dinted, as if it had been stamped there.

"Are ye come light-handed, ye son of a toom whistle?" said Sir Robert. "Zounds! if you are——"

My gudesire, with as gude a countenance as he could put on, made a leg, and placed the bag of money on the table wi' a dash, like a man that does something clever. The laird drew it to him hastily. "Is it all here, Steenie, man?"

"Your honour will find it right," said my gudesire.

"Here, Dougal," said the laird, "gie Steenie a tass of brandy downstairs, till I count the siller and write the receipt."

But they werena weel out of the room when Sir Robert gied a yelloch that garr'd the castle rock. Back ran Dougal—in flew the liverymen—yell on yell gied the laird, ilk ane mair awfu' than the ither. My gudesire knew not whether to stand or flee, but he ventured back into the parlour, where a' was gaun hirdie-girdie—naebody to say "come in" or "gae out." Terribly the laird roared for cauld water to his feet, and wine to cool his throat; and "Hell, hell, hell, and its flames," was aye the word in his mouth. They brought him water, and when then plunged his swoln feet into the tub, he cried out it was burning; and folk say that it *did* bubble and sparkle like a seething caldron. He flung the cup at Dougal's head, and said he had given him blood instead of burgundy; and, sure aneugh, the lass washed clotted blood aff the carpet the neist day. The jackanape they ca'd Major Weir, it jibbered and cried as if it was mocking its master. My gudesire's head was like to turn; he forgot baith siller and receipt, and downstairs he banged; but as he ran, the shrieks came faint and fainter; there was a deep-drawn shivering groan, and word gaed through the castle that the laird was dead.

Weel, away came my gudesire wi' his finger in his mouth, and his best hope was that Dougal had seen the money-bag, and heard the laird speak of writing the receipt. The young laird, now Sir John, came from Edinburgh to see things put to rights. Sir John and his father never gree'd weel. Sir John had been bred an advocate, and afterwards sat in the last Scots Parliament and voted for the Union, having gotten, it was thought, a rug of the compensations; if his father could have come out of his grave he would have brained him for it on his awn hearthstane. Some thought it was easier counting with the auld rough knight than the fair-spoken young ane—but mair of that anon.

Dougal MacCallum, poor body, neither grat nor graned, but gaed about the house looking like a corpse, but directing, as was his duty, a' the order of the grand funeral. Now, Dougal looked aye waur and waur when night was coming, and was aye the last to gang to his bed, whilk was in a little round just opposite the chamber of dais, whilk his master occupied while he was living, and where he now lay in state, as they ca'd it, weel-a-day! The night before the funeral, Dougal could keep his awn counsel nae langer: he came doun with his proud spirit, and fairly asked auld Hutcheon to sit in his room with him for an hour. When they were in the round, Dougal took ae tass of brandy to himsell and gave another to Hutcheon, and wished him all health and lang life, and said that, for himsell he wasna lang for this world; for that, every night since Sir Robert's death, his silver call had sounded from the state chamber, just as it used to do at nights in his lifetime, to call Dougal to help to turn him in his bed. Dougal said that, being alone with the dead on that floor of the tower (for naebody cared to wake Sir Robert Redgauntlet like another corpse), he had never daured to answer the call, but that now his conscience checked him, for neglecting his duty; for, "though death breaks service," said Mac-Callum, "it shall never break my service to Sir Robert; and I will answer his next whistle, so be you will stand by me, Hutcheon."

Hutcheon had nae will to the wark, but he had stood by Dougal in battle and broil, and he wad not fail him at this pinch; so down the carles sat ower a stoup of brandy, and Hutcheon, who was something of a clerk, would have read a chapter of the Bible; but Dougal would hear naething but a blaud of Davie Lindsay, whilk was the waur preparation.

When midnight came, and the house was quiet as the grave, sure aneugh the silver whistle sounded as sharp and shrill as if Sir Robert was blowing it, and up gat the twa auld serving-men and tottered into the room where the dead man lay. Hutcheon saw aneugh at the first glance; for there were torches in the room, which showed him the foul fiend in his ain shape, sitting on the laird's coffin! Ower he couped as if he had been dead. He could not tell how lang he lay in a trance at the door, but when he gathered himself he cried on his neighbour, and getting nae answer, raised the house, when Dougal was found lying dead within twa steps of the bed where his master's coffin was placed.

As for the whistle, it was gane anes and aye; but mony a time was it heard at the top of the house on the bartizan, and amang the auld chimneys and turrets, where the howlets have their nests. Sir John hushed the matter up, and the funeral passed over without mair bogle-wark.

But when a' was ower, and the laird was beginning to settle his affairs, every tenant was called up for his arrears, and my gudesire for the full sum that stood against him in the rental-book. Weel, away he trots to the castle, to tell his story, and there he is introduced to Sir John, sitting in his father's chair, in deep mourning, with weepers and hanging cravat, and a small walking rapier by his side, instead of the auld broadsword that had a hundredweight of steel about it, what with blade, chape, and basket-hilt. I have heard their communing so often tauld ower, that I almost think I was there mysell, though I couldna be born at the time. (In fact, Alan, my companion mimicked, with a good deal of humour, the flattering, conciliatory tone of the tenant's address, and the hypocritical melancholy of the laird's reply. His grandfather, he said, had, while he spoke, his eye fixed on the rental-book, as if it were a mastiff-dog that he was afraid would spring up and bite him.)

"I wuss ye joy, sir, of the head seat, and the white loaf, and the braid Lairdship. Your father was a kind man to friends and followers; muckle grace to you, Sir John, to fill his shoon—his boots, I suld say, for he seldom wore shoon, unless it were muils when he had the gout."

"Ay, Steenie," quoth the laird, sighing deeply, and putting his napkin to his een, "his was a sudden call, and he will be missed in the country; no time to set his house in order: weel prepared Godward, no doubt, which is the root of the matter, but left us behind a tangled hesp to wind, Steenie. Hem! hem! We maun go to business, Steenie; much to do, and little time to do it in."

Here he opened the fatal volume. I have heard of a thing they call Doomsday Book—I am clear it has been a rental of back-ganging tenants.

"Stephen," said Sir John, still in the same soft, sleekit tone of voice —"Stephen Stevenson, or Steenson, ye are down here for a year's rent behind the hand, due at last term."

Stephen. "Please your honour, Sir John, I paid it to your father."

Sir John. "Ye took a receipt then, doubtless, Stephen, and can produce it?"

Stephen. "Indeed I hadna time, an it like your honour; for nae sooner had I set doun the siller, and just as his honour Sir Robert, that's gaen, drew it till him to count it, and write out the receipt, he was ta'en wi' the pains that removed him."

"That was unlucky," said Sir John, after a pause. "But ye maybe paid it in the presence of somebody. I want but a *talis qualis* evidence, Stephen. I would go ower strictly to work with no poor man."

Stephen. "Troth, Sir John, there was naebody in the room but Dougal MacCallum, the butler. But, as your honour kens, he as e'en followed his auld master."

"Very unlucky again, Stephen," said Sir John, without altering his voice a single note. "The man to whom ye paid the money is dead; and the man who witnessed the payment is dead too; and the siller, which should have been to the fore, is neither seen nor heard tell of in the repositories. How am I to believe a' this?"

Stephen. "I dinna ken, your honour; but there is a bit memorandum note of the very coins—for, God help me! I had to borrow out of twenty purses—and I am sure that ilka man there set down will take his grit oath for what purpose I borrowed the money."

Sir John. "I have little doubt ye *borrowed* the money, Steenie. It is the *payment* to my father that I want to have some proof of."

Stephen. "The siller maun be about the house, Sir John. And since your honour never got it, and his honour that was canna have ta'en it wi' him, maybe some of the family may have seen it."

Sir John. "We will examine the servants, Stephen; that is but reasonable."

But lackey and lass, and page and groom, all denied stoutly that they had ever seen such a bag of money as my gudesire described. What was waur, he had unluckily not mentioned to any living soul of them his purpose of paying his rent. Ae quean had noticed something under his arm, but she took it for the pipes.

Sir John Redgauntlet ordered the servants out of the room, and then said to my gudesire, "Now, Steenie, ye see you have fair play; and, as I have little doubt ye ken better where to find the siller than ony other body, I beg, in fair terms, and for your own sake, that you will end this fasherie; for, Stephen, ye maun pay or flit."

"The Lord forgie your opinion," said Stephen, driven almost to his wit's end—"I am an honest man."

"So am I, Stephen," said his honour; "and so are all the folks in the house, I hope. But if there be a knave amongst us, it must be he that tells the story he cannot prove." He paused, and then added, mair sternly, "If I understand your trick, sir, you want to take advantage of some malicious reports concerning things in this family, and particularly respecting my father's sudden death, thereby to cheat me out of the money, and perhaps take away my character, by insinuating that I have received the rent I am demanding. Where do you suppose this money to be? I insist upon knowing."

My gudesire saw everything look sae muckle against him that he grew nearly desperate; however, he shifted from one foot to another, looked to every corner of the room, and made no answer.

"Speak out, sirrah," said the laird, assuming a look of his father's—a very particular ane, which he had when he was angry: it seemed as if the wrinkles of his frown made that selfsame fearful shape of a horse's shoe in the middle of his brow—"speak out, sir! I *will* know your thoughts. Do you suppose that I have this money?"

"Far be it frae me to say so," said Stephen.

"Do you charge any of my people with having taken it?"

"I wad be laith to charge them that may be innocent," said my gudesire; "and if there be any one that is guilty, I have nae proof."

"Somewhere the money must be, if there is a word of truth in your story," said Sir John; "I ask where you think it is, and demand a correct answer."

"In hell, if you *will* have my thoughts on it," said my gudesire, driven to extremity—"in hell! with your father, his jackanape, and his silver whistle."

Down the stairs he ran, for the parlour was nae place for him after such a word, and he heard the laird swearing blood and wounds behind him, as fast as ever did Sir Robert, and roaring for the bailie and the baron-officer.

Away rode my gudesire to his chief creditor, him they ca'd Laurie Lapraik, to try if he could make onything out of him; but when he tauld his story, he got but the warst word in his wame—thief, beggar, and dyvour were the saftest terms; and to the boot of these hard terms, Laurie brought up the auld story of his dipping his hand in the blood of God's saunts, just as if a tenant could have helped riding with the laird, and that a laird like Sir Robert Redgauntlet. My gudesire was by this time far beyond the bounds of patience, and while he and Laurie were at deil speed the liars, he was wanchancie aneugh to abuse Lapraik's doctrine as weel as the man, and said things that garr'd folks' flesh grue that heard them; he wasna just himsell, and he had lived wi' a wild set in his day.

At last they parted, and my gudesire was to ride hame through the wood of Pitmurkie, that is a' fou of black firs, as they say. I ken the wood, but the firs may be black or white for what I can tell. At the entry of the wood there is a wild common, and on the edge of the common a little lonely change-house, that was keepit then by an ostler-

wife—they suld hae ca'd her Tibbie Faw—and there puir Steenie
cried for a mutchkin of brandy, for he had had no refreshment the
haill day. Tibbie was earnest wi' him to take a bite o' meat, but he
couldna think o't, nor would he take his foot out of the stirrup, and
took off the brandy wholely at twa draughts, and named a toast at
each—the first was, the memory of Sir Robert Redgauntlet, and might
he never lie quiet in his grave till he had righted his poor bond-tenant;
and the second was, a health to Man's Enemy, if he would but get him
back the pock of siller, or tell him what came o't, for he saw the haill
world was like to regard him as a thief and a cheat, and he took that
waur than even the ruin of his house and hauld.

On he rode, little caring where. It was a dark night turned, and the
trees made it yet darker, and he let the beast take its ain road through
the wood; when, all of a sudden, from tired and wearied that it was
before, the nag began to spring, and flee, and stend, that my gudesire could hardly keep the saddle; upon the whilk, a horseman, suddenly riding up beside him, said, "That's a mettle beast of yours,
freend; will you sell him?" So saying, he touched the horse's neck with
his riding-wand, and it fell into its auld heigh-ho of a stumbling trot.
"But his spunk's soon out of him, I think," continued the stranger,
"and that is like mony a man's courage, that thinks he wad do great
things till he come to the proof."

My gudesire scarce listened to this, but spurred his horse, with
"Gude e'en to you, freend."

But it's like the stranger was ane that doesna lightly yield his point;
for, ride as Steenie liked, he was aye beside him at the selfsame pace.
At last my gudesire, Steenie Steenson, grew half angry, and, to say
the truth, half feared.

"What is it that ye want with me, freend?" he said. "If ye be a robber, I have nae money; if ye be a leal man, wanting company, I have
nae heart to mirth or speaking; and if ye want to ken the road, I scarce
ken it mysell."

"If you will tell me your grief," said the stranger, "I am one that,
though I have been sair misca'd in the world, am the only hand for
helping my freends."

So my gudesire, to ease his ain heart, mair than from any hope of
help, told him the story from beginning to end.

"It's a hard pinch," said the stranger; "but I think I can help you."

"If you could lend the money, sir, and take a lang day—I ken nae
other help on earth," said my gudesire.

"But there may be some under the earth," said the stranger. "Come,
I'll be frank wi' you; I could lend you the money on bond, but you

would maybe scruple my terms. Now, I can tell you that your auld laird is disturbed in his grave by your curses, and the wailing of your family, and if ye daur venture to go to see him, he will give you the receipt."

My gudesire's hair stood on end at this proposal, but he thought his companion might be some humoursome chield that was trying to frighten him, and might end with lending him the money. Besides, he was bauld wi' brandy, and desperate wi' distress; and he said he had courage to go to the gate of hell, and a step farther, for that receipt.

The stranger laughed.

Weel, they rode on through the thickest of the wood, when, all of a sudden, the horse stopped at the door of a great house; and, but that he knew the place was ten miles off, my father would have thought he was at Redgauntlet Castle. They rode into the outer courtyard, through the muckle faulding yetts, and aneath the auld portcullis; and the whole front of the house was lighted, and there were pipes and fiddles, and as much dancing and deray within as used to be at Sir Robert's house at Pace and Yule, and such high seasons. They lap off, and my gudesire, as seemed to him, fastened his horse to the very ring he had tied him to that morning, when he gaed to wait on the young Sir John.

"God!" said my gudesire. "If Sir Robert's death be but a dream!"

He knocked at the ha' door just as he was wont, and his auld acquaintance, Dougal MacCallum, just after his wont, too, came to open the door, and said, "Piper Steenie, are ye there, lad? Sir Robert has been crying for you."

My gudesire was like a man in a dream; he looked for the stranger, but he was gane for the time. At last he just tried to say, "Ha! Dougal Driveower, are ye living? I thought ye had been dead."

"Never fash yoursell wi' me," said Dougal, "but look to yoursell; and see ye tak naething frae onybody here, neither meat, drink, or siller, except just the receipt that is your ain."

So saying, he led the way out through halls and trances that were weel kend to my gudesire, and into the auld oak parlour; and there was as much singing of profane sangs, and birling of red wine, and speaking blasphemy and sculduddry, as had ever been in Redgauntlet Castle when it was at the blithest.

But, Lord take us in keeping! what a set of ghastly revellers they were that sat round that table! My gudesire kend mony that had long before gane to their place, for often had he piped to the most part in the hall of Redgauntlet. There was the fierce Middleton, and the dissolute Rothes, and the crafty Lauderdale; and Dalyell, with his bald head and a beard to his girdle; and Earlshall, with Cameron's blude on his hand; and wild Bonshaw, that tied blessed Mr. Cargill's limbs till the blude sprung; and Dumbarton Douglas, the twice-turned traitor baith to country and king. There was the Bluidy Advocate MacKenyie, who, for his worldly wit and wisdom, had been to the rest as a god. And there was Claverhouse, as beautiful as when he lived, with his long, dark, curled locks, streaming down over his laced buff-coat, and his left-hand always on his right spule-blade, to hide the wound that the silver bullet had made. He sat apart from them all, and looked at them with a melancholy, haughty countenance; while the rest hallooed, and sung, and laughed, that the room rang. But their smiles were fearfully contorted from time to time; and their laugh passed into such wild sounds as made my gudesire's very nails grow blue, and chilled the marrow in his banes.

They that waited at the table were just the wicked serving-men and troopers that had done their work and cruel bidding on earth. There was the Lang Lad of the Nethertown, that helped to take Argyle; and the bishop's summoner, that they called the Deil's Rattle-bag; and the wicked guardsmen, in their laced coats; and the savage Highland Amorites, that shed blood like water; and mony a proud serving-man, haughty of heart and bloody of hand, cringing to the rich, and making them wickeder than they would be; grinding the poor to powder, when the rich had broken them to fragments. And mony, mony mair were coming and ganging, a' as busy in their vocation as if they had been alive.

Sir Robert Redgauntlet, in the midst of a' this fearful riot, cried, wi' a voice like thunder, on Steenie Piper to come to the board-head where he was sitting, his legs stretched out before him, and swathed up with flannel, with his holster pistols aside him, while the great broadsword rested against his chair, just as my gudesire had seen him the last time upon earth—the very cushion for the jackanape was close to him, but the creature itself was not there; it wasna its hour, it's likely; for he heard them say as he came forward, "Is not the major come yet?" And another answered, "The jackanape will be here betimes the morn." And when my gudesire came forward, Sir Robert, or his ghaist, or the deevil in his likeness, said, "Weel, piper, hae ye settled wi' my son for the year's rent?"

With much ado my father gat breath to say that Sir John would not settle without his honour's receipt.

"Ye shall hae that for a tune of the pipes, Steenie," said the appearance of Sir Robert. "Play us up, 'Weel hoddled, Luckie.'"

Now this was a tune my gudesire learned frae a warlock, that heard

it when they were worshipping Satan at their meetings, and my gudesire had sometimes played it at the ranting suppers in Redgauntlet
Castle, but never very willingly; and now he grew cauld at the very
name of it, and said, for excuse, he hadna his pipes wi' him.

"MacCallum, ye limb of Beelzebub," said the fearfu' Sir Robert,
"bring Steenie the pipes that I am keeping for him!"

MacCallum brought a pair of pipes might have served the piper of
Donald of the Isles. But he gave my gudesire a nudge as he offered
them; and looking secretly and closely, Steenie saw that the chanter
was of steel, and heated to a white heat; so he had fair warning not to
trust his fingers with it. So he excused himself again, and said he was
faint and frightened, and had not wind aneugh to fill the bag.

"Then ye maun eat and drink, Steenie," said the figure; "for we do
little else here; and it's ill speaking between a fou man and a fasting."

Now these were the very words that the bloody Earl of Douglas said
to keep the king's messenger in hand, while he cut the head off Mac-
Lellan of Bombie, at the Threave Castle, and that put Steenie mair
and mair on his guard. So he spoke up like a man, and said he came
neither to eat, or drink, or make minstrelsy, but simply for his ain—
to ken what was come o' the money he had paid, and to get a discharge for it; and he was so stout-hearted by this time, that he charged
Sir Robert for conscience' sake (he had no power to say the holy
name), and as he hoped for peace and rest, to spread no snares for
him, but just to give him his ain.

The appearance gnashed its teeth, and laughed, but it took from a
large pocket-book the receipt, and handed it to Steenie. "There is your
receipt, ye pitiful cur; and for the money, my dog-whelp of a son may
go look for it in the Cat's Cradle."

My gudesire uttered mony thanks, and was about to retire when
Sir Robert roared aloud, "Stop though, thou sack-doudling son of a
whore! I am not done with thee. HERE we do nothing for nothing;
and you must return on this very day twelvemonth to pay your master
the homage that you owe me for my protection."

My father's tongue was loosed of a suddenty, and he said aloud, "I
refer mysell to God's pleasure, and not to yours."

He had no sooner uttered the word that all was dark around him,
and he sunk on the earth with such a sudden shock, that he lost both
breath and sense.

How lang Steenie lay there, he could not tell; but when he came to
himsell, he was lying in the auld kirkyard of Redgauntlet parochine,
just at the door of the family aisle, and the scutcheon of the auld
knight, Sir Robert, hanging over his head. There was a deep morning

fog on grass and gravestane around him, and his horse was feeding quietly beside the minister's twa cows. Steenie would have thought the whole was a dream, but he had the receipt in his hand, fairly written and signed by the auld laird; only the last letters of his name were a little disorderly, written like one seized with sudden pain.

Sorely troubled in his mind, he left that dreary place, rode through the mist to Redgauntlet Castle, and with much ado he got speech of the laird.

"Well, you dyvour bankrupt," was the first word, "have you brought me my rent?"

"No," answered my gudesire, "I have not; but I have brought your honour Sir Robert's receipt for it."

"How, sirrah? Sir Robert's receipt! You told me he had not given you one."

"Will your honour please to see if that bit line is right?"

Sir John looked at every line, and at every letter, with much attention and at last at the date, which my gudesire had not observed— " 'From my appointed place,' " he read, " 'this twenty-fifth of November.' What! That is yesterday! Villain, thou must have gone to Hell for this!"

"I got it from your honour's father; whether he be in Heaven or Hell, I know not," said Steenie.

"I will delate you for a warlock to the privy council!" said Sir John. "I will send you to your master, the devil, with the help of a tar-barrel and a torch!"

"I intend to delate mysell to the presbytery," said Steenie, "and tell them all I have seen last night, whilk are things fitter for them to judge of than a borrel man like me."

Sir John paused, composed himsell, and desired to hear the full history; and my gudesire told it him from point to point, as I have told it to you—word for word, neither more nor less.

Sir John was silent again for a long time, and at last he said, very composedly, "Steenie, this story of yours concerns the honour of many a noble family besides mine; and if it be a leasing-making, to keep yourself out of my danger, the least you can expect is to have a red-hot iron driven through your tongue, and that will be as bad as scaulding your fingers with a red-hot chanter. But yet it may be true, Steenie; and if the money cast up, I shall not know what to think of it. But where shall we find the Cat's Cradle? There are cats enough about the old house, but I think they kitten without the ceremony of bed or cradle."

"We were best ask Hutcheon," said my gudesire; "he kens a' the odd corners about as weel as—another serving-man that is now gane, and that I wad not like to name."

Aweel, Hutcheon, when he was asked, told them that a ruinous turret, lang disused, next to the clock-house, only accessible by a ladder, for the opening was on the outside, and far above the battlements, was called of old the Cat's Cradle.

"There will I go immediately," said Sir John; and he took (with what purpose, Heaven kens) one of his father's pistols from the hall-table, where they had lain since the night he died, and hastened to the battlements.

It was a dangerous place to climb, for the ladder was auld and frail, and wanted ane or twa rounds. However, up got Sir John, and entered at the turret door, where his body stopped the only little light that was in the bit turret. Something flees at him wi' a vengeance, maist dang him back ower; bang gaed the knight's pistol, and Hutcheon, that held the ladder, and my gudesire that stood beside him, hears a loud skelloch. A minute after, Sir John flings the body of the jackanape down to them, and cries that the siller is fund, and that they should come up and help him. And there was the bag of siller sure aneugh, and mony orra things besides that had been missing for mony a day. And Sir John, when he had riped the turret weel, led my gudesire into the dining-parlour, and took him by the hand, and spoke kindly to him, and said he was sorry he should have doubted his word, and that he would hereafter be a good master to him, to make amends.

"And now, Steenie," said Sir John, "although this vision of yours tends, on the whole, to my father's credit, as an honest man, that he should, even after his death, desire to see justice done to a poor man like you, yet you are sensible that ill-dispositioned men might make bad constructions upon it, concerning his soul's health. So, I think, we had better lay the haill dirdum on that ill-deedie creature, Major Weir, and say naething about your dream in the wood of Pitmurkie. You had taken ower muckle brandy to be very certain about ony thing; and, Steenie, this receipt (his hand shook while he held it out), it's but a queer kind of document, and we will do best, I think, to put it quietly in the fire."

"Od, but for as queer as it is, it's a' the voucher I have for my rent," said my gudesire, who was afraid, it may be, of losing the benefit of Sir Robert's discharge.

"I will bear the contents to your credit in the rental-book, and give you a discharge under my own hand," said Sir John, "and that on the spot. And, Steenie, if you can hold your tongue about this matter, you shall sit, from this term downward, at an easier rent."

"Mony thanks to your honour," said Steenie, who saw easily in what corner the wind was; "doubtless I will be conformable to all your honour's commands; only I would willingly speak wi' some powerful minister on the subject, for I do not like the sort of soumons of appointment whilk your honour's father——"

"Do not call the phantom my father!" said Sir John, interrupting him.

"Weel, then, the thing that was so like him," said my gudesire; "he spoke of my coming back to see him this time twelvemonth, and it's a weight on my conscience."

"Aweel, then," said Sir John, "if you be so much distressed in mind, you may speak to our minister of the parish; he is a douce man, regards the honour of our family, and the mair that he may look for some patronage from me."

Wi' that my gudesire readily agreed that the receipt should be burnt, and the laird threw it into the chimney with his ain hand. Burn it would not for them, though; but away it flew up the lum, wi' a lang train of sparks at its tail, and a hissing noise like a squib.

My gudesire gaed down to the manse, and the minister, when he had heard the story, said it was his real opinion that, though my gudesire had gaen very far in tampering with dangerous matters, yet, as he had refused the devil's arles (for such was the offer of meat and drink), and had refused to do homage by piping at his bidding, he hoped, that if he held a circumspect walk hereafter, Satan could take little advantage by what was come and gane. And, indeed, my gudesire, of his ain accord, lang forswore baith the pipes and the brandy; it was not even till the year was out, and the fatal day passed, that he would so much as take the fiddle, or drink usquebaugh or tippenny.

Sir John made up his story about the jackanape as he liked himsell; and some believe till this day there was no more in the matter than the filching nature of the brute. Indeed, ye'll no hinder some to threap that it was nane o' the Auld Enemy that Dougal and my gudesire (Hutcheon) saw in the laird's room, but only that wanchancie creature, the major, capering on the coffin; and that, as to the blawing on the laird's whistle that was heard after he was dead, the filthy brute could do that as weel as the laird himsell, if no better. But Heaven kens the truth, whilk first came out by the minister's wife, after Sir John and her ain gudeman were baith in the moulds. And then, my gudesire, wha was failed in his limbs, but not in his judgment or memory—at least nothing to speak of—was obliged to tell the real narrative to his freends for the credit of his good name. He might else have been charged for a warlock.

Russian

WHEN a Russian sells his soul to the Devil it is no casual bargain. A man of Latin temperament, having completed such a contract, proceeds to enjoy himself until the Money-Lender-on-Souls comes around to foreclose. The German bolstered by diabolical apologists who call themselves philosophers is well aware that there is no such thing as good or evil and that selling one's soul to the Devil is excellent strategy. The Englishman drives as good a bargain as possible and treats the whole affair as though the war in Heaven would eventually be won on the playing fields of Eton; he adds a mental note that it is always wise to have investments outside the tight little island, including a first lien on the furnaces of Hell (considered by the Foreign Office to be merely an outlying part of the British Empire).

But your true Russian goes into the psychological aspects of the deal.

For instance, take the case of Stavrogin, considered by Dostoevski the most important character in *The Possessed*. It is notorious that Katkov refused to publish the chapter of that novel in which Stavrogin has a conference with the Devil. The public was not ready in those days (and might even be shocked today) by the cataloguing of Stavrogin's sins—his unmotivated crimes, his violation of a child, his utterly debauched life in St. Petersburg.

Dostoevski's famous "unwritten masterpiece," *The Life of a Great Sinner,* to which he refers in his notes and letters, would have gone even more deeply into Stavrogin's character. But we know enough of that tortured soul to know what agonies of self-abasement and self-analysis attend the dark Russian mind turned to evil.

Several Russian folk tales are equally melodramatic and pathological, highly colored and bloody. The best of these is *St. John's Eve* as told by Nikolái Vasilévich Gógol—the love story of Petrus and Pidórka aided and abetted by the Devil. Rich as the tale is in Ukrainian folk customs, it is even richer in its revelation of the gruesome subconscious of the Ukrainian peasant mentality in preliterate, prerevolutionary times.

It is interesting to note in passing that Petrus saw the Devil on St. John's Eve, the traditional moment in European folklore for seeing Satan in his true form, and that fern seed was the classical currency used to acquire unearthly treasures from the powers of darkness.

Gorki's ephemeral but bitter satire, *The Devil,* reveals the particularly difficult life any honest creative writer was forced to lead during the czarist regime.

Obviously, dialectical materialism leaves little room for Satan save as he has been metamorphosed into the greedy capitalist or the ferocious fascist. Soviet education striking at superstition has doubtless relegated the Devil to remote mountain valleys. But seeing how efficacious the doctrinaire Marxist can be without Lucifer's assistance, Russia need not mourn the loss.

ST. JOHN'S EVE

Nikolái Vasilévich Gógol

THOMA GRIGOROVICH had a very strange sort of eccentricity: to the day of his death he never liked to tell the same thing twice. There were times when, if you asked him to relate a thing afresh, behold, he would interpolate new matter, or alter it so that it was impossible to recognize it. Once on a time one of those gentlemen (it is hard for us simple people to put a name to them, to say whether they are scribblers, or not scribblers: but it is just the same thing as the usurers at our yearly fairs; they clutch and beg and steal every sort of frippery and issue mean little volumes, no thicker than an A B C book, every month, or even every week)—one of these gentlemen wormed this same story out of Thoma Grigorovich, and he completely forgot about it. But that same young gentleman in the pea-green caftan, whom I have mentioned, and one of whose tales you have already read, I think, came from Poltava, bringing with him a little book and, opening it in the middle, showed it to us. Thoma Grigorovich was on the point of setting his spectacles astride of his nose but recollected that he had forgotten to wind thread about them, and stick them together with wax, so he passed it over to me. As I understand something about reading and writing and do not wear spectacles, I undertook to read it. I had not turned two leaves, when all at once he caught me by the hand and stopped me.

"Stop! Tell me first what you are reading."

I confess that I was a trifle stunned by such a question.

"What! What am I reading, Thoma Grigorovich? These were your very words."

"Who told you that they were my words?"

"Why, what more would you have? Here it is printed: 'Related by such and such a sacristan.'"

"Spit on the head of the man who printed that! He lies, the dog of a

Moscow peddler! Did I say that? ' 'Twas just the same as though one
hadn't his wits about him!' Listen, I'll tell it to you on the spot."
We moved up to the table, and he began.

My grandfather (the kingdom of heaven be his! may he eat only
wheaten rolls and *makovniki* [poppy-seeds cooked in honey and dried
in square cakes] with honey in the other world!) could tell a story
wonderfully well. When he used to begin on a tale you wouldn't stir
from the spot all day but keep on listening. He was no match for the
storyteller of the present day, when he begins to lie, with a tongue as
though he had had nothing to eat for three days, so that you snatch
your cap and flee from the house. As I now recall it, my old mother
was alive then; in the long winter evenings when the frost was crack-
ling out of doors and had so sealed up hermetically the narrow panes
of our cottage, she used to sit before the hackling comb, drawing out a
long thread in her hand, rocking the cradle with her foot, and humming a song which I seem to hear even now.

The fat lamp, quivering and flaring up as though in fear of something, lighted us within our cottage; the spindle hummed, and all of
us children, collected in a cluster, listened to Grandfather, who had
not crawled off the stove for more than five years, owing to his great
age. But the wondrous tales of the incursions of the Zaporogian
Cossacks, the Poles, the bold deeds of Podkova, of Poltor-Kozhukh,
and Sagaidatchnii did not interest us so much as the stories about
some deed of old which always sent a shiver through our frames and
made our hair rise upright on our heads. Sometimes such terror took
possession of us in consequence of them that, from that evening on,
Heaven knows what a marvel everything seemed to us. If you chanced
to go out of the cottage after nightfall for anything, you imagine that
a visitor from the other world has lain down to sleep in your bed; and
I should not be able to tell this a second time were it not that I had
often taken my own smock, at a distance, as it lay at the head of the
bed, for the Evil One rolled up in a ball! But the chief thing about
Grandfather's stories was that he never had lied in his life, and whatever he said was so, was so.

I will now relate to you one of his marvelous tales. I know that there
are a great many wise people who copy in the courts and can even
read civil documents, who, if you were to put into their hand a simple
prayer book, could not make out the first letter in it and would show
all their teeth in derision—which is wisdom. These people laugh at
everything you tell them. Such incredulity has spread abroad in the
world! What then? (Why, may God and the Holy Virgin cease to love

me if it is not possible that even you will not believe me!) Once he
said something about witches. . . . What then? Along comes one of
these head-breakers—and doesn't believe in witches! Yes, glory to God
that I have lived so long in the world! I have seen heretics to whom it
would be easier to lie in confession than it would for our brothers and
equals to take snuff, and those people would deny the existence of
witches! But let them just dream about something, and they won't
even tell what it was! There's no use in talking about them!

No one could have recognized this village of ours a little over a hundred years ago: a hamlet it was, the poorest kind of hamlet. Half a
score of miserable *izbás*, unplastered, badly thatched, were scattered
here and there about the fields. There was not an enclosure or a decent
shed to shelter animals or wagons. That was the way the wealthy
lived; and if you had looked for our brothers, the poor—why, a hole
in the ground—that was a cabin for you! Only by the smoke could
you tell that a God-created man lived there. You ask why they lived
so? It was not entirely through poverty: almost everyone led a wandering, Cossack life, and gathered not a little plunder in foreign lands; it
was rather because there was no reason for setting up a well-ordered
khata (wooden house). How many people were wandering all over
the country—Crimeans, Poles, Lithuanians! It was quite possible that
their own countrymen might make a descent and plunder everything.
Anything was possible.

In this hamlet a man, or rather a devil in human form, often made
his appearance. Why he came, and whence, no one knew. He prowled
about, got drunk, and suddenly disappeared as if into the air, and
there was not a hint of his existence. Then again, behold, and he
seemed to have dropped from the sky and went flying about the street
of the village, of which no trace now remains, and which was not more
than a hundred paces from Dikanka. He would collect together all the
Cossacks he met; then there were songs, laughter, money in abundance, and vodka flowed like water. . . . He would address the
pretty girls and give them ribbons, earrings, strings of beads—more
than they knew what to do with. It is true that the pretty girls rather
hesitated about accepting his presents: God knows, perhaps they had
passed through unclean hands. My grandfather's aunt, who kept a
tavern at the time, in which Basavriuk (as they called that devil-man)
often had his carouses, said that no consideration on the face of the
earth would have induced her to accept a gift from him. And then,
again, how avoid accepting? Fear seized on everyone when he knit his
bristly brows and gave a sidelong glance which might send your feet

God knows whither; but if you accept, then the next night some fiend from the swamp, with horns on his head, comes to call and begins to squeeze your neck when there is a string of beads upon it; or drag you by the hair, if ribbons are braided in it. God have mercy, then, on those who owned such gifts! But here was the difficulty: it was impossible to get rid of them; if you threw them into the water, the diabolical ring or necklace would skim along the surface and into your hand.

There was a church in the village—St. Pantelei, if I remember rightly. There lived there a priest, Father Athanasii of blessed memory. Observing that Basavriuk did not come to church, even on Easter, he determined to reprove him and impose penance upon him. Well, he hardly escaped with his life. "Hark ye, *pannotche* [sir]!" he thundered in reply. "Learn to mind your own business instead of meddling in other people's, if you don't want that goat's throat of yours stuck together with boiling *kutya* [a dish of rice or wheat flour, with honey and raisins, which is brought to the church on the celebration of memorial masses]." What was to be done with this unrepentant man? Father Athanasii contented himself with announcing that anyone who should make the acquaintance of Basavriuk would be counted a Catholic, an enemy of Christ's church, not a member of the human race.

In this village there was a Cossack named Korzh, who had a laborer whom people called Peter the Orphan—perhaps because no one remembered either his father or mother. The church *starost* (elder), it is true, said that they had died of the pest in his second year, but my grandfather's aunt would not hear to that and tried with all her might to furnish him with parents, although poor Peter needed them about as much as we need last year's snow. She said that his father had been in Zaporozhe, taken prisoner by the Turks, underwent God only knows what tortures, and, having by some miracle disguised himself as a eunuch, had made his escape. Little cared the black-browed youths and maidens about his parents. They merely remarked that, if only he had a new coat, a red sash, a black lambskin cap with dandified blue crown on his head, a Turkish saber hanging by his side, a whip in one hand, and a pipe with handsome mountings in the other, he would surpass all the young men. But the pity was that the only thing poor Peter had was a gray *svitka* with more holes in it than there are gold pieces in a Jew's pocket. And that was not the worst of it, but this: that Korzh had a daughter, such a beauty as I think you can hardly have chanced to see. My deceased grandfather's aunt used to say—and you know that it is easier for a woman to kiss the Evil One

than to call anybody a beauty, without malice be it said—that this
Cossack maiden's cheeks were as plump and fresh as the pinkest poppy
when just bathed in God's dew and, glowing, it unfolds its petals and
coquets with the rising sun; that her brows were like black cords, such
as our maidens buy nowadays, for their crosses and ducats, of the
Moscow peddlers who visit the villages with their baskets, and evenly
arched as though peeping into her clear eyes; that her little mouth, at
sight of which the youth smacked their lips, seemed made to emit the
songs of nightingales; that her hair, black as the raven's wing and soft
as young flax (our maidens did not then plait their hair in clubs interwoven with pretty, bright-hued ribbons), fell in curls over her *kuntush*
(upper garment in Little Russia). Eh! may I never intone another
alleluia in the choir, if I would not have kissed her, in spite of the
gray which is making its way all through the old wool which covers my
pate, and my old woman beside me, like a thorn in my side! Well, you
know what happens when young men and maids live side by side. In
the twilight the heels of red boots were always visible in the place
where Pidórka chatted with her Petrus. But Korzh would never have
suspected anything out of the way, only one day—it is evident that
none but the Evil One could have inspired him—Petrus took it into his
head to kiss the Cossack maiden's rosy lips with all his heart in the
passage, without first looking well about him; and that same Evil One
—may the son of a dog dream of the holy cross!—caused the old graybeard, like a fool, to open the cottage door at the same moment. Korzh
was petrified, dropped his jaw, and clutched at the door for support.
Those unlucky kisses had completely stunned him. It surprised him
more than the blow of a pestle on the wall, with which, in our days,
the muzhik generally drives out his intoxication for lack of fusees and
powder.

Recovering himself, he took his grandfather's hunting whip from
the wall and was about to belabor Peter's back with it, when Pidórka's
little six-year-old brother Ivas rushed up from somewhere or other
and, grasping his father's legs with his little hands, screamed out,
"Daddy, Daddy! Don't beat Petrus!" What was to be done? A father's
heart is not made of stone. Hanging the whip again upon the wall, he
led him quietly from the house. "If you ever show yourself in my
cottage again, or even under the windows, look out, Petró! By Heaven,
your black mustache will disappear; and your black locks, though
wound twice about your ears, will take leave of your pate, or my name
is not Terentii Korzh." So saying, he gave him a little taste of his fist
in the nape of his neck, so that all grew dark before Petrus, and he flew
headlong. So there was an end of their kissing. Sorrow seized upon our

doves; and a rumor was rife in the village that a certain Pole, all embroidered with gold, with mustaches, saber, spurs, and pockets jingling like the bells of the bag with which our sacristan Taras goes through the church every day, had begun to frequent Korzh's house. Now, it is well known why the father is visited when there is a black-browed daughter about. So one day Pidórka burst into tears and clutched the hand of her Ivas. "Ivas, my dear! Ivas, my love! Fly to Petrus, my child of gold, like an arrow from a bow. Tell him all: I would have loved his brown eyes; I would have kissed his white face, but my fate decrees not so. More than one towel have I wet with burning tears. I am sad; I am heavy at heart. And my own father is my enemy. I will not marry that Pole, whom I do not love. Tell him they are preparing a wedding, but there will be no music at our wedding: ecclesiastics will sing instead of pipes and *kobzas* [eight-stringed musical instrument]. I shall not dance with my bridegroom; they will carry me out. Dark, dark will be my dwelling—of maple wood; and, instead of chimneys, a cross will stand upon the roof."

Petró stood petrified, without moving from the spot, when the innocent child lisped out Pidórka's words to him. "And I, unhappy man, thought to go to the Crimea and Turkey, win gold and return to thee, my beauty! But it may not be. The evil eye has seen us. I will have a wedding, too, dear little fish, I, too; but no ecclesiastics will be at that wedding. The black crow will caw, instead of the pope, over me; the smooth field will be my dwelling; the dark blue clouds my rooftree. The eagle will claw out my brown eyes; the rain will wash the Cossack's bones, and the whirlwinds will dry them. But what am I? Of whom, to whom, am I complaining? 'Tis plain, God willed it so. If I am to be lost, then so be it!" And he went straight to the tavern.

My late grandfather's aunt was somewhat surprised on seeing Petrus in the tavern, and at an hour when good men go to morning Mass; and she stared at him as though in a dream, when he demanded a jug of brandy, about half a pailful. But the poor fellow tried in vain to drown his woe. The vodka stung his tongue like nettles and tasted more bitter than wormwood. He flung the jug from him upon the ground. "You have sorrowed enough, Cossack," growled a bass voice behind him. He looked round—Basavriuk! Ugh, what a face! His hair was like a brush, his eyes like those of a bull. "I know what you lack; here it is." Then he jingled a leather purse which hung from his girdle, and smiled diabolically. Petró shuddered. "He, he, he! Yes, how it shines!" he roared, shaking out ducats into his hand. "He, he, he! And how it jingles! And I only ask one thing for a whole pile of such shiners."

"It is the Evil One!" exclaimed Petró: "Give them here! I am ready for anything!"

They struck hands upon it. "See here, Petró, you are ripe just in time: tomorrow is St. John the Baptist's day. Only on this one night in the year does the fern blossom. Delay not. I will await thee at midnight in the bear's ravine."

I do not believe that chickens await the hour when the woman brings their corn with as much anxiety as Petrus awaited the evening. And, in fact, he looked to see whether the shadows of the trees were not lengthening, if the sun were not turning red toward setting; and, the longer he watched, the more impatient he grew. How long it was! Evidently, God's day had lost its end somewhere. And now the sun is gone. The sky is red only on one side, and it is already growing dark. It grows colder in the fields. It gets dusky, and more dusky, and at last quite dark. At last! With heart almost bursting from his bosom, he set out on his way and cautiously descended through the dense woods into the deep hollow called the bear's ravine. Basavriuk was already waiting there. It was so dark that you could not see a yard before you. Hand in hand they penetrated the thin marsh, clinging to the luxuriant thornbushes and stumbling at almost every step. At last they reached an open spot. Petró looked about him; he had never chanced to come there before. Here Basavriuk halted.

"Do you see, before you stand three hillocks? There are a great many sorts of flowers upon them. But may some power keep you from plucking even one of them. But as soon as the fern blossoms, seize it, and look not round, no matter what may seem to be going on behind thee."

Petró wanted to ask—and behold, he was no longer there. He approached the three hillocks—where were the flowers? He saw nothing. The wild steppe grass darkled around and stifled everything in its luxuriance. But the lightning flashed, and before him stood a whole bed of flowers, all wonderful, all strange; and there were also the simple fronds of fern. Petró doubted his senses and stood thoughtfully before them, with both hands upon his sides.

"What prodigy is this? One can see these weeds ten times in a day; what marvel is there about them? Was not devil's-face laughing at me?"

Behold! The tiny flower bud crimsons and moves as though alive. It is a marvel, in truth. It moves and grows larger and larger, and flashes like a burning coal. The tiny star flashes up; something bursts softly, and the flower opens before his eyes like a flame, lighting the others about it. "Now is the time," thought Petró, and extended his hand. He sees hundreds of shaggy hands reach from behind him, also for the flower; and there is a running about from place to place in the rear. He half shut his eyes, plucked sharply at the stalk, and the flower remained in his hand. All became still. Upon a stump sat Basavriuk, all blue like a corpse. He moved not so much as a finger. His eyes were immovably fixed on something visible to him alone; his mouth was half open and speechless. All about, nothing stirred. Ugh! It was horrible! But then a whistle was heard, which made Petró's heart grow cold within him; and it seemed to him that the grass whispered, and the flowers began to talk among themselves in delicate voices, like little silver bells; the trees rustled in waving contention. Basavriuk's face suddenly became full of life and his eyes sparkled. "The witch has just returned," he muttered between his teeth. "See here, Petró: a beauty will stand before you in a moment; do whatever she commands; if not—you are lost forever." Then he parted the thornbush with a knotty stick, and before him stood a tiny izbá, on chicken's legs, as they say. Basavriuk smote it with his fist, and the wall trembled. A large black dog ran out to meet them, and with a whine, transforming itself into a cat, flew straight at his eyes. "Don't be angry, don't be angry, you old Satan!" said Basavriuk, employing such words as would have made a good man stop his ears. Behold, instead of a cat, an old woman with a face wrinkled like a baked apple, and all bent into a bow; her nose and chin were like a pair of nutcrackers. "A stunning beauty!" thought Petró, and cold chills ran down his back. The witch tore the flower from his hand, bent over, and muttered over it for a long time, sprinkling it with some kind of water. Sparks flew from her mouth; froth appeared on her lips.

"Throw it away," she said, giving it back to Petró.

Petró threw it, and what wonder was this? The flower did not fall straight to the earth, but for a long while twinkled like a fiery ball through the darkness and swam through the air like a boat; at last it began to sink lower and fell so far away that the little star, hardly larger than a poppy seed, was barely visible. "Here!" croaked the old woman in a dull voice; and Basavriuk, giving him a spade, said, "Dig here, Petró: here you will find more gold than you or Korzh ever dreamed of."

Petró spat on his hands, seized the spade, applied his foot, and turned up the earth, a second, a third, a fourth time. . . . There was something hard; the spade clinked and would go no farther. Then his eyes began to distinguish a small ironbound coffer. He tried to seize it, but the chest began to sink into the earth, deeper, farther, and deeper still; and behind him he heard a laugh, more like a serpent's hiss. "No, you shall not see the gold until you procure human blood," said the witch, and led up to him a child of six, covered with a white sheet, indicating by a sign that he was to cut off his head. Petró was stunned. A trifle, indeed, to cut off a man's or even an innocent child's head for no reason whatever! In wrath he tore off the sheet enveloping his head, and behold! before him stood Ivas. And the poor child crossed his little hands and hung his head. . . . Petró flew upon the witch with the knife like a madman and was on the point of laying hands on her. . . .

"What did you promise for the girl?" thundered Basavriuk, and like a shot he was on his back. The witch stamped her foot: a blue flame flashed from the earth; it illumined it all inside, and it was as if molded of crystal; and all that was within the earth became visible, as if in the palm of the hand. Ducats, precious stones in chests and kettles were piled in heaps beneath the very spot they stood on. His eyes burned; his mind grew troubled. . . . He grasped the knife like a madman, and the innocent blood spurted into his eyes. Diabolical laughter resounded on all sides. Misshaped monsters flew past him in herds. The witch, fastening her hands in the headless trunk, like a wolf, drank its blood. . . . All went round in his head. Collecting all his strength, he set out to run. Everything turned red before him. The trees seemed steeped in blood and burned and groaned. The sky glowed and glowered. . . . Burning points, like lightning, flicked before his eyes. Utterly exhausted, he rushed into his miserable hovel and fell to the ground like a log. A deathlike sleep overpowered him.

Two days and two nights did Petró sleep, without once awakening. When he came to himself, on the third day, he looked long at all the corners of his hut; but in vain did he endeavor to recollect; his memory was like a miser's pocket, from which you cannot entice a quarter of a kopek. Stretching himself, he heard something clash at his feet. He looked—two bags of gold. Then only, as if in a dream, he recollected that he had been seeking some treasure, that something had frightened him in the woods. . . . But at what price he had obtained it, and how, he could by no means understand.

Korzh saw the sacks—and was mollified. "Such a Petrus, quite unheard of! Yes, and did I not love him? Was he not to me as my own son?" And the old fellow carried on his fiction until it reduced him to tears. Pidórka began to tell him some passing gypsies had stolen Ivas; but Petró could not even recall him—to such a degree had the Devil's influence darkened his mind! There was no reason for delay. The Pole was dismissed, and the wedding feast prepared; rolls were baked, towels and handkerchiefs embroidered; the young people were seated at table; the wedding loaf was cut; banduras, cymbals, pipes, kobzi sounded, and pleasure was rife. . . .

A wedding in the olden times was not like one of the present day. My grandfather's aunt used to tell—what doings!—how the maidens —in festive headdresses of yellow, blue, and pink ribbons, above which they bound gold braid; in thin chemisettes embroidered on all the seams with red silk, and strewn with tiny silver flowers; in morocco shoes, with high iron heels—danced the *gorlitza* as swimmingly as peacocks, and as wildly as the whirlwind; how the youths—with their ship-shaped caps upon their heads, the crowns of gold brocade, with a little slit at the nape where the hair net peeped through, and two horns projecting, one in front and another behind, of the very finest black lambskin; in kuntushas of the finest blue silk with red borders— stepped forward one by one, their arms akimbo in stately form, and executed the *gopak;* how the lads—in tall Cossack caps, and light cloth svitkas, girt with silver embroidered belts, their short pipes in their teeth—skipped before them and talked nonsense. Even Korzh could not contain himself, as he gazed at the young people, from getting gay in his old age. Bandura in hand, alternately puffing at his pipe and singing, a brandy glass upon his head, the graybeard began the national dance amid loud shouts from the merrymakers. What will not people devise in merry mood! They even began to disguise their faces. They did not look like human beings. They are not to be compared with the disguises which we have at our weddings nowadays. What do they do now? Why, imitate gypsies and Moscow peddlers. No! Then one used to dress himself as a Jew, another as the Devil; they would begin by kissing each other, and end by seizing each other by the hair. . . . God be with them! You laughed till you held your sides. They dressed themselves in Turkish and Tartar garments. All upon them glowed like a conflagration, and then they began to joke and play pranks. . . . Well, then away with the saints!

An amusing thing happened to my grandfather's aunt, who was at this wedding. She was dressed in a voluminous Tartar robe, and, wineglass in hand, was entertaining the company. The Evil One instigated one man to pour vodka over her from behind. Another, at the same moment, evidently not by accident, struck a light and touched it to her; the flame flashed up; poor aunt, in terror, flung her robe from her, before them all. . . . Screams, laughter, jests arose as if at a fair. In a word, the old folks could not recall so merry a wedding.

Pidórka and Petrus began to live like a gentleman and lady. There was plenty of everything, and everything was handsome. . . . But honest people shook their heads when they looked at their way of living. "From the Devil no good can come," they unanimously agreed. "Whence, except from the tempter of orthodox people, came this wealth? Where else could he get such a lot of gold? Why, on the very day that he got rich, did Basavriuk vanish as if into thin air?" Say, if you can, that people imagine things! In fact, a month had not passed, and no one would have recognized Petrus. Why, what had happened to him? God knows. He sits in one spot and says no word to anyone; he thinks continually and seems to be trying to recall something. When Pidórka succeeds in getting him to speak, he seems to forget himself, carries on a conversation, and even grows cheerful; but if he inadvertently glances at the sacks, "Stop, stop! I have forgotten," he cries, and again plunges into reverie, and again strives to recall something. Sometimes when he has sat long in a place, it seems to him as though it was coming, just coming back to mind . . . and again all fades away. It seems as if he is sitting in the tavern: they bring him vodka; vodka stings him; vodka is repulsive to him. Someone comes along and strikes him on the shoulder; but beyond that everything is veiled in darkness before him. The perspiration streams down his face, and he sits exhausted in the same place.

What did not Pidórka do? She consulted the sorceress; and they poured out fear and brewed stomach-ache ("To pour out fear" is done with us in case of fear; when it is desired to know what caused it, melted lead or wax is poured into water and the object whose form it assumes is the one which frightened the sick person; after this the fear departs. *Sónyashnitza* is brewed for giddiness and pain in the bowels. To this end, a bit of stump is burned, thrown into a jug, and turned upside down into a bowl filled with water, which is placed on the patient's stomach; after an incantation he is given a spoonful of this water to drink)—but all to no avail. And so the summer passed. Many a Cossack had mowed and reaped; many a Cossack, more enterprising than the rest, had set off upon an expedition. Flocks of ducks were already crowding our marshes, but there was not even a hint of improvement.

It was red upon the steppes. Ricks of grain, like Cossacks' caps, dotted the fields here and there. On the highway were to be encountered wagons loaded with brushwood and logs. The ground had become more solid, and in places was touched with frost. Already had the snow begun to besprinkle the sky, and the branches of the trees were covered with rime like rabbitskin. Already on frosty days the red-breasted finch hopped about on the snow heaps like a foppish Polish nobleman and picked out grains of corn; and children, with huge sticks, chased wooden tops upon the ice, while their fathers lay quietly on the stove, issuing forth at intervals with lighted pipes in their lips, to growl, in regular fashion, at the orthodox frost, or to take the air and thresh the grain spread out in the barn. At last the snow began to melt, and the ice rind slipped away, but Petró remained the same; and, the longer it went on, the more morose he grew. He sat in the middle of the cottage as though nailed to the spot, with the sacks of gold at his feet. He grew shy; his hair grew long; he became terrible, and still he thought of but one thing; still he tried to recall something and got angry and ill-tempered because he could not recall it. Often, rising wildly from his seat, he gesticulates violently, fixes his eyes on something as though desirous of catching it; his lips move as though desirous of uttering some long-forgotten word—and remain speechless. Fury takes possession of him: he gnaws and bites his hands like a man half crazy, and in his vexation tears out his hair by the handful, until, calming down, he falls into forgetfulness, as it were, and again begins to recall, and is again seized with fury and fresh tortures. . . . What visitation of God is this?

Pidórka was neither dead nor alive. At first it was horrible to her to remain alone in the cottage; but, in course of time, the poor woman grew accustomed to her sorrow. But it was impossible to recognize the Pidórka of former days. No blush, no smile; she was thin and worn with grief and had wept her bright eyes away. Once, someone who evidently took pity on her advised her to go to the witch who dwelt in the bear's ravine and enjoyed the reputation of being able to cure every disease in the world. She determined to try this last remedy; word by word she persuaded the old woman to come to her. This was St. John's Eve, as it chanced. Petró lay insensible on the bench and did not observe the newcomer. Little by little he rose and looked about him. Suddenly he trembled in every limb, as though he were on the scaffold; his hair rose upon his head, and he laughed such a laugh as pierced Pidórka's heart with fear. "I have remembered, remembered!" he cried in terrible joy; and, swinging a hatchet round his head, he flung it at the old woman with all his might. The hatchet penetrated the oaken door two *vershok* (three inches and a half). The old woman disappeared, and a child of seven in a white blouse, with covered head, stood in the middle of the cottage. . . . The sheet flew off. "Ivas!" cried Pidórka, and ran to him; but the apparition became covered from head to foot with blood and illumined the whole room with red light. . . . She ran into the passage in her terror, but, on recovering herself a little, wished to help him; in vain! The door had slammed to behind her so securely that she could not open it. People ran up and began to knock; they broke in the door, as though there were but one mind among them. The whole cottage was full of smoke; and just in the middle, where Petrus had stood, was a heap of ashes, from which smoke was still rising. They flung themselves upon the sacks: only broken potsherds lay there instead of ducats. The Cossacks stood with staring eyes and open mouths, not daring to move a hair, as if rooted to the earth, such terror did this wonder inspire in them.

I do not remember what happened next. Pidórka took a vow to go upon a pilgrimage, collected the property left her by her father, and in a few days it was as if she had never been in the village. Whither she had gone, no one could tell. Officious old women would have dispatched her to the same place whither Petró had gone, but a Cossack from Kiev reported that he had seen, in a cloister, a nun withered to a mere skeleton, who prayed unceasingly; and her fellow villagers recognized her as Pidórka, by all the signs—that no one had ever heard her utter a word; that she had come on foot and had brought a frame for the icon of God's mother, set with such brilliant stones that all were dazzled at the sight.

But this was not the end, if you please. On the same day that the Evil One made away with Petrus, Basavriuk appeared again; but all fled from him. They knew what sort of bird he was—none else than Satan, who had assumed human form in order to unearth treasures; and, since treasures do not yield to unclean hands, he seduced the young. That same year, all deserted their earth huts and collected in a village; but, even there, there was no peace, on account of that accursed Basavriuk. My late grandfather's aunt said that he was particularly angry with her, because she had abandoned her former tavern, and tried with all his might to revenge himself upon her. Once the village elders were assembled in the tavern, and, as the saying goes, were arranging the precedence at the table, in the middle of which was placed a small roasted lamb, shame to say. They chattered about this, that, and the other—among the rest about various marvels and strange things. Well, they saw something; it would have been nothing if only one had seen it, but all saw it; and it was this: the sheep raised his head; his goggling eyes became alive and sparkled, and the black, bristling mustache, which appeared for one instant, made a significant gesture at those present. All, at once, recognized Basavriuk's countenance in the sheep's head; my grandfather's aunt thought it was on the point of asking for vodka. . . . The worthy elders seized their hats and hastened home.

Another time, the church starost himself, who was fond of an occasional private interview with my grandfather's brandy glass, had not succeeded in getting to the bottom twice, when he beheld the glass bowing very low to him. "Satan take you, let us make the sign of the cross over you!" . . . And the same marvel happened to his better half. She had just begun to mix the dough in a huge kneading trough, when suddenly the trough sprang up. "Stop, stop! Where are you going?" Putting its arms akimbo, with dignity, it went skipping all about the cottage. . . . You may laugh, but it was no laughing matter to your grandfathers. And in vain did Father Athanasii go through all the village with holy water and chase the Devil through the streets with his brush; and my late grandfather's aunt long complained that, as soon as it was dark, someone came knocking at her door and scratching at the wall.

Well! All appears to be quiet now, in the place where our village stands; but it was not so very long ago—my father was still alive—that I remember how a good man could not pass the ruined tavern, which a dishonest race had long managed for their own interest. From the smoke-blackened chimneys smoke poured out in a pillar, and rising high in the air, as if to take an observation, rolled off like a cap, scattering burning coals over the steppe; and Satan (the son of a dog should not be mentioned) sobbed so pitifully in his lair that the startled ravens rose in flocks from the neighboring oakwood and flew through the air with wild cries.

Italian

POSSIBLY because the Papacy had an early toe hold on the Italian boot, the Devil has been particularly active in the ancient pagan regions from the Brenner Pass to Scylla and Charybdis. If Satan was not actually reincarnated in the Borgias and the Medici he could at least count them among his most devout disciples. And there are those who believe that Niccolò Machiavelli served Satan as Moses once served Yahweh—as talented personal secretary.

However that may be, Machiavelli realized that the Devil himself was not a match for a beautiful and evil woman of the sort to be found in Renaissance Italy. Drawing upon a medieval Latin source, both Giovanni Brevio and the author of *The Prince* wrote tales of a minor devil who took an earthly wife and finally left her to return to the comforts of Hell. As satire, this story appealed to later French and German writers, echoing plaintively down the years until Ben Jonson revived the theme in *The Devil Is an Ass*.

More virtuous by far than Machiavelli's scheming female was the "married woman of unimpeachable morality" who was wooed for years by an incubus who haunted Pavia. If we are to trust the word of the Reverend Father Sinistrari of Ameno, who was among the *cognoscenti* on incubi and succubi, this lecherous demon sought in every conceivable way to share the bed of Hieronyma, who lived in the parish of St. Michael. Having first tempted her with "a large cake of peculiar shape," he was soon whispering sweet nothings in her ear, "appearing as a little man of great beauty, with golden locks, a flaxen beard that shone like gold, sea-green eyes calling to mind a flax flower, and arrayed in fancy Spanish dress."

Calling Jesus and Mary, this virtuous woman sought the help of exorcists, priests, and relics in support of her virtue, but for many years the demon came to her bedroom or connived to waylay her.

This lovesick, weeping, and moaning incubus, "incensed at her disdain," had recourse to new kinds of persecution, purloining her rings and holy relics and even snatching her child from her bosom. He capped his concupiscent conniving by stripping the voluptuous young matron on the steps of the church at ten in the morning, when a crowd of people were gathering for Mass. "Her clothes and ornaments fell off to the ground and disappeared in a gust of wind, leaving her stark-naked." Had it not been for "two cavaliers of mature age" who divested themselves of their cloaks to conceal the woman's nudity, few would have attended Mass that morning.

Hieronyma's infuriating purity at last confounded the Evil One, but the similar purity of Beatrice led Dante to write Hell's most famous Baedeker—proving that virginity can be put to a number of unsuspected uses. A casual commentator might imagine that Dante Alighieri pictured the deepest Hell as one of desolate fog and ice in commemoration of the tortures of chastity. His icy inferno, however, was not without tradition and precedent. Actually he was drawing upon ancient Teutonic sources, as all who have perused Saxo Grammaticus, Cædmon, and others can testify. His demon "Dis," with its three faces, is strikingly similar to the evil deity of the north known to Celts and Teutons.

The Comedy of Dante Alighieri, a Florentine by Birth but Not in Character acquired as centuries passed a shorter title, *Divina Commedia,* an expression of the high regard in which the great allegory was held by generations of readers.

To modern ears, and particularly in translation, the *Divine Comedy* often seems shrill and needlessly cantankerous. Those who can read it in the original, however, testify to its extreme beauty of phrase.

Dante's reasons for political satire and his castigation of the inhabitants of the Arno Valley go back to the struggles between the Guelphs and the Ghibellines and subsequent feuding clans. Although Dante was a Guelph, his sympathies were divided in the struggle between the "Blacks" and "Whites," and his attempts to keep the peace drew their usual reward. Exile did not improve his temper.

But that some good may come out of evil is proved by this poet's picture of Hell and hell-on-earth. And the gangsters of the Arno Valley are immortal if only in ridicule. Our thanks to Beatrice and the feuding politicos of Florence.

CANTO XXXIV FROM THE DIVINE COMEDY

Dante Alighieri

THE JUDECCA, or Last Circlet of Cocytus, takes its name from Judas Iscariot, and contains the souls of those "who betrayed their masters and benefactors." The Arch Traitor Satan, "Emperor of the Realm of Sorrow," stands fixed in the Centre of it; and he too is punished by his own Sin. All the streams of Guilt keep flowing back to him, as their source; and from beneath his three Faces (Shadows of his consciousness) issue forth the mighty wings with which he struggles, as it were, to raise himself; and sends out winds that freeze him only the more firmly in his ever-swelling Marsh. Dante has to take a full view of him, too; and then is carried through the Centre by his Mystic Guide—"grappling on the hair of Satan," not without significance; and set down on "the other face of the Judecca." And now the bitter journey of our Pilgrim is over; and a tone of gladness goes through the remaining verses. Hell is now behind him, and, the Stars of Heaven above; he has got beyond the "Everlasting No," and is "sore travailled," and the "way is long and difficult," but it leads from Darkness to the "bright world." After some brief inquiries, "without caring for any repose," by aid of the heaven-sent Wisdom he "plucks himself from the Abyss"; and follows climbing, till they see the Stars in the opposite hemisphere.

"*Vexilla Regis prodeunt inferni*[1] towards us: therefore look in front of thee," my Master said, "if thou discernest him."

As, when a thick mist breathes, or when the night comes on our hemisphere, a mill, which the wind turns, appears at distance:

such an edifice did I now seem to see; and, for the wind, shrunk back behind my Guide, because no other shed was there.

[1]This is a parody of the first line of a Latin hymn by Fortunatus (sixth century) —*Vexilla regis prodeunt*. The advancing standards are the wings of Lucifer.

Already I had come (and with fear I put it into verse) where the souls were wholly covered, and shone through like straw in glass.

Some are lying; some stand upright, this on its head, and that upon its soles; another, like a bow, bends face to feet.

When we had proceeded in so far, that it pleased my Guide to show to me the Creature which was once so fair,

he took himself from before me, and made me stop, saying "Lo Dis! And lo the place where it behoves thee arm thyself with fortitude."

How icy chill and hoarse I then became, ask not, O Reader! for I write it not, because all speech would fail to tell.

I did not die, and did not remain alive: now think for thyself, if thou hast any grain of ingenuity, what I became, deprived of both death and life.

The Emperor of the dolorous realm, from mid breast stood forth out of the ice; and I in size am liker to a giant,

than the giants are to his arms: mark now how great that whole must be, which corresponds to such a part.

If he was once as beautiful as he is ugly now, and lifted up his brows against his Maker, well may all affliction come from him.

Oh how great a marvel seemed it to me, when I saw three faces on his head! The one in front, and it was fiery red;

the others were two, that were adjoined to this, above the very middle of each shoulder; and they were joined at his crest;

and the right seemed between white and yellow; the left was such to look on, as they who come from where the Nile descends.[2]

Under each there issued forth two mighty wings, of size befitting such a bird; sea-sails I never saw so broad.

No plumes had they; but were in form and texture like a bat's: and he was flapping them, so that three winds went forth from him.

Thereby Cocytus all was frozen; with six eyes he wept, and down three chins gushed tears and bloody foam.

In every mouth he champed a sinner with his teeth, like a brake; so that he thus kept three of them in torment.

To the one in front, the biting was nought, compared with the tearing: for at times the back of him remained quite stript of skin.

"That soul up there, which suffers greatest punishment," said the Master, "is Judas Iscariot, he who has his head within, and outside plies his legs.

---

[2]The red, yellow, and black faces have been variously explained. The best interpretation seems to be the one which makes them representative of hatred, impotence, and ignorance—the qualities opposed to those of the Holy Trinity.

Of the other two, who have their heads beneath, that one who hangs from the black visage, is Brutus: see how he writhes himself, and utters not a word;

and the other is Cassius,[3] who seems so stark of limb. But night is reascending;[4] and now must we depart: for we have seen the whole."

As he desired, I clasped his neck; and he took opportunity of time and place; and when the wings were opened far,

applied him to the shaggy sides, and then from shag to shag descended down, between the tangled hair and frozen crusts.

When we had come to where the thigh revolves just on the swelling of the haunch, my Guide with labour and with difficulty

turned his head where he had had his feet before, and grappled on the hair, as one who mounts; so that I thought we were returning into Hell again.

"Hold thee fast! for by such stairs," said my Guide, panting like a man forespent, "must we depart from so much ill."

Thereafter through the opening of a rock he issued forth, and put me on its brim to sit; then towards me he stretched his wary step.

I raised my eyes, and thought to see Lucifer as I had left him; and saw him with the legs turned upwards;

and the gross people who see not what that point is which I had passed, let them judge if I grew perplexed then.

"Rise up!" said the Master, "upon thy feet: the way is long, and difficult the road; and already to middle tierce the Sun returns."[5]

It was no palace-hall, there where we stood, but natural dungeon with an evil floor and want of light.

"Before I pluck myself from the Abyss," said I when risen up, "O Master! speak to me a little, to draw me out of error.

Where is the ice? and this, how is he fixed thus upside down? and how, in so short a time, has the Sun from eve to morn made transit?"

And he to me: "Thou imaginest that thou art still upon the other side of the centre, where I caught hold on the hair of the evil Worm which pierces through the world.

Thou wast on that side, so long as I descended; when I turned myself, thou then didst pass the point to which all gravities from every part are drawn;

---

[3]These three arch sinners betrayed, in the persons of their lords and benefactors, the two most august representatives of Church and State—the founder of Christianity and the founder of the Roman Empire. The other sinners in Giudecca are not specified save in a general way.

[4]It is now about six o'clock on the Saturday evening.

[5]*Tierce* was the first of the four canonical divisions of the day and would, at the equinox, last from six till nine; *middle tierce* is therefore equivalent to half-past seven.

and now thou art arrived beneath the hemisphere opposed to that which canopies the great dry land,[6] and underneath whose summit was consumed

the Man, who without sin was born and lived; thou hast thy feet upon a little sphere, which forms the other face of the Judecca.

Here it is morn, when it is evening there; and this Fiend, who made a ladder for us with his hair, is still fixed as he was before.

On this side fell he down from Heaven; and the land, which erst stood out here, through fear of him veiled itself with sea,

and came to our hemisphere; and perhaps, in order to escape from him, that which on this side appears left here the empty space, and upwards rushed."[7]

Down there, from Beelzebub as far removed as his tomb extends, is a space, not known by sight but by the sound

of a rivulet[8] descending in it, along the hollow of a rock which it has eaten out with tortuous course and slow declivity.

The Guide and I entered by that hidden road, to return into the bright world; and, without caring for any rest,

we mounted up, he first and I second, so far that I distinguished through a round opening the beauteous things which Heaven bears; and thence we issued out, again to see the Stars.[9]

German

IT IS INDEED CURIOUS that a nation which was never thoroughly converted to Christianity should be so deeply steeped in Diabolism. But the German genius for poetry and sadism seems to have found its perfect outlet in the cults of Satan.

Bridges and cathedrals built by the Devil (if legend can be believed) abound in the Reich. The works of such devil-lorists as Wilhelm Hauff and E. Th. A. ("Devil") Hoffmann have been enormously popular. And of course the Faust legend (from Goethe to

[6]The northern hemisphere was held to be covered with land, the southern with water.

[7]This passage has generally been taken to establish a connection between the cone of the Mount of Purgatory and the funnel of Hell. It is obvious, however, that Hell was in existence ready to receive Satan, and that the *empty space* and the *tomb* refer not to Hell, but to the cavern into which the nether bulk of Satan is thrust.

[8]The *rivulet* is Lethe, which bears the memory of sin from Purgatory down to the place of sin in Hell.

[9]The word *stars,* with which each of the three canticles closes, indicates the constant aspiration of the poem, and of the soul whose journey it depicts, toward the highest things.

Spengler's "Faustian Man") is the very pivot of German literature, meriting special attention elsewhere in this volume.

Curious parallels between the orgiastic excesses of the Nazis and ancient Germanic celebrations have been drawn by a number of historians and thoughtful correspondents. They range from violations of the rules of war to gross homosexuality.

Those who believe that the Inquisition reached its full flowering in Spain under Torquemada should read the records of torture on the rack, the wheel, and the "iron virgin" in Nuremberg, Augsburg, and elsewhere in gentle Germany.

Camp commanders at Dachau and Oranienberg were amateurs compared to the Christian fathers who with whips, spikes, burning sulphur, burning brandy, weights, vises, and other instruments of Hell tortured a pregnant woman in the year 1631 as related in König's *Ausgeburten des Menschenwahns.*

Actually no fictional presentation of the Devil is necessary in a nation which has produced Frederick, Wilhelm II, Hitler, and Himmler. Those who would know more about the German Devil might ask the Poles, Czechs, Norwegians, French, Dutch, Belgians, and Jews.

By contrast the Reformation once promised a Christianized and moral Germany. Martin Luther was one German who hated the Devil and all his works, and Luther's "table talk," as proved by the following excerpts, should rival any holy relic as a specific for exorcizing the pan-German Devil.

OF THE DEVIL AND HIS WORKS

Martin Luther

No MALADY comes upon us from God, who is good, and wishes us well; they all emanate from the Devil, who is the cause and author of plagues, fevers, &c. When he is at work with jurisconsults, he engenders all sorts of dissensions and machinations, turning justice into injustice. Approaches he great lords, princes, kings, he gives birth to wars and massacres. Gains he access to divines, he produces the worst mischief of all: false doctrines, which seduce and ruin men's souls. God alone can check so many calamities.

 ☆ ☆ ☆

The Devil vexes and harasses the workmen in the mines. He makes them think they have found fine new veins of silver, which, when they have labored and labored, turn out to be mere illusions. Even in open day, on the surface of the earth, he causes people to think they see a treasure before them, which vanishes when they would pick it up.

☆ ☆ ☆

When I was young, someone told me this story: Satan had, in vain, set all his craft and subtlety at work to separate a married pair that lived together in perfect harmony and love. At last, having concealed a razor under each of their pillows, he visited the husband, disguised as an old woman, and told him that his wife had formed the project of killing him; he next told the same thing to the wife. The husband, finding the razor under his wife's pillow, became furious with anger at her supposed wickedness, and cut her throat. So powerful is Satan in his malice.

☆ ☆ ☆

A pastor, near Torgau, came to Luther, and complained that the Devil tormented him without intermission. The doctor replied: He plagues and harasses me too, but I resist him with the arms of faith. I know of one person at Magdeburg, who put Satan to the rout, by spitting at him; but this example is not to be lightly followed; for the Devil is a presumptuous spirit, and not disposed to yield. We run great risk when, with him, we attempt more than we can do. One man, who relied implicitly on his baptism, when the Devil presented himself to him, his head furnished with horns, tore off one of the horns; but another man, of less faith, who attempted the same thing, was killed by the Devil.

☆ ☆ ☆

When I could not be rid of the Devil with sentences out of the Holy Scripture, I made him often fly with jeering words; sometimes I said unto him: Saint Satan! if Christ's blood, which was shed for my sins, be not sufficient, then I desire that thou wouldst pray to God for me. When he finds me idle, with nothing in hand, he is very busy, and before I am aware, he wrings from me a bitter sweat; but when I offer him the pointed spear, God's Word, he flies; yet, before he goes, makes a grievous hurricane.

There was a citizen, whose child died, for whom he refused to have vigils and Masses sung. The Devil played his freaks, came every night, about twelve o'clock, into the chamber where the boy died, and made a whining like a young child. The good citizen, being therewith full of sorrow, knew not what course to take. . . . I wrote to him from

Wittenberg, and advised him not to suffer any vigils at all to be held, for he might be fully assured that these were merely pranks of the Devil; whereupon, the children and servants in the house jeered at the Devil, and said: What doest thou, Satan? Avoid, thou cursed spirit, get thee gone to the place where thou oughtest to be, to the pit of Hell. When the Devil marked their contempt, he left off his game, and came there no more. He is a proud spirit, and cannot endure scorn.

At Mohlburg, in Thuringia, not far from Erfurt, there was a musician, who gained his living by playing at merry-makings. This man came to the minister of his parish, and complained that he was every day assailed by the Devil, who threatened to carry him off, because he had played at an unlawful marriage. The minister consoled him, prayed for him, recited to him numerous passages of Scripture, directed against the Devil; and, with some other pious men, watched over the unfortunate man, day and night, fastening the doors and windows, so that he might not be carried off. At length the musician said: I feel that Satan cannot harm my soul, but he will assuredly remove my body; and that very night, at eight o'clock, though the watch was doubled, the Devil came in the shape of a furious wind, broke the windows, and carried off the musician, whose body was found next morning, stiff and black, stuck on a nut tree.

A DAY IN NUREMBERG

B. E. König

THE HANGMAN bound the woman, who was pregnant, and placed her on the rack. Then he racked her till her heart would fain break, but had no compassion. When she did not confess, the torture was repeated; the hangman tied her hands, cut off her hair, poured brandy over her head and burned it. He placed sulphur in her armpits and burned it. Her hands were tied behind her, and she was hauled up to the ceiling and suddenly dropped down. This hauling up and dropping down was repeated for some hours, until the hangman and his helpers went to dinner. When they returned, the master hangman tied her feet and hands upon her back; brandy was poured on her back and burned. Then heavy weights were placed on her back and she was pulled up. After this she was again stretched on the rack.

A spiked board was placed on her back, and she was again hauled up to the ceiling. The master again tied her feet and hung on them a block of fifty pounds, which made her think that her heart would burst. This proved insufficient; therefore, the master untied her feet and fixed her legs in a vise, tightening the jaws until the blood oozed out at the toes. Nor was this sufficient; therefore, she was stretched and pinched again in various ways. Now the hangman of Dreissis-gacker began the third grade of torture. When he placed her on the bench and put the "shirt" on her, he said: "I do not take you for one, two, three, not for eight days, nor for a few weeks, but for half a year or a year, for your whole life, until you confess: and if you will not confess, I shall torture you to death, and you shall be burned after all." The hangman's son-in-law hauled her up to the ceiling by her hands. The hangman of Dreissisgacker whipped her with a horse-whip. She was placed in a vise where she remained for six hours. After that she was again mercilessly horsewhipped. This was all that was done on the first day.

Swedish

"FOR THE MOST PART we saw him in a gray Coat, and red and blue stockings; he had a red Beard, a high-crowned Hat, with Linnen of divers Colours wrap'd about it, and long Garters upon his Stockings."

Such was the picture of the Devil painted by the children of the village of Mohra in Sweden in 1669, when the King's Commissioners were sent to investigate a report of rampant witchcraft. It is a strange tale as reported by Joseph Glanvil in his eighteenth-century volume on witches and apparitions, a tale told by an idiot, the legend of the Pied Piper with the pages dipped in blood.

We learn that the confessions of all of the children eventually agreed, "except some very little ones who could not tell all the Circumstances" of their traffic with the Devil. We find that twenty-three of the villagers were found guilty and condemned to death and that many of the others were exiled. Fifteen children were executed. Thirty-six were forced to run the "gantlet" and then were lashed once a week for a year, while twenty children were lashed with rods "upon their hands for three Sundays together at the Church door."

If any further proof were needed of the Devil's entrenchment in Sweden, reference might be made to a fairly common Scandinavian folk tale in which the Devil in the role of Charon bargains with a fisherman to transport a boatload of souls to an island off the coast.

The circumstances of the tale vary slightly, but the fisherman always notices that the weight of the arriving souls gradually brings his gunwales awash, although he can see nothing in his craft, and that his boat rises to its normal level after he has reached the island's shore.

Selma Lagerlöf's "ghost story" which has been taken complete from *The Story of Gösta Berling*, speaks for itself as an atmospheric old wives' tale. It is worth noting, perhaps, that the Devil returns from his nightly trips with black bulls hitched to his carriage, since in Tennessee the legend persists into our own time that the Devil hitches black oxen to his cart.

Today we may assume that the Swedish Devil is an isolationist, a power in the steel trust, righteously indignant at the success of the co-operatives. Satan waxes fatter when there is friction.

GHOST STORY

Selma Lagerlöf

OH, CHILDREN OF THE PRESENT DAY!

I have nothing new to tell you, only what is old and almost forgotten. I have legends from the nursery, where the little ones sat on low stools about the old nurse with her white hair, or from the log fire in the cottage, where the laborers sat and chatted, while the steam reeked from their wet clothes, and they drew knives from leather sheaths at their necks to spread the butter on thick, soft bread, or from the hall where old men sat in their rocking chairs and, cheered by the steaming toddy, talked of old times.

When a child, who had listened to the old nurse, to the laborers, to the old men, stood at the window on a winter's evening, it saw no clouds on the horizon without their being the pensioners; the stars were wax candles, which were lighted at the old house at Borg; and the spinning wheel which hummed in the next room was driven by old Ulrika Dillner. For the child's head was filled with the people of those old days; it lived for and adored them.

But if such a child, whose whole soul was filled with stories, should be sent through the dark attic to the storeroom for flax or biscuits, then the small feet scurried; then it came flying down the stairs, through the passage to the kitchen. For up there in the dark it could not help thinking of the wicked millowner at Fors—of him who was in league with the Devil.

Sintram's ashes have been resting long in Svartsjö churchyard, but no one believes that his soul has been called to God, as it reads on his tombstone.

While he was alive he was one of those to whose home, on long, rainy Sunday afternoons, a heavy coach, drawn by black horses, used to come. A gentleman, richly but plainly dressed, gets out of the carriage and helps with cards and dice to while away the long hours which, with their monotony, have driven the master of the house to despair. The game is carried on far into the night; and when the stranger departs at dawn he always leaves behind some baleful parting gift.

As long as Sintram was here on earth he was one of those whose coming is made known by spirits. They are heralded by visions. Their carriages roll into the yard; their whip cracks; their voices sound on the stairs; the door of the entry is opened and shut. The dogs and people are awakened by the noise, it is so loud; but there is no one who has come; it is only a hallucination which goes before them.

Ugh, those horrible people, whom evil spirits seek out! What kind of big black dog was it which showed itself at Fors in Sintram's time? He had terrible, shining eyes and a long tongue which dripped blood and hung far out of his panting throat. One day, when the menservants had been in the kitchen and eaten their dinner, he had scratched at the kitchen door, and all the maids had screamed with fright; but the biggest and strongest of the men had taken a burning log from the fire, thrown open the door, and hurled it into the dog's gaping mouth.

Then he had fled with terrible howls; flames and smoke had burst from his throat; sparks whirled about him, and his footprints on the path shone like fire.

And was it not dreadful that every time Sintram came home from a journey he had changed the animals which drew him? He left with horses, but when he came home at night he had always black bulls before his carriage. The people who lived near the road saw their great black horns against the sky when he drove by and heard the creatures' bellowing and were terrified by the line of sparks which the hoofs and wheels drew out of the dry gravel.

Yes, the little feet needed to hurry, indeed, to come across the big dark attic. Think if something awful, if he, whose name one may not say, should come out of a dark corner! Who can be sure? It was not only to wicked people that he showed himself. Had not Ulrika Dillner seen him? Both she and Anna Stjärnhök could say that they had seen him.

Friends, children, you who dance, you who laugh! I beg you so earnestly to dance carefully, laugh gently, for there can be so much unhappiness if your thin slippers tread on sensitive hearts instead of on hard boards; and your glad, silvery laughter can drive a soul to despair.

It was surely so; the young people had trodden too hard on old Ulrika Dillner, and the young people's laughter had rung too arrogantly in her ears, for there came over her suddenly an irresistible longing for a married woman's titles and dignities. At last she said "yes" to the evil Sintram's long courtship, followed him to Fors as his wife, and was parted from the old friends at Berga, the dear old work, and the old cares for daily bread.

It was a match which went quickly and gayly. Sintram offered himself at Christmas, and in February they were married. That year Anna Stjärnhök was living in Captain Uggla's home. She was a good substitute for old Ulrika, and the latter could draw back without compunction and take to herself married honors.

Without compunction, but not without regret. It was not a pleasant place she had come to; the big, empty rooms were filled with dreadful terrors. As soon as it was dark she began to tremble and to be afraid. She almost died of homesickness.

The long Sunday afternoons were the hardest of all. They never came to an end, neither they nor the long succession of torturing thoughts which traveled through her brain.

So it happened one day in March, when Sintram had not come home from church to dinner, that she went into the drawing room on the second floor and placed herself at the piano. It was her last consolation. The old piano, with a flute player and shepherdess painted on the white cover, was her own, come to her from her parents' home. To it she could tell her troubles; it understood her.

But is it not both pitiful and ridiculous? Do you know what she is playing? Only a polka, and she who is so heartbroken!

She does not know anything else. Before her fingers stiffened round broom and carving knife she had learned this one polka. It sticks in her fingers, but she does not know any other piece—no funeral march, no impassioned sonata, not even a wailing ballad—only the polka.

She plays it whenever she has anything to confide to the old piano. She plays it both when she feels like weeping and like smiling. When she was married she played it, and when for the first time she had come to her own home, and also now.

The old strings understand her: she is unhappy, unhappy.

A traveler passing by and hearing the polka ring could well believe that Sintram was having a ball for neighbors and friends, it sounds so gay. It is such a brave and glad melody. With it, in the old days, she has played carelessness in and hunger out at Berga; when they heard it everyone must up and dance. It burst the fetters of rheumatism about the joints and lured pensioners of eighty years onto the floor. The whole world would gladly dance to that polka, it sounds so gay— but old Ulrika weeps. Sintram has sulky, morose servants about him and savage animals. She longs for friendly faces and smiling mouths. It is this despairing longing which the lively polka shall interpret.

People find it hard to remember that she is Madam Sintram. Everybody calls her Mamselle Dillner. She wants the polka tune to express her sorrow for the vanity which tempted her to seek for married honors.

Old Ulrika plays as if she would break the strings. There is so much to drown: the lamentations of the poor peasants, the curses of overworked cottagers, the sneers of insolent servants, and, first and last, the shame—the shame of being the wife of a bad man.

To those notes Gösta Berling has led young Countess Dohna to the dance. Marianne Sinclair and her many admirers have danced to them, and the major's wife at Ekeby has moved to their measure when Altringer was still alive. She can see them, couple after couple in their youth and beauty, whirl by. There was a stream of gaiety from them to her, from her to them. It was her polka which made their cheeks glow, their eyes shine. She is parted from all that now. Let the polka resound —so many memories, so many tender memories to drown!

She plays to deaden her anguish. Her heart is ready to burst with terror when she sees the black dog, when she hears the servants whispering of the black bulls. She plays the polka over and over again to deaden her anguish.

Then she perceives that her husband has come home. She hears that he comes into the room and sits down in the rocking chair. She knows so well the sound as the rockers creak on the deal floor that she does not even look around.

All the time she is playing the rocking continues; she soon hears the music no longer, only the rocking.

Poor old Ulrika, so tortured, so lonely, so helpless, astray in a hostile country, without a friend to complain to, without any consoler but a cracked piano, which answers her with a polka.

It is like loud laughter at a funeral, a drinking song in a church.

While the rocking chair is still rocking she hears suddenly how the piano is laughing at her sorrows, and she stops in the middle of a bar. She rises and turns to the rocking chair.

But the next instant she is lying in a swoon on the floor. It was not her husband who sat in the rocking chair, but another—he to whom little children do not dare to give a name, he who would frighten them to death if they should meet him in the deserted attic.

Can anyone whose soul has been filled with legends ever free himself from their dominion? The night wind howls outside; the trees whip the pillars of the balcony with their stiff branches; the sky arches darkly over the far-stretching hills, and I, who sit alone in the night and write, with the lamp lighted and the curtain drawn, I, who am old and ought to be sensible, feel the same shudder creeping up my back as when I first heard this story, and I have to keep lifting my eyes from my work to be certain that no one has come in and hidden himself in that further corner; I have to look out on the balcony to see if there is not a black head looking over the railing. This fright never leaves me when the night is dark and solitude deep, and it becomes at last so dreadful that I must throw aside my pen, creep down in my bed, and draw the blanket up over my eyes.

It was the great, secret wonder of my childhood that Ulrika Dillner survived that afternoon. I should never have done so.

I hope, dear friends, that you may never see the tears of old eyes. And that you may not have to stand helpless when a gray head leans against your breast for support, or when old hands are clasped about yours in a silent prayer. May you never see the old sunk in a sorrow which you cannot comfort.

What is the grief of the young? They have strength; they have hope. But what suffering it is when the old weep; what despair when they, who have always been the support of your young days, sink into helpless wailing.

There sat Anna Stjärnhök and listened to old Ulrika, and she saw no way out for her.

The old woman wept and trembled. Her eyes were wild. She talked and talked, sometimes quite incoherently, as if she did not know where she was. The thousand wrinkles which crossed her face were twice as deep as usual; the false curls, which hung down over her eyes, were straightened by her tears, and her whole long, thin body was shaken with sobs.

At last Anna had to put an end to the wailings. She had made up her mind. She was going to take her back with her to Berga. Of course she was Sintram's wife, but she could not remain at Fors. He would drive her mad if she stayed with him. Anna Stjärnhök had decided to take old Ulrika away.

Ah, how the poor thing rejoiced, and yet trembled at this decision! But she never would dare to leave her husband and her home. He would perhaps send the big black dog after her.

But Anna Stjärnhök conquered her resistance, partly by jests, partly by threats, and in half an hour she had her beside her in the sledge. Anna. was driving herself, and old Disa was in the shafts. The road was wretched, for it. was late in March, but it did old Ulrika good to drive once. more in the well-known sledge, behind the old horse who had been a faithful servant at Berga almost as long as she.

As she had naturally a cheerful spirit, she stopped crying by the time they passed Arvidstorp; at Högberg she was already laughing, and when they passed Munkeby she was telling how it used to be in her youth, when she lived with the countess at Svaneholm.

They drove up a steep and stony road in the lonely and deserted region north of Munkeby. The road sought out all the hills it possibly could find; it crept up to their tops by slow windings, rushed down them in a steep descent, hurried across the even valley to find a new hill to climb over.

They were just driving down Vestratorp's Hill, when old Ulrika stopped short in what she was saying and seized Anna by the arm. She was staring at a big black dog at the roadside.

"Look!" she said.

The dog set off into the wood. Anna did not see much of him.

"Drive on," said Ulrika; "drive as fast as you can! Now Sintram will hear that I have gone."

Anna tried to laugh at her terror, but she insisted.

"We shall soon hear his sleigh bells, you will see. We shall hear them before we reach the top of the next hill."

And when Disa drew breath for a second at the top of Elots Hill sleigh bells could be heard behind them.

Old Ulrika became quite mad with fright. She trembled, sobbed, and wailed as she had done in the drawing room at Fors. Anna tried to urge Disa on, but she only turned her head and gave her a glance of unspeakable surprise. Did she think that Disa had forgotten when it was time to trot and when it was time to walk? Did she want to teach her how to drag a sledge, to teach her who had known every stone, every bridge, every gate, every hill for more than twenty years?

All this while the sleigh bells were coming nearer.

"It is he, it is he! I know his bells," wails old Ulrika.

The sound comes ever nearer. Sometimes it seems so unnaturally loud that Anna turns to see if Sintram's horse has not got his head in her sledge; sometimes it dies away. They hear it now on the right, now on the left of the road, but they see no one. It is as if the jingling of the bells alone pursues them.

Just as it is at night, on the way home from a party, is it also now. These bells ring out a tune; they sing, speak, answer. The woods echo with their sound.

Anna Stjärnhök almost wishes that their pursuer would come near enough for her to see Sintram himself and his red horse. The dreadful sleigh bells anger her.

"Those bells torture me," she says.

The word is taken up by the bells. "Torture me," they ring. "Torture me, torture, torture, torture me," they sing to all possible tunes.

It was not so long ago that she had driven this same way, hunted by wolves. She had seen their white teeth, in the darkness, gleam in their gaping mouths; she had thought that her body would soon be torn to pieces by the wild beasts of the forest, but then she had not been afraid. She had never lived through a more glorious night. Strong and beautiful had the horse been which drew her; strong and beautiful was the man who had shared the joy of the adventure with her.

Ah, this old horse, this old, helpless, trembling companion. She feels so helpless that she longs to cry. She cannot escape from those terrible, irritating bells.

So she stops and gets out of the sledge. There must be an end to it all. Why should she run away as if she were afraid of that wicked, contemptible wretch?

At last she sees a horse's head come out of the advancing twilight, and after the head a whole horse, a whole sledge, and in the sledge sits Sintram himself.

She notices, however, that it is not as if they had come along the road—this sledge, and this horse, and their driver—but more as if they had been created just there before her eyes and had come forward out of the twilight as soon as they were made ready.

Anna threw the reins to Ulrika and went to meet Sintram.

He stops the horse.

"Well, well," he says; "what a piece of luck! Dear Miss Stjärnhök, let me move my companion over to your sledge. He is going to Berga tonight, and I am in a hurry to get home."

"Where is your companion?"

Sintram lifts his blanket and shows Anna a man who is lying asleep on the bottom of the sledge. "He is a little drunk," he says, "but what does that matter? He will sleep. It's an old acquaintance, moreover; it is Gösta Berling."

Anna shudders.

"Well, I will tell you," continues Sintram, "that she who forsakes the man she loves sells him to the Devil. That was the way I got into his claws. People think they do so well, of course; to renounce is good, and to love is evil."

"What do you mean? What are you talking about?" asks Anna, quite disturbed.

"I mean that you should not have let Gösta Berling go from you, Miss Anna."

"It was God's will."

"Yes, yes, that's the way it is; to renounce is good, and to love is evil. The good God does not like to see people happy. He sends wolves after them. But if it was not God who did it, Miss Anna? Could it not just as well have been I who called my little gray lambs from the Dovre mountains to hunt the young man and the young girl? Think, if it was I who sent the wolves, because I did not wish to lose one of my own! Think, if it was not God who did it!"

"You must not tempt me to doubt that," says Anna in a weak voice, "for then I am lost."

"Look here," says Sintram, and bends down over the sleeping Gösta Berling; "look at his little finger. That little sore never heals. We took the blood there when he signed the contract. He is mine. There is a peculiar power in blood. He is mine, and it is only love which can free him, but if I am allowed to keep him he will be a fine thing."

Anna Stjärnhök struggles and struggles to shake off the fascination which has seized her. It is all madness, madness. No one can swear away his soul to the odious tempter. But she has no power over her thoughts; the twilight lies so heavy over her; the woods stand so dark and silent. She cannot escape the dreadful terror of the moment.

"You think, perhaps," continues Sintram, "that there is not much left in him to ruin. But don't think that! Has he ground down the peasants; has he deceived poor friends; has he cheated at cards? Has he, Miss Anna, has he been a married woman's lover?"

"I think you are the Devil himself!"

"Let us exchange. You take Gösta Berling, take him and marry him. Keep him, and give them at Berga the money. I yield him up to you, and you know that he is mine. Think that it was not God who sent the wolves after you the other night and let us exchange!"

"What do you want as compensation?"

Sintram grinned.

"I—what do I want? Oh, I am satisfied with little. I only want that old woman there in your sledge, Miss Anna."

"Satan, tempter," cries Anna, "leave me! Shall I betray an old friend who relies on me? Shall I leave her to you, that you may torture her to madness?"

"There, there, there; quietly, Miss Anna! Think what you are doing! Here is a fine young man, and there an old, worn-out woman. One of them I must have. Which of them will you let me keep?"

Anna Stjärnhök laughed wildly.

"Do you think that we can stand here and exchange souls as they exchange horses at the market at Broby?"

"Just so, yes. But if you will, we shall put it on another basis. We shall think of the honor of the Stjärnhöks."

Thereupon he begins to call in a loud voice to his wife, who is sitting in Anna's sledge; and, to the girl's unspeakable horror, she obeys the summons instantly, gets out of the sledge, and comes, trembling and shaking, to them.

"See, see, see!—such an obedient wife," says Sintram. "You cannot prevent her coming when her husband calls. Now, I shall lift Gösta out of my sledge and leave him here—leave him for *good,* Miss Anna. Whoever may want to can pick him up."

He bends down to lift Gösta up, but Anna leans forward, fixes him with her eyes, and hisses like an angry animal:

"In God's name, go home! Do you not know who is sitting in the rocking chair in the drawing room and waiting for you? Do you dare to let him wait?"

It was for Anna almost the climax of the horrors of the day to see how these words affect him. He drags on the reins, turns, and drives homeward, urging the horse to a gallop with blows and wild cries down the dreadful hill, while a long line of sparks crackle under the runners and hoofs in the thin March snow.

Anna Stjärnhök and Ulrika Dillner stand alone in the road, but they do not say a word. Ulrika trembles before Anna's wild eyes, and Anna has nothing to say to the poor old thing, for whose sake she has sacrificed her beloved.

She would have liked to weep, to rave, to roll on the ground and strew snow and sand on her head.

Before, she had known the sweetness of renunciation; now she knew its bitterness. What was it to sacrifice her love compared to sacrificing her beloved's soul? They drove on to Berga in the same silence, but when they arrived and the hall door was opened Anna Stjärnhök fainted for the first and only time in her life. There sat both Sintram and Gösta Berling, and chatted quietly. The tray with toddy had been brought in; they had been there at least an hour.

Anna Stjärnhök fainted, but old Ulrika stood calm. She had noticed that everything was not right with him who had followed them on the road.

Afterward the captain and his wife arranged the matter so with Sintram that old Ulrika was allowed to stay at Berga. He agreed good-naturedly.

"He did not want to drive her mad," he said.

I do not ask anyone to believe these old stories. They cannot be anything but lies and fiction. But the anguish which passes over the heart, until it wails as the floor boards in Sintram's room wailed under the swaying rockers; but the questions which ring in the ears, as the sleigh bells rang for Anna Stjärnhök in the lonely forest—when will they be as lies and fiction?

Oh, that they could be!

English

POSSIBLY you remember the brief cable stories filed early in October of 1944 and emanating from the remote village of Great Leighs in Essex County. An American bulldozer pushed away a huge stone which had pinned down the Witch of Scrapfaggot Green for more than two hundred years and released (so we are told) a particularly malicious poltergeist.

Villagers insisted that church bells rang in the dark hours, heavy scaffolding poles were "scattered like matchsticks," large haystacks "blew over" on still nights, and enormous stones were carried considerable distances.

Wars and great disasters have always played curious tricks upon the mass mind.

The appearance of the crucified Christ over England, attested by eminent divines and other impressionable souls, reminds us of the spine-chilling manifestations of World War I in which the Archers of Agincourt swept in with shadowy longbows and deadly arrows to turn the desperate tide of battle and save the day for England.

By curious coincidence, England is once again utilizing the Witchcraft Act of 1735 to punish dabblers in the occult. On April 3, 1944, Mrs. Helen Duncan, a forty-six-year-old medium (or "witch," as she would have been called in an earlier era), was sentenced in Old Bailey to nine months' imprisonment. To make the "witch burning" perfect in every detail, the conviction came on a Friday. There were three other defendants (magic number); the trial lasted seven days (seven is a natural in any language); and the bewildered "witch" held traditional silence for all seven days, crying out at the sentence: "I've done nothing. O God! Is there a God?"

But those who make a pact with the Devil have a powerful friend. Let inquisitors beware. You know what happened to Old Bailey! It was struck by German bombs.

That the Devil had a merry time in Merry England for many centuries is attested by the vast literature of Diabolism, the naïve fulminations against witches and sorcerers, and the truly diabolic persecutions of those suspected of having intercourse with the Devil.

While it is true that the Roman and later the Christian influence seemed rather quickly to destroy the ancient paganism of the Druids, it is also true that fertility rites and "Sabbaths" of prehistoric origin were celebrated up to the eighteenth century. The dances and feasts of Candlemas (February 2), Roodmas (May 3), Lammas (August 1), and Allhallow Eve were night-long celebrations, often of a bacchanalian variety.

The similarity of these celebrations throughout Europe, and the similar methods by which the Christian hierarchy backed by civil law sought to destroy this earlier and rival form of religion, give recognizable pattern to every "witch" and "devil" story in European folklore.

England's legal definition of a witch is "a person who hath conference with the Devil to consult with him or to do some act." Since any sort of testimony save that of the accused was given credence, thousands went to their deaths through the monomaniacal efforts of bigots hysterically certain that they were fighting the Devil.

Devil lore in England (and elsewhere) might be divided into four categories: (1) the naïve testimony of accused or accuser in witchcraft trials; (2) the pseudo-philosophical studies of eminent divines and other dabblers; (3) serious and enlightened works by scientific students, and (4) artistic representations (both naïve and sophisticated) in fiction, verse, and drama.

In the fourth category are a great many delightful and fanciful works of art from the earliest morality plays through Byron's *Cain* to George Bernard Shaw's *Man and Superman* and Sylvia Townsend Warner's *Lolly Willows*. Generally speaking, the modern reader will find them readable in inverse proportion to his belief in the subject. For as A. E. Housman once observed:

Malt does more than Milton can
To justify God's way toward man.

The material in this section runs the gamut from naïveté to sophistication; in fact, from Fryer Bacon to John Collier. The selection from William J. Thoms's early English romances pictures the wily fiend as a very real menace to the soul of a gentleman who made the usual infernal bargain. But fortunately in this case the sophistry of the clergy was more than a match for the greed of banker or barrister from the nether regions. And it must have comforted many a sinful wretch to see the Devil thus hoisted on his own petard.

The selection from Alfred, Lord Tennyson is interesting chiefly as evidence of the fact that Queen Victoria's poet laureate was as good a poet at fourteen as he would ever become—though in later years he drew his inspiration from less diabolical sources.

The current laureate, John Masefield, in *The Devil and the Old Man,* would seem to testify that in the days of wooden ships and iron men the master of a ship was everything that name implies. Masefield, drawing upon an old fisherman's legend, has the Devil pay "nine and twenty silver pennies" in earnest money. Heine noted a similar folk theme involving similar coins. And the tale rings other pieces of silver down the years from the thirty which betrayed Christ and those that paid Charon's ferrying fee to the solid silver service on which the Devil spread a feast for the artist in William Makepeace Thackeray's *The Painter's Bargain.*

The Collier extravaganza runs the gamut of fantasy usually reserved for Hollywood musical productions. It embodies the fundamental appeals of sin, sex, and sophistry—with ironic observations upon feminine psychology. Even Einstein might be confused by Collier's discovery that the universe is shaped like a vast pint of beer.

Drink up, old chap!

HOW FRYER BACON SAVED A GENTLEMAN THAT HAD GIVEN HIMSELFE TO THE DEVILL

Edited by William J. Thoms

IN OXFORDSHIRE there lived a gentleman, that had through his riotous expences wasted a faire inheritance that was left him by his father: after which hee grew so poore, that he had not wherwith to buy himselfe so much bread as would mainteine his miserable life: the memory of his former state that hee had lived in, and the present want that he now sustained, made him to grow desperate and regardlesse both of his soule and bodies estate: which gave the Devill occasion to worke upon his weaknesse in this manner following.

On a time, hee being alone full of griefe and care (griefe for his folies past, and care how to get a poore living for the remainder of his dayes), the Devill came to him and asked him what hee wanted (hee came not in a shape terrible, but like an old penny-father). This gentleman was amazed at his sodaine presence, but hearing him demand of his wants, hee tooke to him courage and said: I want all things, I want money to buy my apparell, money to buy mee meat, money to redeeme my land and money to pay my debts: can or will you helpe mee in this misery? I will answered the Devill, on some conditions helpe you to money for to supply all these wants and that sodainly. On any condition, said the Gentleman, helpe mee, and I sweare for to performe them: I take no oathes (answered the Devill). I must have bonds, if you will doe so, meet mee by the woods side to morrow morning, and there I will have the moneys ready: I will said the gentleman (for hee poore man was glad of it on any conditions, as he said before). The next day hee went to the wood where the Devill had promised to meet him: long had he not been there, but he beheld the Devill comming, and after him two other like servingmen with bagges of money: this reioyced the poore gentlemans heart to thinke that hee should once again live like a man. The Devill comming to him said: sonne I will performe my promise unto you if that you will seale to the conditions that I have here already drawne: willingly said the gentleman, I will, I pray read them. The Devill read them to this effect: that he lent him so much money as he should have need of, to be imployed to these uses following: First, to redeeme his mortgaged land: next to pay his debts: lastly, to buy him such necessaries as hee wanted: this to be lent on this condition, that so soone as he had paid all his debts, that he should be at the lenders disposing, and his without any delay, freely to yeeld himselfe to him upon the first demand of the aforesaid lender. To this the gentleman sealed, and had the money carried to his chamber, with which money hee in short time redeemed his land, and bought such things as he needed, and likewise payed all his debts, so that there was not any man that coulde aske him one penny.

Thus lived this gentleman once againe in great credit, and grew so great a husband that he increased his estate, and was richer than ever his father before him was: but long did this joy of his not continue, for one day hee being in his studie the Devill appeared unto him, and did tell him that now his land was redeemed, and his debts paid, and therefore the time was come that hee must yeeld himselfe to his mercy, as hee was bound by bond. This troubled the gentleman to heare, but more to thinke how he must become a slave to a stranger that hee did not know (for hee knew not as yet that he was the Devill) but being urged to answer for himselfe (by the Devill) hee said that hee had not as yet paid all his debts, and therefore as yet hee was not liable to the bonds strait conditions. At this the Devill seemed angry and with a fearefull noyse transfformed himselfe to an ugly shape, saying, alas poore wretch, these are poore excuses that thou framest, I know them all to be false, and so will prove them to thy face to morrow morning, till when I leave thee to despaire: So with great noyse he went his way, leaving the gentleman halfe dead with feare.

When he was gone, the gentleman reviving bethought himselfe in what a miserable state he was now in, then wished he that he had lived and died poorely, then cursed he all his ambitious thoughts, that led him first to desire againe that wealth which he had so vainly by his riot lost: then would hee curse his prodigall expences that were the originall of all his misery: thus was he tormented a long time in his minde, at last he fully resolved to end his wretched life by some violent death, and to that end he went forth thinking to kill himselfe, which he had done, had it not beene for the Fryer: for as he was falling upon his sword, Fryer Bacon came by and called to him to hold, which he did. Fryer Bacon demanded of him the cause why he was so desperate that he would run headlong to hell? O sir, said he, the cause is great, and the relation is so terrible to me, that I would intreat you not to trouble me any more, but to leave me to my owne will: his answer filled the Fryer with amazement and pitty both at once, which made him to urge him in this manner. Sir, should I leave you to this wilfull damnation, I were unfit ever hereafter to weare or touch any robe that belongeth unto the holy order, whereof I am a brother: you know (I doubt not) that there is given power to the church to absolve penitent sinners, let not your wilfulnesse take away from you that benefit which you may receive by it: freely confesse your selfe (I pray you) unto me, and doubt not but I shall give your troubled conscience ease: Father (said this Gentleman) I know all that you have spoken is truth, and I have many times received comfort from the mother church (I dare not say our, for I feare that shee will never receive me for a childe), I have no part in her benediction, yet since you request so earnestly the cause, I will tell you, heare it and tremble. Know then that I have given my selfe to the Devill for a little wealth, and he to morrow in this wood must have me: now have you my griefe, but I know not how to get comfort. This is strange (quoth Fryer Bacon), yet be of good comfort, penitentiall teares may doe much, which see you doe not spare; soone I will visit you at your house, and give you that comfort (I hope) that will beget you againe to goodnesse: the Gentleman with these words was somewhat comforted and returned home. At night Fryer Bacon came to him, and found him full of teares for his haynous offences, for these teares he gave him hope of pardon, demanded further what conditions hee had made with the Devill; the gentleman told him, how that he had promised himselfe to him so soone as hee had paid all his debts: which he now had done, for he owed not one peny to any man living. Well said Fryer Bacon, continue thy sorrow for thy sinnes, and to morrow meete him without feare, and be thou content to stand to the next mans judgement that shall come that way, whether thou doest belong to the Devill or no: feare not, but do so, and be thou assured that I will be he that shall come by, and will give such judgement on thy side, that thou shalt bee free from him: with that Fryer Bacon went home, and the Gentleman went to his prayers.

In the morning the gentleman (after that hee had blessed himselfe) went to the wood where he found the Devill ready for him, so soone as he came neere, the Devill said, now deceiver are you come, now shall thou see that I can and will prove that thou hast paid all thy debts, and therefore thy soule belongeth to me. Thou art a deceiver (said the gentleman) and gavest me money to cheat me of my soule, for else why wilt thou be thy own judge: let me have some other to judge between us. Content said the Devill, take whom thou wilt: then I will have (said the gentleman) the next man that commeth this way: hereto the Devill agreed. No sooner were these words ended, but Fryer Bacon came by, to whom this gentleman speake, and requested, that he would be judge in a waighty matter betweene them two: the Fryer said, he was content, so both parties were agreed: the Devill said they were, and told Fryer Bacon how the case stood between them in this manner.

Know Fryer, that I seeing this prodigall like to starve for want of food, lent him money, not onely to buy him victuals, but also to re-deeme his lands and pay his debts, conditionarily that so soone as his debts were paid, that hee should give himselfe freely to mee, to this, here is his hand (shewing him the bond) now my time is expired, for all his debts are paid, which hee cannot denie. This case is plaine, if it be so that his debts are paid: his silence confirmes it said the Devill, therefore give him a just sentence. I will said Fryer Bacon: but first tell me (speaking to the gentleman) didst thou never yet give the Devill any of his money back, nor requite him any wayes: never had hee any thing of me as yet (answered the gentleman): then never let him have any thing of thee and thou art free; deceiver of mankind, said he (speaking to the Devill) it was thy bargaine, never to meddle with him so long as hee was indebted to any, now how canst thou demand of him any thing, when he is indebted for all that hee hath to thee, when hee payeth thee thy money, then take him as thy due; till then thou hast nothing to doe with him: and so I charge thee to be gone. At this, the Devill vanished with great horror, but Fryer Bacon comforted the gentleman, and sent him home with a quiet conscience bidding him never to pay the Devills money backe as he tendred his owne safety: which he promised for to observe.

THE DEVIL AND THE LADY

Alfred, Lord Tennyson

(A poetic drama in 3 acts, written by Tennyson when he was 14 years old.)

ACT I

The Devil comes, having been summoned by Magus, a necromancer

I come, O I Come, at the sound of my name
From the depths and the caverns of Hell where I lie,
I can rush through the torrent and ride on the flame
Or mount on the whirlwind that sweeps thro' the sky—
What wilt thou have me do for thee? Shall I weave
The sunbeams to a crown for thy bald brows?
Shall I ungarter the Plëiades for thee
And twist their glittering *periscelides*[1]
To keep the hose up on thy minishing calves?
Shall I unchair Cassiopeia's brightness
And fetch her close stool for thee? or pluck the Nanny-goat
From off the back of that old blade whose haunches
Quiver beneath the feather'd foot of Perseus?
Shall I ungird Orion's strength, or bring thee
A grinder of that mighty snake, whose folds
Far stretching through the unconfined space
Involve seven worlds?

[1] Greek word meaning "garters."

MAGUS. A truce with thine heroics!
A murrain take thine ill tim'd pleasantry!
If thou art not the most impertinent Devil
That ever smelt bitumen, pri'thee hear me.
Affairs of high importance call me hence,
Nor would I borrow of that usurer
Procrastination, whose vast interest
Is almost higher than his principal.
Procrastination, like the wayward tide,
With imperceptible and secret course
Gains hourly on us till that we are left
No landing place whereon to set our feet—
So lost and tangled is the maze of cares
Protracted and put off from day to day.

DEVIL. What is the end and purport of thy words?
And wherewith can I serve thee?

MAGUS.   Thou shalt hear
For I forthwith upon the yeasty wave
With hasty expedition of swift oars
Shall now embark—but to thee I commit
(Until such time as I retrace my way)
My loving wife, to guard her chaste and pure
As stainless snow, brush'd by the windy wing
Of Eagle on the stormy mountain top,
Or like the virgin lily, whose rare sweets
Combining with the ambient atmosphere,
Do make a paradise of this fair earth,
So delicate are its odours.

DEVIL.   Gentle master,
I would do ought but this—I'd dive i'th' sea,
I'd ride the chariot of the rocking winds
Alarum'd by the hornéd corners of the Moon
I'd pluck the charméd flowers that flourish there;
I'd visit far Arcturus, the bright length
Of the Ecliptic and the spangled Lyre,
Or that dim star which in Boötes' wain
Shines nightly, or I'd bring thee gems from out
The stilly chambers of the mighty deep,
The boundless halls of porphyry, where sit
The ancient fathers of the sea with beards
That sweep the burnish'd chrysolite beneath 'em—
All this and more I'd do for thee, for these

Are trifles to that weighty task, to guard
A woman 'gainst her will.

    MAGUS.   This once, good Friend,
Exert thy power—the task is short—eftsoones
I shall be here again—til then farewell!
      Exit MAGUS

SCENE II

    DEVIL. A very decent, tolerable task—
Outwit a woman—that were difficult;
Place in one scale my graceless Devilship—
Her ladyship in t'other—weight us both,
I do much fear me lest her ladyship
Untwist my meshes, foil my purposes
And by her subtile intricacy of wit
Mislead my choicest, noblest, nicest guile.
The very fuscous and embrownéd cheek
Of his Satanick Majesty might blanch
Before a woman's art. O Styx and Acheron!
What deprecations, amulets and charms,
What exorcisms, crossings and bead countings,
What Ave-Maries will be play'd against me!
I value not your amulets and charms
The twentieth part of half a rotten murphy
Or a split pea, albeit I do confess me
I'm apt to turn tail on an Ave-Mary,
And quail a little at a Pater-Noster,
Except when it's said backwards. I remember me
When I was summon'd up by this same Magus
And unto this same office ('twas the dead
Of a most chilly winter) that I lit
I' th' grey o' th' morning on a blue nos'd Monk
And pluck'd him by the beard, whereat he shrunk
In all his sinews like a sensitive plant
And chatter'd from the bottom of his cowl
"*Apage Sathanus iniquissime!*"
Whereat I tripp'd him up and laid him prone
Holding close conference with his Mother Earth
About the damage of his splinter'd nose,
And having punch'd him fundamentally
With my strong hooves, I left him bruised and battered
As a beefsteak.

THE DEVIL AND THE OLD MAN

John Masefield

UP AWAY NORTH, in the old days, in Chester, there was a man who never throve. Nothing he put his hand to ever prospered, and as his state worsened, his friends fell away and he grew desperate. So one night when he was alone in his room, thinking of the rent due in two or three days and the money he couldn't scrape together, he cried out, "I wish I could sell my soul to the Devil like that man the old books tell about."

Now just as he spoke the clock struck twelve, and, while it chimed, a sparkle began to burn about the room, and the air, all at once, began to smell of brimstone, and a voice said:

"Will these terms suit you?"

He then saw that someone had just placed a parchment there. He picked it up and read it through; and being in despair, and not knowing what he was doing, he answered, "Yes," and looked round for a pen.

"Take and sign," said the voice again, "but first consider what it is you do; do nothing rashly. Consider."

So he thought awhile; then, "Yes," he said, "I'll sign," and with that he groped for the pen.

"Blood from your left thumb and sign," said the voice.

So he pricked his left thumb and signed.

"Here is your earnest money," said the voice, "nine and twenty silver pennies. This day twenty years hence I shall see you again."

Now early next morning our friend came to himself and felt like one of the drowned. "What a dream I've had," he said. Then he woke up and saw the nine and twenty silver pennies and smelled a faint smell of brimstone.

So he sat in his chair there and remembered that he had sold his soul to the Devil for twenty years of heart's desire; and whatever fears he may have had as to what might come at the end of those twenty years, he found comfort in the thought that, after all, twenty years is a good stretch of time, and that throughout them he could eat, drink, merrymake, roll in gold, dress in silk, and be carefree, heart at ease, and jib sheet to windward.

So for nineteen years and nine months he lived in great state, having his heart's desire in all things; but, when his twenty years were nearly run through, there was no wretcheder man in all the world than that poor fellow. So he threw up his house, his position, riches, everything, and away he went to the port of Liverpool, where he signed on as A.B., aboard a Black Ball packet, a tea clipper, bound to the China Seas.

They made a fine passage out, and when our friend had only three days more, they were in the Indian Ocean, lying lazy, becalmed.

Now it was his wheel that forenoon, and it being dead calm, all he had to do was just to think of things, the ship of course having no way on her.

So he stood there, hanging onto the spokes, groaning and weeping till, just twenty minutes or so before eight bells were made, up came the captain for a turn on deck.

He went aft of course, took a squint aloft, and saw our friend crying at the wheel. "Hello, my man," he says, "why, what's all this? Ain't you well? You'd best lay aft for a dose o' salts at four bells tonight."

"No, Cap'n," said the man, "there's no salts'll ever cure my sickness."

"Why, what's all this?" says the old man. "You must be sick if it's as bad as all that. But come now; your cheek is all sunk, and you look as if you ain't slept well. What is it ails you, anyway? Have you anything on your mind?"

"Captain," he answers very solemn, "I have sold my soul to the Devil."

"Oh," said the old man, "why, that's bad. That's powerful bad. I never thought them sort of things ever happened outside a book."

"But," said our friend, "that's not the worst of it, Captain. At this time three days hence the Devil will fetch me home."

"Good Lord!" groaned the old man. "Here's a nice hurrah's nest to happen aboard my ship. But come now," he went on, "did the Devil give you no chance—no saving clause like? Just think quietly for a moment."

"Yes, Captain," said our friend, "just when I made the deal, there came a whisper in my ear. And," he said, speaking very quietly, so as not to let the mate hear, "if I can give the Devil three jobs to do which he cannot do, why, then, Captain," he says, "I'm saved, and that deed of mine is canceled."

Well, at this the old man grinned and said, "You just leave things to me, my son. *I'll* fix the Devil for you. Aft there, one o' you, and relieve the wheel. Now you run forrard, and have a good watch below, and be quite easy in your mind, for I'll deal with the Devil for you. You rest and be easy."

And so that day goes by, and the next, and the one after that, and the one after that was the day the Devil was due.

Soon as eight bells was made in the morning watch, the old man called all hands aft.

"Men," he said, "I've got an all-hands job for you this forenoon.

"Mr. Mate," he cried, "get all hands onto the main-tops'l halyards and bouse the sail stiff up and down."

So they passed along the halyards and took the turns off, and old John Chantyman piped up:

> *"There's a Black Ball clipper*
> *Comin' down the river."*

And away the yard went to the masthead till the bunt robands jammed in the sheave.

"Very well that," said the old man. "Now get my dinghy off o' the half deck and let her drag alongside."

So they did that too.

"Very well that," said the old man. "Now forrard with you, to the chain locker, and rouse out every inch of chain you find there."

So forrard they went, and the chain was lighted up and flaked along the deck all clear for running.

"Now, Chips," says the old man to the carpenter, "just bend the spare anchor to the end of that chain and clear away the fo'c'sle rails ready for when we let go."

So they did this too.

"Now," said the old man, "get them tubs of slush from the galley. Pass that slush along there, doctor. Very well that. Now turn to, all hands, and slush away every link in that chain a good inch thick in grease."

So they did that, too, and wondered what the old man meant.

"Very well that," cries the old man. "Now get below, all hands! Chips, onto the fo'c'sle head with you and stand by! I'll keep the deck, Mr. Mate! Very well that."

So all hands tumbled down below; Chips took a fill o' 'baccy to leeward of the capstan, and the old man walked the weather poop, looking for a sign of hell-fire.

It was still dead calm—but presently, toward six bells, he raised a black cloud away to leeward and saw the glimmer of the lightning in it; only the flashes were too red and came too quick.

"Now," says he to himself, "stand by."

Very soon that black cloud worked up to windward, right alongside, and there came a red flash, and a strong sulphurous smell, and then a loud peal of thunder as the Devil steps aboard.

"Mornin', Cap'n," says he.

"Mornin', Mr. Devil," says the old man, "and what in blazes do you want aboard *my* ship?"

"Why, Captain," said the Devil, "I've come for the soul of one of your hands as per signed agreement; and, as my time's pretty full up in these wicked days, I hope you won't keep me waiting for him longer than need be."

"Well, Mr. Devil," says the old man, "the man you come for is down below, sleeping, just at this moment. It's a fair pity to call him till it's right time. So supposin' I set you them three tasks. How would that be? Have you any objections?"

"Why, no," said the Devil, "fire away as soon as you like."

"Mr. Devil," said the old man, "you see that main-tops'l yard? Suppose you lay out on that main-tops'l yard and take in three reefs singlehanded."

"Ay, ay, sir," the Devil said, and he ran up the ratlines, into the top, up the topmast rigging, and along the yard.

Well, when he found the sail stiff up and down, he hailed the deck:

"Below there! On deck there! Lower away ya halyards!"

"I will not," said the old man, "nary a lower."

"Come up your sheets, then," said the Devil. "This main-topsail's stiff up and down. How'm I to take in three reefs when the sail's stiff up and down?"

"Why," said the old man, *"you can't do it.* Come out o' that! Down from aloft, you hoof-footed son. That's one to me."

"Yes," says the Devil, when he got on deck again, "I don't deny it, Cap'n. That's one to you."

"Now, Mr. Devil," said the old man, going toward the rail, "suppose you was to step into that little boat alongside there. Will you please?"

"Ay, ay, sir," he said, and he slid down the forrard fall, got into the stern sheets, and sat down.

"Now, Mr. Devil," said the skipper, taking a little salt spoon from his vest pocket, "supposin' you bail all the water on that side the boat onto this side the boat, using this spoon as your dipper."

Well!—the Devil just looked at him.

"Say!" he said at length. "Which of the New England States d'ye hail from anyway?"

"Not Jersey, anyway," said the old man. "That's two up, all right; ain't it, sonny?"

"Yes," growls the Devil as he climbs aboard. "That's two up. Two to you and one to play. Now, what's your next contraption?"

"Mr. Devil," said the old man, looking very innocent, "you see, I've ranged my chain ready for letting go anchor. Now Chips is forrard there, and when I sing out, he'll let the anchor go. Supposin' you stopper the chain with them big hands o' yourn and keep it from running out clear. Will you, please?"

So the Devil takes off his coat and rubs his hands together and gets away forrard by the bitts and stands by.

"All ready, Cap'n," he says.

"All ready, Chips?" asked the old man.

"All ready, sir," replies Chips.

"Then, stand by. Let *go* the anchor," and clink, clink, old Chips knocks out the pin, and away goes the spare anchor and greased chain into a five-mile deep of God's sea. As I said, they were in the Indian Ocean.

Well—there was the Devil, making a grab here and a grab there, and the slushy chain just slipping through his claws, and at whiles a bight of chain would spring clear and rap him in the eye.

So at last the cable was nearly clean gone, and the Devil ran to the last big link (which was seized to the heel of the foremast), and he put both his arms through it and hung onto it like grim death.

But the chain gave such a *yank* when it came to that the big link carried away, and oh, roll and go, out it went through the hawsehole, in a shower of bright sparks, carrying the Devil with it. There is no Devil now. The Devil's dead.

As for the old man, he looked over the bows, watching the bubbles burst, but the Devil never rose. Then he went to the fo'c'sle scuttle and banged thereon with a hand spike.

"Rouse out, there, the port watch," he called, "an' get my dinghy inboard."

THE DEVIL, GEORGE, AND ROSIE

John Collier

THERE WAS a young man who was invariably spurned by the girls, not because he smelled at all bad, but because he happened to be as ugly as a monkey. He had a good heart, but this soured it, and though he would still grudgingly admit that the female kind were very agreeable in shape, size, and texture, he thought that in all other respects they were the most stupid, blind, perverse, and ill-natured bitches that had ever infested the earth.

He expressed this view very forcefully, and on all possible occasions. One evening he was holding forth to a circle of his cronies: it was in the Horseshoe Bar, at the bottom of the Tottenham Court Road. He could not help noticing that his remarks attracted the interest of a smart and saturnine individual seated at the next table, who had the rather repulsive look of a detective dressed up in evening clothes for the purpose of spying on a night club.

Our friend was in no wise abashed by this scrutiny but continued to say exactly what girls were and what they did whenever they got the chance. He, who had least evidence for it of any man in the world, seemed to think they were unduly inclined to lasciviousness. "Or else," said he, "in the other extreme, they are mercenary prudes, or sadistical Dianas, whose delight it is to kindle the fires of Hell in a man's bosom and elsewhere, and triumphantly to describe his agonies to their little friends. I speak of the fires of Hell—I wish they existed in reality, so that these harpies and teasers might be sent there, and I myself would go willingly, if only I could watch them frizzle and fry."

With that, he got up and went home. You may imagine his astonishment, when he had climbed the high stairs to his poor student's room, to find the dark and cynical stranger, who had been watching him in the bar, now standing very much at his ease upon the hearthrug. At the very first glance he realized this was none other than the Devil himself, in whom for many years he had had no belief at all. "I cannot easily describe," said that worthy, with the smile of a man of the world, "the pleasure it gives me to meet one of such insight and intelligence as Mr. George Postlethwaite."

George made several sorts of protest, but the Devil smiled and bowed like an ambassador. In the end he had buttered up George to some effect and carried him off to supper in a little restaurant in Jermyn Street. It must be admitted he stood a superb bottle of wine.

"I was vastly intrigued," said he, "by the views I heard you expressing earlier this evening. Possibly, of course, they were born of a mere passing petulance, pique, wounded vanity—call it what you will."

"The Devil take me if they were!" cried George.

"Splendid!" said his companion. "We are getting on like a house on fire. Now, my dear chap, my little difficulty is this. The domain over which I have the honor and pleasure to preside was designed originally on the most ample scale, but, nevertheless, certain recent tendencies are fast rendering its confines too narrow, and its supervision too onerous, for one who is not as young as he was."

"Sorry to hear that," said George.

"I could cope with the increase of the population of this planet," said the Devil. "I might have coped even with the emancipation of women. But unfortunately the two are connected and form a vicious circle——"

"I see exactly what you mean," said George.

"I wish I had never invented that particular sin," said the Devil. "I do indeed. There are a thousand million women in the world at this moment, and, with one or two negligible exceptions, every one of them is damned."

"Fine!" said George.

"Very fine indeed," said the Devil, "from the artistic point of view. But consider the pressure on space and the ceaseless strain of organization."

"Squeeze 'em in!" cried George with enthusiasm. "Pack 'em tight. That's what I say."

"They would then imagine themselves at a party," replied his new friend, "and that would never do. No, no. Everyone who comes to me must have individual attention. I intend to open a new department. The site is chosen. The builders are at work. All that I need is a superintendent of iron personality."

"I should like to know a little about the climate, salary, and prospects," said George in a businesslike tone.

"The climate, much like that of Oxford Street on a summer afternoon," replied the Devil. "The salary is power, and the prospects are infinite. But if you are interested, my dear fellow, allow me to show you over the place. In any case, I should value your opinion on it."

No sooner said than done: they sank into the bowels of the earth and came out in a suburb of Sydney, N.S.W.

"Here we are, then!" cried George.

"No, no," said the Devil. "Just a little farther on."

They proceeded with the speed of rockets to the northeast corner of the universe, which George perceived to be shaped exactly like a pint of beer in which the nebulae were the ascending bubbles. He observed with alarm a pair of enormous lips approaching the upper rim of our space. "Do not be alarmed," said the Devil. "That is a young medical student called Prior, who has failed his exam three times in succession. However, it will be twenty million billion light years before his lips reach the glass, for a young woman is fixing him with her eye, and by the time he drinks all the bubbles will be gone, and all will be flat and stale."

"Poor fellow!" cried our hero. "Damn these women!"

"Do not pity him," said the Devil very tolerantly. "This is his fifth, and he is already as drunk as a lord, and closing time draws near. What's more, our destination is at hand."

George saw that they were nearing what is sometimes called a "fish" in this considerable pint of beer. As they approached it he saw it was a dark star of gigantic proportions, about which circled a satellite many hundred times larger than the earth.

"That satellite," said his conductor, "is the spot I am proposing to colonize with my new department. We will go straight there, if you wish."

George assenting, they landed in a sterile and saturnine country, close by a palace of black basalt, which covered seven square miles of ground.

"That's a snug-looking box!" cried our hero.

"Merely a pioneer's hut," said his companion. "My future overseer will have to rough it there until something better can be run up."

George, however, observed a prodigious number of barrels being run down into a cellar on the hinder side of this palace. What's more, he saw several groups of fiends, who should have been at their work, squatting in one of the unfinished galleries with cards in their hands.

"You actually play poker here?" said he, in tones of the liveliest satisfaction.

"We are connoisseurs of every pleasure," replied the Devil with a smile. "And when we play cards everybody has an excellent hand."

He showed George a number of masterly pictures: some of them were a little indecent. There were also very splendid kitchens, already staffed with cooks; kennels, stables, falconries, gun rooms, music rooms, grand halls, little cozy rooms, rooms devoted to every sort of pastime, and gardens laid out rather like those of Versailles, only much larger. There was a whole cellar full of fireworks of every description. Not only these, but there were a number of other delights, of a nature entirely new to the visitor. There was an observatory, for example, from which the behavior of any young woman in the world could be closely inspected. "This is really a very interesting device," murmured our hero.

"Come!" said the fiend. "We must not stay here all day. Doubtless you will want to see the rest of your domain."

"Yes indeed," said George. "For of course I could not have the prisoners here, unless now and then I had one haled up for special admonishment."

The Devil then flew with him over the whole surface of the planet, which, once they were clear of the palace and its lands, proved to have an aspect not unlike that of the Great West Road, where it approaches London. On every hand rows of cells were being run up; to add the final refinement and misery, they were designed exactly like modern villas. Imitation husbands, who could neither speak nor hear, were planted in armchairs with their feet on the mantelpieces. The wardrobes were full of unfashionable garments. Small imps disguised as children were already rehearsing by dozens in all the upper rooms. The peculiar property of the walls was to translate the noise of those next door into the sound of a party going on, while the windows were so designed as to make the dowdiest passer-by appear to be arrayed in the very latest mode.

Vast bunion factories belched smoke among the crazy villas; lorryloads of superfluous hair clattered along the streets. George was shown the towering gasometers of the halitosis works and a number of other things I do not dare imagine. He saw a great concourse of fiends being instructed in door-to-door salesmanship; others were being fitted out as relations-in-law, rent collectors, and bailiffs. He himself made two suggestions that were immediately put into force: one was for a stocking ladderer and the other for an elastic that would break in the middle of any crowded thoroughfare.

As a final encouragement, the Devil took him over to the mainland of Hell itself, which is girdled by the Styx as Saturn by his ring. Charon's vast liner had just come to dock, and our hero had the pleasure of seeing a multitude of film stars, baby blondes, unfaithful wives, disobedient daughters, frivolous typists, lazy serving maids, wantons, careless waitresses, cruel charmers, naggers, sirens, clogs, unpunctual sweethearts, bridge-playing grandmas, extravagant helpmeets, mischief-making gossips, tantalizers, female novelists, crazy debutantes, possessive mothers, neglectful mothers, modern mothers, unmarried mothers, would-be, should-be—in fact, all who could be—mothers: they were all there, as naked as your hand, and they filed down the gangway, some weeping, some brazen, and some in attitudes of affected modesty.

"This is a magnificent sight," remarked our hero.

"Well, my dear sir," said the Devil, "are you the man for the job?"

"I will do my best!" cried George enthusiastically.

They shook hands on it; all the little details were arranged; before evening George was installed as principal vassal of all the Devil's host and overlord of a planet populated only by women and fiends.

It must be admitted he enjoyed himself with a vengeance. Every day he would go out, having donned his cap of invisibility, and regale himself upon his subjects' endeavors to cope with the hardships he had designed for them. Sometimes he would hold up the ceaseless self-dirtying of plates, put the children to sleep, and amuse them with the prospect of a matinee. He saw to it, though, that they had to queue up for the cheap seats and arranged for it to rain. In the end he would announce that the show was postponed.

He had a thousand other ways of tantalizing them: I shall not enumerate them all. One of the best was to send for any newly arrived young thing who was reported to be vain of her beauty and give her the impression for an hour or two that she had made a conquest of him, and then (as far as was possible) undeceive her.

When the day's work was done he sat down to cards with his principal officers, and, sure enough, everyone had a good hand, but his was the best. They drank like champions: the Devil was constantly sending over the choicest delicacies from Hell; the word "fine" was continually upon our hero's lips, and the time passed like lightning.

One day, toward the end of the second year, our potentate had just got through his levee and was refreshing himself with a stroll on a little private terrace which he much affected, when word was brought to him that the senior port official desired an audience. Our hero was the easiest fellow in the world to approach; never stood upon his dignity. "Send the old chap along here," said he. "And, hi! Bring a bottle and a couple of glasses back with you when you come."

The fact is, George dearly loved a chat with these old petty officers, who occasionally brought him reports of diverting little incidents at the Ellis Island of Hell, or scraps of gossip concerning the irrelevant affairs of the world, such as sometimes strayed in among Charon's cargo, as lizards or butterflies travel to Covent Garden among the bananas.

On this occasion, however, the harbor master's face bore an extremely worried expression. "I'm afraid, sir," he said, "I've got a little irregularity to report."

"Well, we all make mistakes sometimes," said George. "What's the trouble?"

"It's like this here, sir," replied the old salt. "Young gal come along o' the last cargo—seems as if she didn't ought to be here at all."

"Oh, that'll be all right," cried George. "Bound to be. It's understood we take the whole issue in these days. She's a woman: that's enough. What's on her charge sheet, anyway?"

"Lot o' little things, sir, what don't amount to much," replied the honest fellow. "Fact is, sir, it ain't added up." And he pursed his lips.

"Not added up?" cried George in amazement.

"That's how it is, sir," said his subordinate glumly. "This young gal *ain't properly dead.*"

George was absolutely bowled over. *"Whew!"* said he. "But this is serious, my man."

"It *is* serious, sir," said the old chap. "I don't know what's to be done, I'm sure."

A score of fine legal points were involved. George dispatched an S O S for one of the leading casuists of Hell proper. Unfortunately they were all engaged in committee, on some fine point concerning an illuminated address which was being prepared for the saviors of Germany. George, therefore, had nothing but precedent to go on, and precedent made it clear that a mortal must sin in such and such a way, die in such and such a condition, be checked in, checked out: it was as complicated as a case in Court Leet under a Statute of Ed. Tert. Rex., that statute being based on precedents from the Saxon and Norman codes dually and differently derived from a Roman adaptation of a Greco-Egyptian principle influenced prehistorically by rites and customs from the basin of the Euphrates or the Indus. It was quite like an income-tax form. George scratched his head in despair.

What made it all the worse was the Devil himself had given him most serious warning against the least infringement of privilege. "This is," he had said, "little better than mandated territory. We have built up, step by step, and with incredible ingenuity, a system under which we live very tolerably, but we have only done it by sailing devilishly near the metaphysical wind. One single step beyond the strict legal limits and I am back on my red-hot throne, in that pit whose bottomlessness I shall heartily envy. As for you——"

George, therefore, had every incentive to caution. He turned over a large number of volumes, tapped his teeth: in the end he knew not what to make of it. "Send the young person in to me," said he.

When she arrived she proved to be no more than seventeen years of age. I should be telling a downright lie if I said she was less beautiful than a peri.

George was not a bad fellow at heart. Like most of us, he was capable of tyranny upon the featureless mass, but when he came to grips with an individual his bark was a good deal worse than his bite. Most of the young women he had had up for admonishment had complained of little except his fickleness.

This young girl was ushered into his presence; the very lackeys who brought her in rolled their eyes till the whites flickered like the Eddystone Lighthouse. She was complete in every particular, and all of the highest quality; she was a picture gallery, an anthology of the poets, a precipitation of all that has ever been dreamed of love: her goodly eyes lyke Saphyres shining bright, her forehead yvory white, her cheekes lyke apples which the sun hath rudded, her lips lyke cherryes charming men to byte, her brest lyke to a bowle of creame uncrudded, her paps lyke lyllies budded, her snowie necke lyke to a marble towre; and all her body like a pallace fayre, ascending up, with many a stately stayre, to honours seat and chastities sweet bowre.

Her name was Rosie Dixon. Moreover, she gained enormously in contrast to her surroundings, by the mere fact of being alive. It was as though a cowslip were to bloom miraculously between the dark and sterile metals of the Underground; as if its scent were wafted to one's nostrils on the nasty, sultry, canned sirocco of that region. It is no exaggeration to say that she was as good as she was beautiful. It is true her pretty face was a little blubbered with tears. "My dear," said George, taking her hand, "there is no reason for you to cry in that fashion. Don't you know the good old saying, 'Never holler before you're hurt'?"

"Pray, sir," cried she, having taken a long, dewy peep at his monkey phiz, and seeing a vast amount of good nature there. "Pray, sir," said she, "tell me only, where am I?"

"Why, in Hell, to be sure," said he with a hearty laugh.

"Oh, thank goodness!" cried she. "I thought I was in Buenos Aires."

"Most of 'em think that," said our hero, "owing to the liner. But I must say, you are the first who has shown any gratification on learning otherwise."

They had a little more conversation of this sort; he questioned her pretty closely as to how she came to be stowed away on Charon's vessel. It appeared that she was a shopgirl who had been much tormented by her workmates; why, she could not say. However, she had to serve a young man who came in to buy some stockings for his sister. This young man had addressed to her a remark that brought her soul fluttering to her lips. At that very moment the cruelest of her envious colleagues had maneuvered to pass behind her and had bestowed on her a pinch so spiteful, so sudden, and so intensely and laceratingly agonizing, that her poised soul was jolted from its perch; it had spread its wings and borne off her swooning body as a woodcock bears off its young. When she had regained her senses she was locked in one of the narrow staterooms of a vast ship, stewarded by what she took to be black men, and resounding with the hysterical laughter and screams of captives of her own sex.

George was very thorough: he minutely examined what little evidence she had to offer. "There is no doubt," said he at length, speaking in tones of the greatest sympathy, "that you have received a very cruel pinch. When your tormentor comes into my hands I myself will repay it a hundredfold."

"No, no," said she. "She did not mean so much harm. I'm sure she is a good girl at heart. It is just her little way."

George was overcome with admiration at this remark, which, however, caused a tremor to pass through the whole of the vast black palace. "Upon my word!" said he. "I can't keep you here. You will bring the whole place crashing about my ears. I dare not put you in one of our punishment cells, for, if I did so against your will, all our system of home rule would be snatched away from us and we should return to the crude discomforts of primitive times. That would be intolerable. There is a museum over on the mainland that would make your blood run cold."

"Could you not send me back to earth?" said she.

"No woman has ever left this place alone!" cried he in despair. "My position is so delicate I dare not make an innovation."

"Do not take on so," said she. "I cannot bear to think of so kind a gentleman being plunged into fiery torments. I will stay voluntarily, and perhaps then no fuss will be made. I hope it will not be terribly painful."

"You adorable creature!" cried he. "I must give you a kiss for that. I believe you have solved the difficulty."

She gave him back his kiss, as sweetly and purely as you can possibly imagine. "Oh, hell!" he cried in great anguish of spirit. "I cannot bear to think of you undergoing the miseries of this place. My dear, good girl——"

"I don't mind," she said. "I have worked in a shop in Oxford Street."

He gave her a pat or two and signed up a form for her: "Remanded in custody at own request."

"This is only temporary, after all," he said. "Otherwise I would not permit it."

Very well, she kept a stiff upper lip and was carted off to a hateful box as cruelly equipped as any of the others. For a whole week George kept his head, reading love lyrics to distract his mind. At the end he could put the matter behind him no longer. "I must go," said he, "and see how she is getting on."

In Hell all the officials travel with incredible speed. In a very few minutes George had passed over a couple of continents and was tapping at the mean front door of poor Rosie's little habitation. He had not chosen to put on his cap of fern-seed virtue, or perhaps he never thought of it; anyway, she came to the door with three or four of the imps hanging about her apron strings and recognized him at once. He observed that she had on the drab and unfashionable garments provided by the authorities, in which her appearance was that of a rose in a jam pot.

What raised an intolerable burden from his heart was the fact that the superfluous hair had obviously failed to take root upon her living flesh. He found on inquiry that she had used it to stuff a pillow with, which she had placed behind the head of the snoring imitation husband who gracelessly sprawled before the fire. She admitted a little tuft flourished on the bruise where she had been pinched.

"No doubt it will fall off," said our hero scientifically, "when the tissues resume their normal condition. These things were designed to flourish upon carrion only, whereas you——" And he smacked his lips.

"I hope it will fall off," said she, "for scissors will not cut it. And since I promised some to the eldest of these toddlers, to make him a false mustache of, no more has arrived."

"Shall I try to cut it off?" said our hero.

"No, no," said she with a blush. "He has stopped crying now. They were all very querulous when first I came here, but now they are improved out of all knowledge."

While she spoke she busied her fingers with a succession of little tasks. "You seem to be terribly busy," complained George.

"Forgive me," said she with a smile, "but there is such a terrible lot to do. Still, it makes the time pass."

"Do you never," said he, "wish to go to the matinee?"

"That would never do," she replied. "Supposing *he* should wake up"—pointing to the imitation husband—"and call for his tea. Besides, I have plenty of entertainment: the people next door seem always to have a party; it does me good to hear them laugh and sing. What's more, when I'm cleaning the windows, as needs doing pretty often, I always see the most beautifully dressed creatures go by. I love to see people in pretty clothes."

"Your own are not very attractive," said George in a melancholy tone.

"They are plain enough," said she with a laugh. "But I'm far too busy to think about that. All I could wish is that they were of slightly stronger materials. The stockings laddered so often I've had to give up wearing them. And whenever I go out shopping—— Still, you don't want to hear all this."

George was so devoured by remorse that he had not the spirit to ask an interesting question. "Good-by," said he, pressing her hand.

She gave him the sweetest glance: he felt it no more than his duty to offer her an encouraging kiss. The doors began to bang; the fire belched smoke; the imps opened their mouths to yell.

"No, no," said she with just so much of inexpressible regret as to soften the cruelty of it. And she pointed to the dummy husband before the fire.

"Don't worry about him!" cried our hero. "He's only a dummy." With that he gave the image a kick, capsizing it into the hearth.

"Well, if he's not a real husband," said Rosie, "I suppose there is nothing wrong in it," and with that she gave George a kiss, which he found altogether delightful, except that as it increased the high esteem in which he held her, so also it increased his misery in having placed her in such a condition.

When he got home the poor fellow could neither eat nor sleep. He called up a few of his officers to pass away the night at poker, but though he held four straight flushes in succession he could take no pleasure in it. In the morning the telephone bell rang. George's was the only instrument on the planet which did not go wrong as soon as one began to speak; on this occasion he would willingly have surrendered the advantage. The Devil was at the other end, and he was in a towering rage. He made no bones about accusing our hero of downright morality.

"You curse and swear very well," said the victim in an injured tone. "All the same, it was not my fault she came here. I clearly see she may prove a disintegrating influence if I keep her, but, if I may not send her back, I don't see what else I can do."

"Why, tempt her, you idiot!" replied the Devil. "Have you never tempted woman before?"

"As far as I know, no," said George frankly.

"Well, do so now," said the Devil in quite a silky tone, which nevertheless caused blue sparks to crackle from the instrument. "Once we get possession of her soul, there will not be much fuss made about her body. I leave the matter in your hands entirely. If you fail me there are one or two ancient institutions over here which I shall take pleasure in reviving entirely for your benefit."

George detested the idea of tempting this singularly good and beautiful young girl; however, the prospect was not so unredeemingly repulsive as that of immersion in boiling brimstone. He took a glass or two, to stifle what regrets he had, and sent for Rosie to attend him in a silken pavilion, which he had rigged up among the groves and fountains which enclosed his citadel. He considered this fabric to be preferable to blocks of black basalt, in the event of some disruptive phrase of hers bringing the roof about their ears.

It was not very long before she arrived, although it seemed so. Heaven knows how she preserved her radiant health in the nasty gray air of Hell's outer suburbs: she looked as fresh and bright as ever and seemed to glow through her cheerless wrappings as a peach glows through tissue paper. Nevertheless, George was naturally a slow starter, especially when his conscience was involved. He certainly greeted her very warmly, but if all the scientists in the world had had these hugs and kisses in a test tube, they could not have separated one atom of sin out of them, for they were as simple and natural as could possibly be desired.

I admit the simple and natural is as good a beginning as any other. George, however, proceeded only to the offer of a cup of tea, which is not sinful except at the university. They began to chat: he was unable to resist telling her of his joys and sorrows in the neighborhood of the Tottenham Court Road, and the reason for this was that he wished her to know everything about him. She herself was no less frank: it is impossible to describe the emotion with which George heard that she had become an orphan at the age of fourteen and had since then lived with an old aunt, who was inclined to severity. The moments passed like flowers of that precious edelweiss joy which blooms on the brink of the abyss.

The light began to fade; the warbling of blackbirds and thrushes now sank into a stillness from which soon rose the diviner strains of the nightingale. Our young people, seated at the entrance of the tent, found their tongues fall idle and sat in a divine languor which, also, like a silence of the being, permitted the first faint notes of a new music to become audible in their hearts. In this far, wild corner of the garden the effect was a little Chinese, with a profusion of willow trees, which now turned blue in the dimming air.

Their fingers interlocked. The moon, which in those parts is of gigantic size, being no other than Hell itself, rose behind the shadowy trees. "They say," said Rosie in a dreamy voice, "that those marks on it are craters."

One person's dream may well be another's awakening. George was at once galvanized into activity. "Come," said he. "It is time we began dinner. It's my birthday, so there's lots of champagne."

He hoped by these words to inveigle the simple girl into making a feast of it. However, he started under a handicap, for he was already as drunk as a lord on the very sound of her voice. A man's true nature appears when he is in that condition: George was prepared to jeopardize his whole future for an amorous whim. His brain reeled under the onslaught of a legion of virtuous thoughts. He even conceived the notion of suggesting to the Devil that it should be the dummy husband who should be cast into the boiling brimstone and that he should take that useless effigy's place, but from this act of madness the thought of the imps restrained him.

The remembrance of his master brought him back to Hell for a moment. "My dear," said he, patting her hand, "how would you like to be a film star?"

"Not at all," said she.

"What?" said he.

"Not at all," said she.

"Oh!" said he. "Well! Well! Well!"

He had a diamond necklace in his pocket, ready to tempt her with, but could not restrain himself from hanging it unconditionally about her neck, he was so delighted by this answer of hers.

She was pleased, even more than by the gift itself, by the spirit in which it was given. She thought George the kindest and the best of men, and (whether it was the wine or not, I'll not say) she would have even stuck to it that he was handsome.

Altogether, the meal went off as merry as a marriage bell; the only drawback was that George could see no signs of a fitting sequel. Some would say the brimstone was a sequel sufficiently appropriate: that was not George's idea at all. In fact, when he had played all his cards in this halfhearted fashion he was suddenly overcome by a hideous prevision of his fate and could not repress a most alarming groan.

"What is it, my dear?" cried Rosie in the tenderest of voices.

"Oh, nothing," said he, "nothing at all. Only that I shall burn forever if I fail to seduce you."

"That is what the young man said at the stocking counter," said she in dismay.

"But I mean it," said he dolorously, "and in brimstone, which, I assure you, is altogether a different proposition from love, whatever the poets may say."

"You are right," said she in a happier voice than seemed entirely fitting, "love is altogether different from brimstone," and with that she squeezed his hand.

"I fear it will give me no peace in which to remember you," said he, positively photographing her with his eyes.

"You shall not go there," said she.

"He said I must!" cried George.

"Not," said she, "if—if it will save you to——"

"To what?" cried George.

"To seduce me," faltered Rosie.

George protested very little; he was altogether carried away by the charming manner in which she expressed herself. He flung his arms about her and endeavored to convey, in one single kiss, all his gratitude for her kindness, his admiration for her beauty, his respect for her character, and his regret that she should have been orphaned at the age of fourteen and left to the care of an aunt who was a little inclined to severity. This is a great deal to be expressed in one single kiss; nevertheless, our hero did his best.

Next morning he had to telephone his report to the Devil. "I'll hold your hand," said Rosie.

"Very well, my darling," said he. "I shall feel better so."

His call was put through like lightning. The Devil, like thunder, asked him how he had got on.

"The young woman is seduced," said George in a rather brusque tone.

"Excellent!" returned his master. "Now tell me exactly how it happened."

"I thought," said George, "that you were supposed to be a gentleman."

"I am inquiring," said the Devil, "in a strictly professional capacity. What I wish to get at is her motive in yielding to your almost too subtle charm."

"Why?" cried George. "You don't think that splendid girl would see me frizzling and frying in a lake of boiling brimstone?"

"Do you mean to say," cried the Devil in a terrifying voice, "that she has sacrificed her virtue merely to save you from punishment?"

"What other inducement," asked our hero, "do you imagine would have been likely to prevail?"

"You besotted fool!" cried his master, and proceeded to abuse him ten times more roundly than before.

George listened in fear and rage. When he had done cursing him the Devil continued in a calmer voice, "There is only one thing to be done," said he, "and you may consider yourself very fortunate that you (you worm!) are needed to play a part in it. Otherwise you would be frizzling before sunset. As it is, I see I must give the matter my individual attention, and the first step is that you must marry the girl."

"By all means," replied our hero briskly.

"I shall send you a bishop to perform the ceremony," continued the fiend, "and next week, if I am better of my present fit of the gout, I shall require you to present me to your wife, and I myself will undertake her temptation."

"Temptation to what?" asked George in a tone of great anxiety.

"To that sin to which wives are peculiarly fitted," replied the Devil. "Does she like a waxed mustache?"

"Oh dear! He says," whispered George to Rosie, "do you like a waxed mustache?"

"No, darling," said Rosie. "I like a bristly, sandy one, like yours."

"She says she likes a bristly, sandy one, like mine," said George, not entirely without complacency.

"Excellent! I will appear in one yet bristlier and sandier," replied the fiend. "Keep her by you. I have never failed yet. And, Postlethwaite——"

"Oh yes, yes," said George. "What is it now?"

"Be discreet," said the Devil in a menacing tone. "If she gets wind of my intentions you shall be in the brimstone within an hour."

George hung up the receiver. "Excuse me, my dear," he said, "I really must go and think over what I have just heard."

He walked out among his groves of willows, which were then all freshened by the morning dew and resounding with the songs of birds. It was, of all the mornings of his life, that on which he would most have appreciated his first cigarette, had it not been for his conversation with the Devil. As it was, he did not bother to light one. "The thing is," he said to himself, "he must either succeed or fail. In the latter case his fury will be intolerable; in the former case mine will be."

The problem seemed to defy solution, and so it would have done, had it not been that love, whose bemusing effects have been celebrated often enough in song and story, has another and an ungratefully neglected aspect, in which the mind receives the benefit of clarifying calm. When the first flurry of his perturbation had passed our hero found himself in possession of a mind as cool and unclouded as the sea-strand sky of earliest dawn. He immediately lit his cigarette.

"After all, we have some days to go," he murmured, "and time is entirely relative. Consider, for example, that fellow Prior, who is at this very moment about to drink up the universe and who will still be arrested in the act of doing so long after all our little lives have passed away. On the other hand, it is certainly not for me to deny that certain delightful moments can take on the aspect of eternity. Besides, we might always escape."

The thought had entered his mind as unostentatiously as, no doubt, the notion of writing *Paradise Lost* entered Milton's—"H'm, I'll write *Paradise Lost*." "Besides, we might always escape." Just a few words, which, however, made all the difference. All that remained, in one case as in the óther, was to work out the little details.

Our hero was ingenious. What's more, he was assisted in his reflections by the hoarse cry, like that of a homing swan, of Charon's siren. It was the hour when that worthy, having cast loose from the quays of Hell, where he dropped his male cargo, turned his great ship toward George's planet. It came into sight, cleaving the morning blue, flashing in the beams of the local sun, leaving behind it a wake like that of a smoke-trailing airplane, only altogether better. It was a glorious sight. Soon George could see the women scampering up and down the decks and hear their cry: "Is that Buenos Aires?"

He lost no time, but, repairing to his palace and seating himself in the most impressive of its salons, he sent forth a messenger to the docks, saying, "Bid the skipper come up and have a word with me."

Charon soon came stumping along in the wake of the messenger. He might have been inclined to grumble, but his eyes brightened at the sight of a bottle George had on his desk. This contained nothing less than the Old Original Rum of Hell, a liquor of the fieriest description, and now as rare as it is unappreciated.

"Skipper," said George, "you and I have got on well enough hitherto, I believe. I have to ask you a question which may seem to reflect a little on your capacities. However, I don't ask it on my own behalf, you may be sure, and in order to show my private estimation of you as a friend, as a man, and above all as a sea dog of the old school, I am going to ask you to do me the favor of taking a little tipple with me first."

Charon was a man of few words. "Aye! Aye!" said he.

George then poured out the rum. When Charon had wet his whistle, "The chief," said George, "is in a secret fury with you over Mrs. Soames of Bayswater."

"Avast," said Charon with a frown.

"Has it slipped your memory that I mentioned her to you on two previous occasions?" continued our hero. "She is now a hundred and four and as cross as two sticks. The chief wants to know why you have not brought her along months ago." As he spoke he refilled Charon's glass.

"Avast," said that worthy again.

"Perhaps," said George, "among your manifold onerous duties, his express commands concerning one individual may have seemed unworthy of your attention. I'm sure I should have forgotten the matter altogether, had I such a job as yours. Still, you know what he is. He has been talking of changes at the Admiralty; however, pay no attention to that. I have to visit the earth myself on important business, and I find that the young woman you brought by such a regrettable mistake has had training as a hospital nurse. Between us, I assure you, we will shanghai the old geezer in a brace of shakes; the chief will find her here when he recovers from his gout, and foul weather between you will be entirely averted."

With that he poured the rest of the rum into the old salt's glass.

"Aye! Aye!" said that worthy.

George at once pressed the bell and had Rosie ushered in, in a bewitching uniform. "To the ship, at once!" he cried.

"Aye! Aye!" cried Charon.

"I can take you back," whispered George to his beloved, "as long as you don't look round. If you do, we are lost."

"Depend upon me," she said. "Nothing will ever make me cast a single glance behind while you and I are together."

Very well, they got aboard. Charon believed all landlubbers were mad; moreover, he had long suspected machinations against him at headquarters and was obliged to George for giving him word of them. George ordered a whole case of the admirable rum (the last case in existence) to be placed in his cabin, lest Charon should remember that old Mrs. Soames had never been mentioned to him at all.

Amid hoots and exclamations in technical language the great ship left her moorings. George, on the pretext that he had to maintain constant communication with his chief, took over the wireless operator's cabin. You may be sure Satan was in a fury when he heard what had happened, but the only effect of that was that his gouty members became a thousand times worse inflamed and grew still more so when he found it impossible to establish communication with the ship.

The best he could do was to conjure up, in the trackless wastes of space, such dumb images as might tempt Rosie to glance behind her. A Paris hat would bob up like a buoy on the starboard bow and a moment later (so great was the speed of the ship) be tossing far astern. On other occasions the images of the most famous film actors would be descried sitting on the silver planets of far constellations, combing their hair. She was exposed to a hundred temptations of this sort, and, what was crueler, she was subjected, by pursuant imps, to ceaseless tweakings of the hair, tuggings of the garments, sensations as of a spider down her back, and to all sorts of odious familiarities, far better imagined than described. The devoted girl, holding fast to the forward rail of the boat deck, never so much as flickered an eye.

The result of this devotion, coupled with George's vigilance at the earphones and Charon's drunkenness below, was that they soon heaved to in the latitudes of the earth. George and Rosie were set to slide at dizzy speed down an invisible rope, and they found themselves safely in bed beside the old centenarian, Mrs. Soames.

She was in a tearing rage when she found this young couple beside her. "Get out of here at once!" she cried.

"All right," they said, "we will."

The very next day I met them in Oxford Street, looking in the windows of the furniture shops, and George acquainted me with the whole story.

"And you say," said I, "that the universe is really a vast pint of beer?"

"Yes," said he. "It is all true. To prove it, I will show you the very place where Rosie was pinched by the envious young woman."

"The very place?" I cried.

"Yes," said he. "It was in that shop over there, at the counter to the right as you go in, just at the end of the stockings, and before the beginning of the lingerie."

THE WAR IN HEAVEN

———————◆———————

GOD AND THE DEVIL, light and darkness, Mazda and Ahriman, they exist through contrast and by reason of each other. A belief in God in a dualistic philosophy presupposes a belief in an opposing force of evil, and, if the deity is anthropomorphic, then the darkness, too, takes on the form of man to become the familiar Devil with horns, a cloven hoof, and telltale caudal appendage, or proud Lucifer with Stygian wings, the Prince of Darkness.

It is further axiomatic that, once called into existence, these forces must be in active opposition. In its most sublime conception this titanic struggle is the War in Heaven—God and the heavenly hosts in ceaseless battle with Satan and his minions.

From Isaiah's "How art thou fallen from heaven, O Lucifer, son of the morning!" down to the present day, the story has captured the imagination of the creative artist.

Nicodemus in his apocryphal gospel (attributed to the third century) brings the war into close focus: Jesus of Nazareth descends into Hell, and his advent precipitates a trenchant passage in which Satan (in this case differentiated from the Prince of Hell) is given a thorough going over, raising an almost impenetrable demonic smoke further to confuse future hagiographers.

And while Satan and the prince of hell were discoursing thus to each other, on a sudden there was a voice as of thunder and the rushing of winds, saying, Lift up your gates, O ye princes; and be ye lift up, O everlasting gates, and the King of Glory shall come in.

When the prince of hell heard this, he said to Satan, Depart from me and begone out of my habitations; if thou art a powerful warrior, fight with the King of Glory. But what hast thou to do with him? And then he cast him forth from his habitations. And the prince said to his impious officers, Shut the brass gates of cruelty and make them fast with iron bars, and fight courageously, lest we be taken captives.

But when all the company of the saints heard this they spake with a loud voice of anger to the prince of hell, Open thy gates that the King of Glory may come in.

Satan "hurl'd headlong flaming from th' Ethereal Sky" and condemned "to dwell in Adamantine Chains and penal Fire" becomes in *Paradise Lost* the occasion for John Milton's investigation of the creation of the world and his elaborately allusive cosmos. But hell's fire had to burn less brightly and the threat of excommunication loom less vital before the artist could give his imagination full play. A conception such as that of Anatole France in *The Revolt of the Angels* would have been tantamount to a most painful suicide in Milton's day and for another hundred years thereafter.

Anatole France toys cheerfully with Milton's "vain war with Heaven" and lets his Satan vision the effects of final conquest. Satan, with his brain filled with the "dense fumes of theology," realizes in his dream the inevitable result of victory if it should fall into his hands.

Satan sees himself seated on the throne of God and then he wakes in an icy sweat. Turning to his entourage, he says:

"No, we will not conquer the heavens. Enough to have the power. War engenders war, and victory defeat.

"God, conquered, will become Satan; Satan, conquering, will become God. May the fates spare me this terrible lot; I love the hell which formed my genius."

Greatly oversimplified, that is the essence of Anatole France's closing chapter from *The Revolt of the Angels* which has been included in this section along with the brief excerpt from *Paradise Lost*.

In *War in Heaven*, Philip Barry once posed an even more daring theological hypothesis. His novel is intricate in structure and plays on two levels. On one level it is the story of a group of down-at-heel vaudeville troupers; on another it is an allegory with startling implications. Produced on Broadway under the title *Here Come the Clowns*, it seemed to baffle most audiences, but, in both the play and the novel, Max Pabst is a most superior modern devil. And it is a strange commentary that even today the story seems to take on added meaning and depth every time the Devil makes his appearance.

Mr. Barry conceives the awesome possibility that the Devil has won the war in Heaven but that for reasons of policy he has kept the news of his victory from mankind, the better to discredit the concept of a God who is actually no longer able to take part in the affairs of our universe.

That is the most devastating communiqué ever to reach us from this eternal front.

SELECTION FROM BOOK I OF PARADISE LOST

John Milton

SAY FIRST, for Heav'n hides nothing from thy view
Nor the deep Tract of Hell, say first what cause
Mov'd our Grand Parents in that happy State,
Favour'd of Heav'n so highly, to fall off
From their Creator, and transgress his Will
For one restraint, Lords of the World besides?
Who first seduc'd them to that foul revolt?
Th' infernal Serpent; he it was, whose guile
Stirr'd up with Envy and Revenge, deceiv'd
The Mother of Mankind, what time his Pride
Had cast him out from Heav'n, with all his Host
Of Rebel Angels, by whose aid aspiring
To set himself in Glory above his Peers,
He trusted to have equall'd the most High,
If he oppos'd; and with ambitious aim
Against the Throne and Monarchy of God
Rais'd impious War in Heav'n and Battle proud
With vain attempt. Him the Almighty Power
Hurl'd headlong flaming from th' Ethereal Sky
With hideous ruin and combustion down
To bottomless perdition, there to dwell
In Adamantine Chains and penal Fire,
Who durst defy th' Omnipotent to Arms.
Nine times the Space that measures Day and Night
To Mortal men, he with his horrid crew
Lay vanquisht, rolling in the fiery Gulf
Confounded though immortal: But his doom
Reserv'd him to more wrath; for now the thought
Both of lost happiness and lasting pain
Torments him; round he throws his baleful eyes
That witness'd huge affliction and dismay
Mixt with obdúrate pride and steadfast hate:
At once as far as Angels ken he views
The dismal Situation waste and wild,
A dungeon horrible, on all sides round
As one great Furnace flam'd, yet from those flames

No light, but rather darkness visible
Serv'd only to discover sights of woe,
Regions of sorrow, doleful shades, where peace
And rest can never dwell, hope never comes
That comes to all; but torture without end
Still urges, and a fiery Deluge, fed
With ever-burning Sulphur unconsum'd:
Such place Eternal Justice had prepar'd
For those rebellious, here their Prison ordained
In utter darkness, and their portion set
As far remov'd from God and light of Heav'n
As from the Centre thrice to th' utmost Pole.
O how unlike the place from whence they fell!
There the companions of his fall, o'erwhelm'd
With Floods and Whirlwinds of tempestuous fire,
He soon discerns, and welt'ring by his side
One next himself in power, and next in crime,
Long after known in *Palestine,* and nam'd
Beëlzebub. To whom th' Arch-Enemy,
And thence in Heav'n call'd Satan, with bold words
Breaking the horrid silence thus began.

   If thou beest he; But O how fall'n! how chang'd
From him, who in the happy Realms of Light
Cloth'd with transcendent brightness didst outshine
Myriads though bright: If he whom mutual league,
United thoughts and counsels, equal hope,
And hazard in the Glorious Enterprise,
Join'd with me once, now misery hath join'd
In equal ruin: into what Pit thou seest
From what highth fall'n, so much the stronger prov'd
He with his Thunder: and till then who knew
The force of those dire Arms? yet not for those,
Nor what the Potent Victor in his rage
Can else inflict, do I repent or change,
Though chang'd in outward lustre; that fixt mind
And high disdain, from sense of injur'd merit,
That with the mightiest rais'd me to contend,
And to the fierce contention brought along
Innumerable force of Spirits arm'd
That durst dislike his reign, and me preferring,
His utmost power with adverse power oppos'd
In dubious Battle on the Plains of Heav'n,

And shook his throne. What though the field be lost?
All is not lost; the unconquerable Will,
And study of revenge, immortal hate,
And courage never to submit or yield:
And what is else not to be overcome?
That Glory never shall his wrath or might
Extort from me. To bow and sue for grace
With suppliant knee, and deify his power
Who from the terror of this Arm so late
Doubted his Empire, that were low indeed,
That were an ignominy and shame beneath
This downfall; since by Fate the strength of Gods
And this Empyreal substance cannot fail,
Since through experience of this great event
In Arms not worse, in foresight much advanc't,
We may with more successful hope resolve
To wage by force or guile eternal War
Irreconcilable, to our grand Foe,
Who now triúmphs, and in th' excess of joy
Sole reigning holds the Tyranny of Heav'n.
   So spake th' Apostate Angel, though in pain,
Vaunting aloud, but rackt with deep despair:
And him thus answer'd soon his bold Compeer.
   O Prince, O Chief of many Throned Powers,
That led th' imbattl'd Seraphim to War
Under thy conduct, and in dreadful deeds
Fearless, endanger'd Heav'n's perpetual King;
And put to proof his high Supremacy,
Whether upheld by strength, or Chance, or Fate,
Too well I see and rue the dire event,
That with sad overthrow and foul defeat
Hath lost us Heav'n, and all this mighty Host
In horrible destruction laid thus low,
As far as Gods and Heav'nly Essences
Can perish: for the mind and spirit remains
Invincible, and vigor soon returns,
Though all our Glory extinct, and happy state
Here swallow'd up in endless misery.
But what if he our Conqueror, (whom I now
Of force believe Almighty, since no less
Than such could have o'erpow'rd such force as ours)
Have left us this our spirit and strength entire

Strongly to suffer and support our pains,
That we may so suffice his vengeful ire,
Or do him mightier service as his thralls
By right of War, whate'er his business be
Here in the heart of Hell to work in Fire,
Or do his Errands in the gloomy Deep;
What can it then avail though yet we feel
Strength undiminisht, or eternal being
To undergo eternal punishment?
Whereto with speedy words th' Arch-fiend repli'd.
   Fall'n Cherub, to be weak is miserable
Doing or Suffering: but of this be sure,
To do aught good never will be our task,
But ever to do ill our sole delight,
As being the contrary to his high will
Whom we resist. If then his Providence
Out of our evil seek to bring forth good,
Our labour must be to pervert that end,
And out of good still to find means of evil;
Which oft-times may succeed, so as perhaps
Shall grieve him, if I fail not, and disturb
His inmost counsels from their destin'd aim.
But see the angry Victor hath recall'd
His Ministers of vengeance and pursuit
Back to the Gates of Heav'n: the Sulphurous Hail
Shot after us in storm, o'erblown hath laid
The Fiery Surge, that from the Precipice
Of Heav'n receiv'd us falling, and the Thunder,
Wing'd with red Lightning and impetuous rage,
Perhaps hath spent his shafts, and ceases now
To bellow through the vast and boundless Deep.
Let us not slip th' occasion, whether scorn,
Or satiate fury yield it from our Foe.
Seest thou yon dreary Plain, forlorn and wild,
The seat of desolation, void of light,
Save what the glimmering of these livid flames
Casts pale and dreadful? Thither let us tend
From off the tossing of these fiery waves,
There rest, if any rest can harbour there,
And reassembling our afflicted Powers,
Consult how we may henceforth most offend
Our Enemy, our own loss how repair,

How overcome this dire Calamity,
What reinforcement we may gain from Hope,
If not what resolution from despair.

THE REVOLT OF THE ANGELS[1]

Anatole France

CLIMBING the seven steep terraces which rise up from the bed of the
Ganges to the temples muffled in creepers, the five angels reached, by
half-obliterated paths, the wild garden filled with perfumed clusters
of grapes and chattering monkeys, and, at the far end thereof, they
discovered him whom they had come to seek. The archangel lay with
his elbow on black cushions embroidered with golden flames. At his
feet crouched lions and gazelles. Twined in the trees, tame serpents
turned on him their friendly gaze. At the sight of his angelic visitors
his face grew melancholy. Long since, in the days when, with his brow
crowned with grapes and his scepter of vine leaves in his hand, he had
taught and comforted mankind, his heart had many times been heavy
with sorrow; but never yet, since his glorious downfall, had his beautiful face expressed such pain and anguish.

Zita told him of the black standards assembled in crowds in all the
waste places of the globe; of the deliverances premeditated and prepared in the provinces of Heaven, where the first revolt had long ago
been fomented.

"Prince," she went on, "your army awaits you. Come, lead it on to
victory."

"Friends," replied the great archangel, "I was aware of the object
of your visit. Baskets of fruit and honeycombs await you under the
shade of this mighty tree. The sun is about to descend into the roseate
waters of the sacred river. When you have eaten, you will slumber
pleasantly in this garden, where the joys of the intellect and of the
senses have reigned since the day when I drove hence the spirit of the
old demiurge. Tomorrow I will give you my answer."

Night hung its blue veils over the garden. Satan fell asleep. He had
a dream, and in that dream, soaring over the earth, he saw it covered
with angels in revolt, beautiful as gods, whose eyes darted lightning.
And from pole to pole one single cry, formed of a myriad cries,
mounted toward him, filled with hope and love. And Satan said:

[1]Final chapter of book by the same name.

"Let us go forth! Let us seek the ancient Adversary in His high abode." And he led the countless host of angels over the celestial plains. And Satan was cognizant of what took place in the heavenly citadel. When news of this second revolt came thither, the Father said to the Son:

"The irreconcilable foe is rising once again. Let us take heed to ourselves, and in this, our time of danger, look to our defenses, lest we lose our high abode."

And the Son, consubstantial with the Father, replied:

"We shall triumph under the sign that gave Constantine the victory."

Indignation burst forth on the Mountain of God. At first the faithful seraphim condemned the rebels to terrible torture, but afterward decided on doing battle with them. The anger burning in the hearts of all inflamed each countenance. They did not doubt of victory, but treachery was feared, and eternal darkness had been at once decreed for spies and alarmists.

There was shouting and singing of ancient hymns and praise of the Almighty. They drank of the mystic wine. Courage, overinflated, came near to giving way, and a secret anxiety stole into the inner depths of their souls. The archangel Michael took supreme command. He reassured their minds by his serenity. His countenance, wherein his soul was visible, expressed contempt for danger. By his orders the chiefs of the thunderbolts, the kerûbs, grown dull with the long interval of peace, paced with heavy steps the ramparts of the Holy Mountain, and, letting the gaze of their bovine eyes wander over the lightning-flashed clouds of their Lord, strove to place the divine batteries in position. After inspecting the defenses, they swore to the Most High that all was in readiness. They took counsel together as to the plan they should follow. Michael was for the offensive. He, as a consummate soldier, said it was the supreme law. Attack, or be attacked— there was no middle course.

"Moreover," he added, "the offensive attitude is particularly suitable to the ardor of the Thrones and Dominations."

Beyond that, it was impossible to obtain a word from the valiant chief, and this silence seemed the mark of a genius sure of himself.

As soon as the approach of the enemy was announced Michael sent forth three armies to meet them, commanded by the archangels Uriel, Raphael, and Gabriel. Standards, displaying all the colors of the Orient, were unfurled above the ethereal plains, and the thunders rolled over the starry floors. For three days and three nights was the lot of the terrible and adorable armies unknown on the Mountain of God.

Toward dawn on the fourth day news came, but it was vague and confused. There were rumors of indecisive victories; of the triumph now of this side, now of that. There came reports of glorious deeds which were dissipated in a few hours.

The thunderbolts of Raphael, hurled against the rebels, had, it was said, consumed entire squadrons. The troops commanded by the impure Zita were thought to have been swallowed up in the whirlwind of a tempest of fire. It was believed that the savage Istar had been flung headlong into the gulf of perdition so suddenly that the blasphemies begun in his mouth had been forced backward with explosive results. It was popularly supposed that Satan, laden with chains of adamant, had been plunged once again into the abyss. Meanwhile, the commanders of the three armies had sent no messages. Mutterings and murmurs, mingling with the rumors of glory, gave rise to fears of an indecisive battle, a precipitate retreat. Insolent voices gave out that a spirit of the lowest category, a guardian angel, the insignificant Arcade, had checked and routed the dazzling host of the three great archangels.

There were also rumors of wholesale defection in the seventh heaven, where rebellion had broken out before the beginning of time, and some had even seen black clouds of impious angels joining the armies of the rebels on earth. But no one lent an ear to the odious rumors, and stress was laid on the news of victory which ran from lip to lip, each statement readily finding confirmation. The high places resounded with hymns of joy; the seraphim celebrated on harp and psaltery Sabaoth, God of Thunder. The voices of the elect united with those of the angels in glorifying the Invisible, and at the thought of the bloodshed that the ministers of holy wrath had caused among the rebels, sighs of relief and jubilation were wafted from the heavenly Jerusalem toward the Most High. But the beatitude of the most blessed, having swelled to the utmost limit before due time, could increase no more, and the very excess of their felicity completely dulled their senses.

The songs had not yet ceased when the guards watching on the ramparts signaled the approach of the first fugitives of the divine army: seraphim on tattered wing, flying in disorder, maimed kerûbs going on three feet. With impassive gaze, Michael, prince of warriors, measured the extent of the disaster, and his keen intelligence penetrated its causes. The armies of the living God had taken the offensive, but by one of those fatalities in war which disconcert the plans of the greatest captains, the enemy had also taken the offensive, and the effect was evident. Scarcely were the gates of the citadel opened to receive the glorious but shattered remnants of the three armies, when a rain of fire fell on the Mountain of God. Satan's army was not yet in sight, but the walls of topaz, the cupolas of emerald, the roofs of diamond, all fell in with an appalling crash under the discharge of the electrophores. The ancient thunderclouds essayed to reply, but the bolts fell short, and their thunders were lost in the deserted plains of the skies.

Smitten by an invisible foe, the faithful angels abandoned the ramparts. Michael went to announce to his God that the Holy Mountain would fall into the hands of the demon in twenty-four hours and that nothing remained for the Master of the Heavens but to seek safety in flight. The seraphim placed the jewels of the celestial crown in coffers. Michael offered his arm to the Queen of Heaven, and the Holy Family escaped from the palace by a subterranean passage of porphyry. A deluge of fire was falling on the citadel. Regaining his post once more, the glorious archangel declared that he would never capitulate, and straightway advanced the standards of the living God. That same evening the rebel host made its entry into the thrice-sacred city. On a fiery steed Satan led his demons. Behind him marched Arcade, Istar, and Zita. As in the ancient revels of Dionysus, old Nectaire bestrode his ass. Thereafter, floating out far behind, followed the black standards.

The garrison laid down their arms before Satan. Michael placed his flaming sword at the feet of the conquering archangel.

"Take back your sword, Michael," said Satan. "It is Lucifer who yields it to you. Bear it in defense of peace and law." Then, letting his gaze fall on the leaders of the celestial cohorts, he cried in a ringing voice:

"Archangel Michael, and you, Powers, Thrones, and Dominations, swear all of you to be faithful to your God."

"We swear it," they replied with one voice.

And Satan said:

"Powers, Thrones, and Dominations, of all past wars, I wish but to remember the invincible courage that you displayed and the loyalty which you rendered to authority, for these assure me of the steadfastness of the fealty you have just sworn to me."

The following day, on the ethereal plain, Satan commanded the black standards to be distributed to the troops, and the winged soldiers covered them with kisses and bedewed them with tears.

And Satan had himself crowned God. Thronging round the glittering walls of heavenly Jerusalem, apostles, pontiffs, virgins, martyrs, confessors, the whole company of the elect, who during the fierce battle had enjoyed delightful tranquillity, tasted infinite joy in the spectacle of the coronation.

The elect saw with ravishment the Most High precipitated into Hell and Satan seated on the throne of the Lord. In conformity with the will of God which had cut them off from sorrow, they sang in the ancient fashion the praises of their new master.

And Satan, piercing space with his keen glance, contemplated the little globe of earth and water where of old he had planted the vine and formed the first tragic chorus. And he fixed his gaze on that Rome where the fallen God had founded his empire on fraud and lie. Nevertheless, at that moment a saint ruled over the Church. Satan saw him praying and weeping. And he said to him:

"To thee I entrust my spouse. Watch over her faithfully. In thee I confirm the right and power to decide matters of doctrine, to regulate the use of the sacraments, to make laws, and to uphold purity of morals. And the faithful shall be under obligation to conform thereto. My Church is eternal, and the gates of Hell shall not prevail against it. Thou art infallible. Nothing is changed."

And the successor of the apostles felt flooded with rapture. He prostrated himself and, with his forehead touching the floor, replied:

"O Lord, my God, I recognize Thy voice! Thy breath has been wafted like balm to my heart. Blessed be Thy name. Thy will be done on earth, as it is in Heaven. Lead us not into temptation, but deliver us from evil."

And Satan found pleasure in praise and in the exercise of his grace; he loved to hear his wisdom and his power belauded. He listened with joy to the canticles of the cherubim who celebrated his good deeds, and he took no pleasure in listening to Nectaire's flute, because it celebrated nature's self, yielded to the insect and to the blade of grass their share of power and love, and counseled happiness and freedom. Satan, whose flesh had crept, in days gone by, at the idea that suffering prevailed in the world, now felt himself inaccessible to pity. He regarded suffering and death as the happy results of omnipotence and sovereign kindness. And the savor of the blood of victims rose upward toward him like sweet incense. He fell to condemning intelligence and to hating curiosity. He himself refused to learn anything more, for fear that in acquiring fresh knowledge he might let it be seen that he had not known everything at the very outset. He took pleasure in mystery, and, believing that he would seem less great by being understood, he affected to be unintelligible. Dense fumes of theology filled his brain. One day, following the example of his predecessor, he conceived the notion of proclaiming himself one god in three persons. Seeing Arcade smile as this proclamation was made, he drove him from his presence. Istar and Zita had long since returned to earth. Thus centuries passed like seconds. Now, one day, from the altitude of his throne, he plunged his gaze into the depths of the pit and saw Ialdabaoth in the Gehenna, where he himself had long lain enchained. Amid the everlasting gloom Ialdabaoth still retained his lofty mien. Blackened and shattered, terrible and sublime, he glanced upward at the palace of the King of Heaven with a look of proud disdain, then turned away his head. And the new god, as he looked upon his foe, beheld the light of intelligence and love pass across his sorrow-stricken countenance. And lo! Ialdabaoth was now contemplating the earth and, seeing it sunk in wickedness and suffering, he began to foster thoughts of kindliness in his heart. On a sudden he rose up and, beating the ether with his mighty arms, as though with oars, he hastened thither to instruct and to console mankind. Already his vast shadow shed upon the unhappy planet a shade soft as a night of love.

And Satan awoke bathed in an icy sweat.

Nectaire, Istar, Arcade, and Zita were standing round him. The finches were singing.

"Comrade," said the great archangel, "no—we will not conquer the Heavens. Enough to have the power. War engenders war, and victory defeat.

"God, conquered, will become Satan; Satan, conquering, will become God. May the fates spare me this terrible lot; I love the Hell which formed my genius. I love the earth where I have done some good, if it be possible to do any good in this fearful world where beings live but by rapine. Now, thanks to us, the God of old is dispossessed of His terrestrial empire, and every thinking being on this globe disdains Him or knows Him not. But what matter that men should be no longer submissive to Ialdabaoth if the spirit of Ialdabaoth is still in them; if they, like Him, are jealous, violent, quarrelsome and greedy, and the foes of the arts and of beauty? What matter that they have rejected the ferocious demiurge, if they do not hearken to the friendly demons who teach all truths; to Dionysus, Apollo, and the Muses? As to ourselves, celestial spirits, sublime demons, we have destroyed Ialdabaoth, our tyrant, if in ourselves we have destroyed Ignorance and Fear."

And Satan, turning to the gardener, said:

"Nectaire, you fought with me before the birth of the world. We were conquered because we failed to understand that Victory is a spirit, and that it is in ourselves and in ourselves alone that we must attack and destroy Ialdabaoth."

THE FAUST LEGEND

<hr/>

HE MUST HAVE BEEN an engaging rascal—the original Dr. Faust (or Faustus).

He called himself Magister Georgius Sabellicus Faustus Junior and was a mountebank of the first water. His dog and his horse were thought to be minions of the Devil. And certainly Faustus was, if nothing else, a diabolical liar.

Should the complete works of Plato and Aristotle be destroyed, Dr. Faustus insisted he could restore them from memory. He scoffed at the miracles of Jesus, claiming he could work even more startling magic without divine help. In the end, of course, the Devil came and carried him off.

The erudite Benedictine, Johann Tritheim, abbot of Spanheim, mentions the old necromancer in a letter dated August 20, 1507. And Luther himself took cognizance of this bespangled blight on German Christianity—showing that men in the show business have always recognized the value of unfavorable publicity from the pulpit.

There is little doubt that this "wicked, cheating, useless, and unlearned doctor" actually lived, having been born, according to some accounts, at Kundling and having studied the occult arts at Cracow.

Few scholars now hold that he was Johann Fust, the printer, whose name is often associated with Gutenberg. But black letters and the devilish art of printing take on an unholy significance if the two men were indeed one. What a patron saint for Dr. Goebbels!

That Faust was hated because of his interest in the natural sciences is fairly well established. One legend says he preached at Luther's own Wittenberg, where he seems to have made merry with riotous students. His finest trick was the restoration of Helen of Troy, which should have held any classroom of young men spellbound.

This episode, slightly altered, found its way (via the early German accounts) into Marlowe's mighty lines:

> *Was this the face that launched a thousand ships*
> *And burnt the topless towers of Ilium?*

The Elizabethan dramatist's magnificent *Doctor Faustus*, first performed September 30, 1594, follows by only seven years the first German book on Faust published in 1587. Marlowe in turn seems to have reinspired the Germans to write additional plays and stories on the "bestial" savant.

Puppet shows and traveling theatrical companies capitalized for nearly a century upon the comedy of Dr. Faust before Lessing wrote and lost his play on the subject and Goethe immortalized the legend.

It is important that Goethe's Mephistopheles is a cynic above good and evil—a Germanic concept so utterly immoral that via Nietzsche and other German thinkers it has come very near to scorching what remains of Christendom.

It is also significant that Goethe's Faust is a restless seeker of all knowledge as well as all sensation and limitless power.

The concept of Faust and his tempter is essential to German *Kultur*. A nation which committed five wars of aggression in seventy-five years obviously not only sold its soul to the Devil, but went to Hell as the classical and logical aftermath.

No wonder Oswald Spengler in *The Decline of the West* calls Western culture "Faustian" and holds his fellow Germans as the highest breed of "Faustian Man."

SELECTION FROM PART I OF FAUST

Johann Wolfgang von Goethe

A STREET

FAUST   MARGARET *passing by*
FAUST. My fair young lady, may I make so free
As to lend you my arm and company?
MARGARET. I'm not a lady, am not fair;
I can go home without your care.
She frees herself and exits

FAUST. By heaven, but this child is fair!
I've never seen her equal anywhere!
So virtuous, through and through,
Yet with a bit of curtness too.
Her ruby lips, her cheek's clear bloom,
I'll not forget till the day of doom!
And then how she casts down her eyes,
Stamped deeply in my heart it lies!
How curt and short were her replies,
That fills me with sheer ecstasy!

     MEPHISTOPHELES *appears*

FAUST. Hear, you must get that girl for me!

MEPHISTOPHELES.   Well, which one, then?

FAUST.   She just went by.

MEPHISTOPHELES. That one? She was just coming from her priest,
Absolved from every sin, down to the least.
Hard by the chair I stole quite nigh.
She's innocent in deed and thought
And went to confession all for naught.
Over her I have no power.

     FAUST. She's over fourteen years old even so.

     MEPHISTOPHELES. My word! You talk like gay Lothario
Who covets for himself each lovely flower
And fancies, puffed up, there's no honour, no
Nor favour that he may not cull;
But yet that is not always possible.

     FAUST. Sir Master Worshipful, I beg you, pause
And leave me in peace with all your laws!
And this I say—few words are best—
Unless that sweet young maiden lays
Her head this night upon my breast,
At midnight we've gone different ways.

     MEPHISTOPHELES. Consider well what can and can not be.
I'll need at least some fourteen days
But to scent out an opportunity.

     FAUST. Had I but seven hours' rest, no need
Of devil would I have, to lead
A little creature such as this astray.

     MEPHISTOPHELES. You're talking almost like a Frenchman. Pray
Don't let yourself be vexed beyond due measure.
What good is it to reap immediate pleasure?
The joy's not near so great, I say,

As if you first prepare the ground
With every sort of idle folly,
Knead and make ready your pretty dolly,
As many Romance tales expound.

FAUST. I've appetite without that too.

MEPHISTOPHELES. Now jests aside, no more ado.
With that good, lovely child, indeed,
I tell you once for all, we can't use speed.
There's nothing here to take by storm;
To strategy we must conform.

FAUST. Get something that the angel owns for me!
Oh, lead me to her place of rest!
Get me a kerchief from her breast,
A garter to my ecstasy!

MEPHISTOPHELES. Now just to prove that I will be
Of helpful service in your agony,
We'll lose no moment in delay.
I'll lead you to her room this very day.

FAUST. And shall I see her? have her?

MEPHISTOPHELES. No!
For she'll be at a neighbour's for a chat or so.
While she is gone, all by yourself you may
Enjoy her atmosphere till you are sated
And feast on all the hope of joys anticipated.

FAUST. Can we go there?

MEPHISTOPHELES. It is too early yet.

FAUST. Provide a gift for her and don't forget.
    Exit

MEPHISTOPHELES. Ah, gifts at once? That's good! He'll make a hit!
Full many a lovely place I know
And many a treasure buried long ago.
I must survey the ground a bit.
    Exit

EVENING

A neat little room

MARGARET *plaiting and binding up her braids of hair.*
I would give something, could I say
Who was that gentleman today!

Right gallant did he seem to be
And of some noble family.
That from his brow I could have told—
Else he would not have been so bold.
> *Exit*

MEPHISTOPHELES FAUST

MEPHISTOPHELES. Come! come in! and on tiptoe!
FAUST *after a silence.* Leave me alone here, I entreat!
MEPHISTOPHELES *peering about.*
Not every girl keeps things so neat.
> *Exit*

FAUST *looking up and around.* Welcome, O thou sweet twilight
  glow
That through this shrine art stirring to and fro.
Sweet agony of love, possess this heart of mine,
Thou who on dews of hope dost live and yet dost pine.
What sense of quiet breathes around,
Of order, of contentedness!
What riches in this poverty abound!
Within this prison, ah! what blessedness!
> *He throws himself on the leather armchair by the bed*

Oh, welcome me, thou who the world now gone
Didst once receive in joy and sorrow, open-armed!
How often, ah! around this fathers'-throne
A flock of children clinging swarmed!
And, thankful for the Christmas gift, maybe
My darling here, her childish cheeks filled out,
Kissed grandsire's withered hand devotedly.
I feel, O maid, thy spirit radiate
Abundance, order, round about,
That, motherly, instructs thee day by day,
Bids thee the cloth upon the table neatly lay,
Even make the sand at thy feet decorate.
O darling hand! So godlike in thy ministry!
The hut becomes a realm of Heaven through thee.
And here!
> *He lifts one of the bed curtains*

What bliss and awe lay hold on me!
Here for whole hours I fain would tarry.
O Nature! Here didst thou in visions airy
Mould her, an angel in nativity.
Here lay the child; with warm life heaving

The tender bosom filled and grew;
And here, with pure and holy weaving,
The image of the gods was wrought anew!
 And thou, O Faust, what led thee here? I feel
My very inmost being reel!
What wouldst thou here? What weights thy heart so sore?
O wretched Faust! I know thee now no more.
 Does magic play about me, sweet and rare?
Some force impelled me to enjoy without delay,
And now in dreams of love I seem to float away!
Are we the sport of every puff of air?
 And if this very moment she might enter here,
For thy rash conduct how wouldst thou atone!
Thou, great big lout, how small wouldst thou appear!
How, melted at her feet, thou wouldst lie prone!

 Mephistopheles *enters.* Be quick! I see her coming down the lane.

Faust. Away! I'll never come back here again!

Mephistopheles. Here is a casket, of some weight,
Which I got elsewhere as a bait.
Here, put it in the press, this minute;
She'll lose her senses, I swear it to you.
In fact, I put some trinkets in it,
Enough another nobler maid to woo;
But still a child's a child, and play is play.

 Faust. I don't know if I should?

 Mephistopheles. Why ask you, pray?
Do you perhaps intend to hoard the treasure?
Then I'd advise you in your lustfulness
To waste no more sweet hours of leisure
And spare me further strain and stress.
I hope that you're not greedy!
I rub my hands, I scratch my head—
  He puts the casket in the press and turns the lock again
Away and speedy!—
To turn the sweet young child that she be led
To satisfy your heart's desire and will;
And you look around
As if to a lecture you were bound,
As if before you, living still,
Stood Physics and Metaphysics grey!
But off! away!
  Exeunt

MARGARET *with a lamp.* Here is such close, such sultry air!
    She opens the window
And yet it's really not so warm out there.
I feel so strange—I don't know how—
I wish that Mother came home now.
From head to foot I'm shuddering—
I'm but a foolish, fearsome thing!
    She begins to sing while she undresses
        There was in Thule olden
        A king true till the grave,
        To whom a beaker golden
        His dying mistress gave.

        Naught prized he more, this lover,
        He drained it at each bout;
        His eyes with tears brimmed over,
        As oft he drank it out.

        And when he came to dying,
        His towns and his lands he told,
        Naught else his heir denying
        Except the beaker of gold.

        Around him knight and vassal,
        At a royal feast sat he
        In his fathers' lofty castle,
        The castle by the sea.

        There the old pleasure-seeker
        Drank, standing, life's last glow,
        Then hurled the sacred beaker
        Into the waves below.

        He saw it plunging, drinking,
        And seeking in the sea,
        And so his eyes were sinking,
        Never one drop more drank he.
  She opens the press to put away her clothes and
    catches sight of the little jewel casket
How came this lovely casket in my press?
Indeed I turned the lock most certainly.
It's very strange! What's in it I can't guess.
Someone has brought it as a pledge maybe,
And on it Mother loaned a bit.
Here on the ribbon hangs a little key,
I really think I'll open it.
What is that? God in Heaven! See!

I've never seen such things as here!
Jewels! A noble lady might appear
With these on any holiday.
This chain—how would it look on me?
Ah, whose can all this splendour be?

      She adorns herself with it and steps before the mirror

Were but the earrings mine! I say
One looks at once quite differently.
What good is beauty? blood of youth?
All that is nice and fine, in truth;
However, people pass and let it be.
They praise you—half with pity, though, be sure.
Toward gold throng all,
To gold cling all,
Yes, all! Alas, we poor.

A PROMENADE

    Faust *walking thoughtfully up and down.* Mephistopheles
    joins him

Mephistopheles. By every despisèd love! By the red-hot fires of
    Hell!
Would I knew something worse, to curse by it as well!
    Faust. What is the matter? What's so badly vexing you?
I've never seen before a face that looked that way.
    Mephistopheles. Off to the Devil I'd betake myself this day
If I myself was not a devil too!
    Faust. What has gone wrong? Why thus behave?
It suits you well to rant and rave!
    Mephistopheles. Just think, the gems for Gretchen that I got,
A wretched priest has bagged the lot!
The mother gets to see the stuff
And starts at once to feel a secret shuddering.
The woman has a scent that's fine enough,
Forever in her prayer-book she delights to snuff,
And smells it out in every single thing
If it be sacred or profane;
So in those gems she noses till it's plain
That they held little blessing, little good.
"My child," she cried, "to keep unrighteous gain
Perturbs the soul, consumes the blood.
We'll dedicate it to the Mother of our Lord,

With heavenly manna She'll reward!"
Then Gretchen drew her mouth askew;
She thought: "It is a gift-horse, it is true,
And surely godless is not he
Who brought it here so handsomely."
The mother summoned in a priest who came
And when he'd scarce perceived the game,
Got much contentment from the sight.
He said: "So one is minded right!
Who overcometh, winneth a crown.
The Church hath a good stomach ever,
Whole countries hath she gobbled down,
And yet hath over-eaten never;
The Church alone, dear ladies, best
Can all unrighteous goods digest."

    FAUST. That is a custom that men oft pursue;
A Jew and king can do it too.

    MEPHISTOPHELES. With that he bagged brooch, chain, and rings,
As if mere toadstools were the things,
And thanked them neither less nor more
Than were it a basketful of nuts he bore.
He promised them all heavenly pay
And greatly edified thereby were they.

    FAUST. And Gretchen?

    MEPHISTOPHELES. Now sits restless. What she would
She knows not, neither what she should,
Thinks of the jewels night and day,
Still more on him who brought them to her.

    FAUST. The darling's grief distresses me.
Quick! get new ornaments to woo her.
The first ones were not much to see.

    MEPHISTOPHELES. Oh yes, Milord thinks all is mere child's-play!

    FAUST. Make haste and do things as I like them done.
Into her neighbour's graces win your way!
Devil, don't be like mush and move so slow.
Fetch some new ornaments—up, now, and run!

    MEPHISTOPHELES. Yes, gracious sir, with all my heart I'll go.
       Exit FAUST

Such an enamoured fool would puff and blow
Sun, moon, and stars into thin air
Just as a pastime for his lady fair.
       Exit

THE NEIGHBOUR'S HOUSE

MARTHA *alone*. God pardon my dear husband! He
Has truly not done well by me!
Off in the world to go and roam
And leave me on the straw at home!
Sure, I did naught to vex him, truly,
And, God knows, always loved him duly.
  She weeps
Perhaps he's even dead!—Oh, cruel fate!
If I but had a death-certificate!
  MARGARET *enters*
MARGARET. Dame Martha!
MARTHA. Gretchen dear, what can it be?
MARGARET. My knees almost sink under me!
There in my press I've found again
Just such a casket—and of ebony,
And things! magnificent they are,
Much richer than the first, by far!
MARTHA. You must not tell that to your mother;
She would confess it like the other.
MARGARET. Ah, only look! ah, see now, do!
MARTHA *decking her out*. You lucky, lucky creature, you!
MARGARET. Alas, these jewels I can never wear
At church or on the street, I'd never dare!
MARTHA. Come often over here to me
And here put on the jewels secretly.
Stroll up and down before the mirror for a season;
We'll have our own sweet joy of it.
And then there'll be a feast-day or some other reason
When one lets people see them, bit by bit.
A chain at first, a pearl then in your ear; your mother
Scarce will see it, we'll coin some fib or other.
MARGARET. But both the caskets! Who could bring
Them both? Some wrong is in this thing!
  Someone knocks
Good Heaven! My mother—can that have been?
MARTHA *peeping through the curtain*.
It's some strange gentleman! Come in!
  MEPHISTOPHELES *enters*

MEPHISTOPHELES. I'm very bold to walk in right away;
The pardon of the ladies I must pray.

He steps back respectfully in the presence of MARGARET

Dame Martha Schwerdtlein I would like to find!

MARTHA. I'm she! What has the gentleman upon his mind?

MEPHISTOPHELES *aside to her*. I know you now, that is enough
    for me.
You have a most distinguished guest, I see.
Excuse the liberty I took! If it is not too soon,
I'll come again this afternoon.

MARTHA *aloud*. Imagine, child, of all things on this earth!
The gentleman thinks you of noble birth.

MARGARET. I am a poor, young thing, as you can see.
The gentleman is far too kind to me.
The ornaments and jewels aren't my own.

MEPHISTOPHELES. Ah, it is not the ornaments alone;
You've such a manner, so refined a way!
How glad I am that I may stay!

MARTHA. What is your errand? I would like to hear—

MEPHISTOPHELES. I wish my tidings brought more cheer!
I hope you'll not make me repent this meeting:
Your husband's dead and sends a greeting.

MARTHA. Is dead? That faithful heart! Oh, woe!
My husband's dead! I'm dying! Oh!

MARGARET. Ah! don't despair, Dame Martha dear!

MEPHISTOPHELES. Prepare the mournful tale to hear!

MARGARET. That's why I would not love while I draw breath;
Such loss as this would make me grieve to death.

MEPHISTOPHELES. Joy must sorrow, sorrow joy must know.

MARTHA. Relate the ending of his life to me!

MEPHISTOPHELES. In Padua he's buried, midst a row
Of graves close to St. Anthony,
In holy ground that was well blessed,
Forever cool his bed of rest.

MARTHA. Did you bring nothing else beside?

MEPHISTOPHELES. Oh yes, a weighty, great petition:
Three hundred masses are you to provide!
My pockets? They have naught. Thus endth my commission!

MARTHA. What? Not a medal? Not a trinket? Such
As every journeyman deep in his pouch doth hide,
As a remembrance puts aside,
And rather hungers, rather begs, than touch?

MEPHISTOPHELES. Madame, that grieves me much, but let me say,
He truly did not throw his cash away;
And deeply did he all his faults deplore,
Yes, and bewailed his ill luck still much more.

MARGARET. Alas, the bad luck men do meet!
Full many a requiem for him will I pray.

MEPHISTOPHELES. You're fit, I think, to wed this very day;
You are so lovable and sweet.

MARGARET. That would not do as yet. Ah, no!

MEPHISTOPHELES. If not a husband, be it for the while a beau.
For, of the greatest gifts of Heaven, it is one
To have within our arms a lover dear.

MARGARET. That's not the custom of the country here.

MEPHISTOPHELES. Custom or not! At any rate it's done.

MARTHA. Tell on, oh, please!

MEPHISTOPHELES. I stood where dying he was laid.
'Twas not a dung-heap; somewhat better it was made
Of rotting straw; but as a Christian did he die,
Thinking he owed far greater penance for his life.
"How deeply must I hate myself," I heard him cry,
"To leave my business so, my wife!
Alas, the recollection's killing me.
If she could but forgive me in this life!"

MARTHA *weeping*. The good man! I forgave him long since—
truthfully!

MEPHISTOPHELES. "But she, God knows, was more to blame than
I!"

MARTHA. He lies! What! at the grave's brink—so to lie!

MEPHISTOPHELES. He fabled as he breathed his last, be sure,
If I am only half a connoisseur.
"I could not gape for pastime," so he said;
"First children, then to get them bread,
And bread in all the broadest sense, I swear;
Yet never could I eat in peace my share."

MARTHA. To all my love, fidelity, he gave no thought,
Nor to my drudgery by night and day?

MEPHISTOPHELES. Not so; he thought of it most warmly as he
ought.
He said: "From Malta once I sailed away
And ardently for wife and children did I pray.
Then Heaven favoured us in gracious measure
Because our ship a Turkish vessel caught

Which to the mighty Sultan bore a treasure.
Then valour was rewarded as was fit,
And I received moreover, as one ought,
My own well-measured share of it."
   MARTHA. Oh what? Oh where? Perhaps he buried it?
   MEPHISTOPHELES. Who knows where the four winds have carried it?
A pretty miss adopted him as her dear friend
When he, in Naples strange, was circulating;
She gave him love and troth so unabating
That he felt the results until his blessèd end.
   MARTHA. The scamp! The robber of his children, he!
And all that want and all that misery
Could not prevent the shameful life he led!
   MEPHISTOPHELES. Well, he has paid for it and now he's dead.
If I were now in your place here,
I'd mourn for him a well-bred year,
Meanwhile be on the lookout for a sweetheart new.
   MARTHA. Ah, God! Another like the first I knew,
I'll hardly find on earth again!
There scarce could be a dearer little fool than mine.
Only to roam he was too much inclined, and then
He loved those foreign women, also foreign wine,
And that accursed dice-throwing.
   MEPHISTOPHELES. Now, now, things could have gone and still be going,
If he perchance as much in you
Had overlooked on his part too.
I swear, on terms like these, if you'd agree,
I'd ask you to exchange a ring with me.
   MARTHA. The gentleman is pleased to jest.
   MEPHISTOPHELES *aside*. Now to make off betimes were best!
She'd hold the very Devil to his word.
     To GRETCHEN
How is your heart? Has it been stirred?
   MARGARET. What means the gentleman?
   MEPHISTOPHELES *aside*. You innocent, sweet dear!
     Aloud
Ladies, good-by!
   MARGARET. Good-by!
   MARTHA. Oh, quickly let me hear
The evidence I'd like to have and save;

Where, how, and when my darling died and where his grave.
Of order I have always been a friend,
And in our "Weekly" I would like to read his end.

MEPHISTOPHELES. Yes, my good woman, what two witnesses attest
Is always known as truth made manifest,
And with me I've a splendid mate.
I tell you, I'll take him before a magistrate.
I'll bring him here.

MARTHA. Oh, do that, do!

MEPHISTOPHELES. And this young lady, will she be here too?
A gallant chap! and travelled far has he
And shows young ladies every courtesy.

MARGARET. Before the gentleman I'd flush with shame.

MEPHISTOPHELES. Before no king this earth could name.

MARTHA. Behind my house and in my garden then,
This evening we'll await the gentlemen.

A STREET

FAUST   MEPHISTOPHELES

FAUST. How goes it? Will it work? soon win the game?

MEPHISTOPHELES. Ah, bravo! Do I find you all aflame?
Gretchen will in a brief time be your own.
This evening you will see her all alone
At Neighbour Martha's; that's a woman made
For go-between and gypsy trade.

FAUST. 'Tis well!

MEPHISTOPHELES. Yet something's wanted from us too.

FAUST. One service may demand another as its due.

MEPHISTOPHELES. We have in due form only to attest
That her good spouse's outstretched limbs repose
In Padua, in consecrated soil at rest.

FAUST. Most wise! We first must make the journey, I suppose!

MEPHISTOPHELES. *Sancta Simplicitas!* Of that there is no need;
You don't know much, but still depose.

FAUST. If that's your best, I tear your plan asunder.

MEPHISTOPHELES. O saintly man! Then you would be a saint indeed!
Is it the first time in your life
You've borne false witness? Well, I wonder!
Of God, the world, and what therein is rife,

Of man, what stirs within his heart and brain,
Have you no definition given with might and main?
With brazen brow and dauntless breast?
And if you'll only probe things truly,
You knew of them—you must confess it duly—
No more than of this Schwerdtlein's death and place of rest!
    FAUST. You are and you remain a liar, sophist too.
    MEPHISTOPHELES. Yes, if one did not have a little deeper view.
Will you not presently cajole
Poor Gretchen—in all honour too—and swear
To her the love of all your soul?
    FAUST. Aye, swear it from my heart.
    MEPHISTOPHELES. Fine, I declare!
Then there'll be talk of love, fidelity eternal,
Of one almighty force supernal—
Will that too issue from your heart alone?
    FAUST. Have done! It will!—And when I'm feeling,
When for the feeling, for my senses' reeling,
I seek for names and yet find none,
Then through the world with every sense sweep on,
Toward all the loftiest phrases, grasping, turn,
And this the glow from which I burn,
Endless, eternal, aye, eternal name,
Is that a devilish, lying game?
    MEPHISTOPHELES. And yet I'm right!
    FAUST. Take heed! Mark this from me,
I beg of you, and spare my lungs:
He who maintains he's right—if his the gift of tongues—
Will have the last word certainly.
So come, this prating rouses my disgust;
I'll say you're right, especially since I must.

A GARDEN

    MARGARET *on* FAUST'S *arm,* MARTHA *and* MEPHISTOPHELES,
      walking up and down
    MARGARET. I feel the gentleman is only sparing me,
So condescends that I am all confused.
A traveller is so much used
To bear with things good-naturedly.
I know too well, my poor talk hardly can
Amuse you, an experienced man.

FAUST. One glance from you, one word, more entertains
Than all the wisdom that this world contains.

He kisses her hand

MARGARET. Don't incommode yourself! How can my hand be
kissed by you?
It is so ugly and so rough!
What work is there that I've not had to do?
My mother's more than strict enough.

They pass on

MARTHA. And you, sir, are you always on the go?
MEPHISTOPHELES. Alas, that business, duty, drive us so!
With how much pain one goes from many a place,
And even so, one simply must not stay.
MARTHA. In active years perhaps 'tis well this way,
Thus freely round and round the world to race;
But then the evil times come on apace,
And as a bachelor to drag on to the grave alone,
That has been good for no one, you must own.
MEPHISTOPHELES. With dread I see it far away.
MARTHA. Then, worthy sir, consider while you may!

They pass on

MARGARET. Yes, out of sight is out of mind!
To you so easy is this courtesy;
But many friends you always find,
More sensible than I can be.
FAUST. O dear one! Trust me, that which men call sense
Is oft but vanity and narrowness.
MARGARET. But why? Tell me.
FAUST. Ah, that simplicity, that innocence,
That neither its own sacred value knows!
That lowliness, humility, those gifts supreme
That loving Nature's bounteous hand bestows—
MARGARET. Though you may think of me a moment only,
I'll have, ah, time enough to think of you and dream.
FAUST. You are then often lonely?
MARGARET. Yes, for our household is but small,
And yet one has to look to all.
We have no maid—must cook, sweep, sew, and knit,
And early run about and late;
And Mother is in all of it
So accurate!
Not that in spending she must feel confined;
We could branch out far more than many do.

My father left a pretty property behind,
A house outside the town, a little garden too.
Yet now I've pretty quiet days. My brother,
He is a soldier lad.
My little sister's dead.
A deal of trouble with the child did I go through;
Yet once more would I gladly undertake the bother,
I loved the child so much.

    FAUST. An angel, if like you.

    MARGARET. I brought it up and it was fond of me.
Father had died when it was born;
We gave our mother up for lost, so worn
And wretched, lying there, was she.
And she grew well so slowly, bit by bit,
She could not think of suckling it
Herself, the poor babe pitifully wee,
And so I brought it up, and quite alone,
With milk and water; so it became my own.
Upon my arm and in my lap it threw
Itself about, was friendly too, and grew.

    FAUST. You've surely felt the purest happiness.

    MARGARET. But also many weary hours, I must confess.
The wee thing's cradle stood at night
Beside my bed; it scarcely might
Just stir; I was awake;
Sometimes I had to give it drink, sometimes to take
It in with me, sometimes from bed arise
And dandle up and down the room to hush its cries;
And at the wash-tub stand at daylight's break
Then to the marketing and to the hearth attend.
Tomorrow too just like today, so without end.
Thus, sir, one's spirits are not always of the best,
But in return one relishes both food and rest.

     They pass on

    MARTHA. Poor women have things hard, it's true;
A bachelor's not easy to convert.

    MEPHISTOPHELES. It but depends upon the like of you,
For then my present ways I might desert.

    MARTHA. Speak out, sir, is there none you've ever met?
Has your heart never bound itself as yet?

    MEPHISTOPHELES. One's own good wife and hearth, we're told,
Are worth as much as pearls and gold.

    MARTHA. I mean, if you have never felt a passion?

MEPHISTOPHELES. I've always been received in very courteous
fashion.

MARTHA. I mean: has love in earnest never stirred your breast?

MEPHISTOPHELES. With ladies one should never dare to jest.

MARTHA. Ah, you don't understand me!

MEPHISTOPHELES. That distresses me!

And yet I understand—most kindly would you be.

They pass on

FAUST. Did you, O little angel, straightway recognize
Me when I came into the garden?

MARGARET. Did you not see that I cast down my eyes?

FAUST. That liberty I took, you'll pardon?

The daring impudence that day
When coming from the church you went your way?

MARGARET. I was confused; to me it never had

Occurred; no one could say of me what's bad.
Ah, thought I, in your manner, then, has he
Seen something bold, unmaidenly?
It seemed to strike him right away
To have some dealings with this girl without delay.
Yet I confess I know not why my heart
Began at once to stir to take your part.
But with myself I was right vexed, it's true,
That I could not become more vexed toward you.

FAUST. Sweet darling!

MARGARET. Wait a bit!

*She plucks a starflower and picks off the petals, one after the
other*

FAUST. What's that? A nosegay?

MARGARET. No,

It's just a game.

FAUST. What?

MARGARET. You will laugh at me, do go!

She pulls off the petals and murmurs

FAUST. What are you murmuring?

MARGARET *half aloud.* He loves me—loves me not!

FAUST. Sweet, heavenly vision!

MARGARET *goes on.* Loves me—not—loves me—not—

He loves me! *Plucking off the last petal with lovely joy*

FAUST. Yes, my child! and let this blossom's word

Be oracle of gods to you! He loves you!
You understand that word and what it means? He loves you!

He seizes both her hands

MARGARET. I'm all a-tremble!

FAUST. Oh, shudder not! But let this look,
Let this hand-pressure say to you
What is unspeakable:
To give one's self up wholly and to feel
A rapture that must be eternal!
Eternal!—for its end would be despair.
No! no end! no end!

> MARGARET *presses his hands, frees herself, and runs away. He stands a moment in thought and then follows her*

> MARTHA *coming.* The night comes on.

MEPHISTOPHELES. Yes, and we must away.

MARTHA. I'd ask you make a longer stay;
But it's a wicked place, here roundabout,
As if no one had naught to carry through
And naught to do
But gape at all the neighbours going in and out.
One's talked about, do all one may.
And our dear couple?

MEPHISTOPHELES. Up that walk I saw them whirr,
The wanton butterflies!

MARTHA. He seems to take to her.

MEPHISTOPHELES. And she to him. So runs the world away.

A GARDEN HOUSE

> MARGARET *runs in, hides behind the door, holds the tip of her finger to her lips, and peers through the crevice*

MARGARET. He's coming!

FAUST *enters.* Rogue, it's thus you tease!
I've caught you!

> *He kisses her*

> MARGARET *embracing him and returning the kiss.*

Best of men, I love you from my heart!

> MEPHISTOPHELES *knocks*

FAUST *stamping.* Who's there?

MEPHISTOPHELES. A friend!

FAUST. A beast!

MEPHISTOPHELES. I think it's time
to part.

MARTHA *enters.* Yes, sir, it's late.

FAUST. Mayn't I escort you, please?

MARGARET. My mother would—— Good-by!
FAUST.   Must I go then?
Good-by!
MARTHA. Adieu!
MARGARET.   But soon to meet again!
        FAUST *and* MEPHISTOPHELES *exeunt*
    MARGARET. Dear God! The things that such a man
Can think of! Everything! I only can
Stand there before him shamed and quivering
And answer "yes" to everything.
I am a poor unknowing child, and he—
I do not see what he can find in me.
        Exit

THE TRAGICAL HISTORY OF DOCTOR FAUSTUS

Christopher Marlowe

CHORUS
DOCTOR FAUSTUS
WAGNER, his servant
GOOD and EVIL ANGEL
VALDES and CORNELIUS, conjurors
THREE SCHOLARS
MEPHISTOPHILIS, a devil
THE CLOWN
BALIOL, BELCHER, LUCIFER, BELZEBUB and other devils
THE SEVEN DEADLY SINS
THE POPE
CARDINAL OF LORRAIN
FRIARS
ROBIN, the ostler
RAFE
A VINTNER
THE EMPEROR
A KNIGHT and attendants
SPIRITS OF ALEXANDER and his PARAMOUR
A HORSE-COURSER
THE DUKE OF VANHOLT and his DUCHESS
AN OLD MAN
The Spirit of HELEN OF TROY

Scene: Mainly the study of Doctor Faustus; otherwise a grove, the Pope's privy chamber at Rome, the courts of the Emperor and the Duke of Vanholt and elsewhere.

Enter Chorus

Chorus. Not marching now in field of Trasimene,
Where Mars did mate the Carthaginians;
Nor sporting in the dalliance of love,
In courts of kings where state is overturned;
Nor in the pomp of proud audacious deeds,
Intends our Muse to vaunt his heavenly verse:
Only this, gentlemen—we must perform
The form of Faustus' fortunes, good or bad;
To patient judgments we appeal our plaud,
And speak for Faustus in his infancy.
Now is he born, his parents base of stock,
In Germany, within a town called Rhodes;
Of riper years to Wittenberg he went,
Whereas his kinsmen chiefly brought him up.
So soon he profits in divinity,
The fruitful plot of scholarism graced,
That shortly he was graced with doctor's name,
Excelling all whose sweet delight disputes
In heavenly matters of theology;
Till swollen with cunning, of a self-conceit,
His waxen wings did mount above his reach,
And, melting, heavens conspired his overthrow;
For, falling to a devilish exercise,
And glutted now with learning's golden gifts,
He surfeits upon cursèd necromancy.
Nothing so sweet as magic is to him,
Which he prefers before his chiefest bliss.
And this the man that in his study sits!
Exit

SCENE I

Enter Faustus *in his study*

Faust. Settle thy studies, Faustus, and begin
To sound the depth of that thou wilt profess;
Having commenced, be a divine in show;
Yet level at the end of every art,
And live and die in Aristotle's works.

Sweet Analytics, 'tis thou hast ravished me—
 Reads
Bene dissere est finis logices.
Is to dispute well logic's chiefest end?
Affords this art no greater miracle?
Then read no more, thou hast attained the end;
A greater subject fitteth Faustus' wit:
Bid ὅν χαὶ μὴ ὅν farewell; Galen come,
Seeing *Ubi desinit philosophus ibi incipit medicus;*
Be a physician, Faustus, heap up gold,
And be eternized for some wondrous cure.
 Reads
Summum bonum medicinæ sanitas,
The end of physic is our body's health.
Why, Faustus, hast thou not attained that end?
Is not thy common talk sound aphorisms?
Are not thy bills hung up as monuments,
Whereby whole cities have escaped the plague,
And thousand desperate maladies been eased?
Yet art thou still but Faustus and a man.
Wouldst thou make men to live eternally,
Or, being dead, raise them to life again,
Then this profession were to be esteemed.
Physic, farewell.—Where is Justinian?
 Reads
Si una eademque res legatur duobus, alter rem, alter valorem rei, etc.
A pretty case of paltry legacies!
 Reads
Exhoereditare filium non potest pater nisi, etc.
Such is the subject of the Institute
And universal body of the law.
His study fits a mercenary drudge,
Who aims at nothing but external trash;
Too servile and illiberal for me.
When all is done divinity is best;
Jerome's Bible, Faustus, view it well.
 Reads
Stipendium peccati mors est. Ha! *Stipendium,* etc.
The reward of sin is death. That's hard.
 Reads
Si peccasse negamus, fallimur, et nulla est in nobis veritas.
If we say that we have no sin we deceive ourselves, and there's

no truth in us. Why, then, belike we must sin, and so consequently die.
Ay, we must die an everlasting death.
What doctrine call you this, *Che sera sera,*
What will be, shall be? Divinity, adieu!
These metaphysics of magicians
And necromantic books are heavenly:
Lines, circles, scenes, letters, and characters:
Ay, these are those that Faustus most desires.
O, what a world of profit and delight,
Of power, of honor, of omnipotence
Is promised to the studious artisan!
All things that move between the quiet poles
Shall be at my command: emperors and kings
Are but obeyèd in their several provinces,
Nor can they raise the wind or rend the clouds;
But his dominion that exceeds in this
Stretcheth as far as doth the mind of man,
A sound magician is a mighty god:
Here, Faustus, try thy brains to gain a deity.
Wagner!

   Enter WAGNER
   Commend me to my dearest friends,
The German Valdes and Cornelius;
Request them earnestly to visit me.
  WAG. I will, sir.
   Exit
  FAUST. Their conference will be a greater help to me
Than all my labors, plod I ne'er so fast.

   Enter the GOOD ANGEL *and the* EVIL ANGEL
  G. ANG. O Faustus! lay that damnèd book aside,
And gaze not on it lest it tempt thy soul,
And heap God's heavy wrath upon thy head.
Read, read the Scriptures: that is blasphemy.
  E. ANG. Go forward, Faustus, in that famous **art,**
Wherein all Nature's treasure is contained:
Be thou on earth as Jove is in the sky,
Lord and commander of these elements.
   Exeunt ANGELS
  FAUST. How am I glutted with conceit of this!
Shall I make spirits fetch me what I please,
Resolve me of all ambiguities,
Perform what desperate enterprise I will?

I'll have them fly to India for gold,
Ransack the ocean for orient pearl,
And search all corners of the new-found world
For pleasant fruits and princely delicates;
I'll have them read me strange philosophy
And tell the secrets of all foreign kings;
I'll have them wall all Germany with brass,
And make swift Rhine circle fair Wittenberg,
I'll have them fill the public schools with silk,
Wherewith the students shall be bravely clad;
I'll levy soldiers with the coin they bring,
And chase the Prince of Parma from our land,
And reign sole king of all the provinces;
Yea, stranger engines for the brunt of war
Than was the fiery keel at Antwerp's bridge,
I'll make my servile spirits to invent.

Enter VALDES *and* CORNELIUS

Come, German Valdes and Cornelius,
And make me blest with your sage conference.
Valdes, sweet Valdes, and Cornelius,
Know that your words have won me at the last
To practise magic and concealèd arts:
Yet not your words only, but mine own fantasy
That will receive no object; for my head
But ruminates on necromantic skill.
Philosophy is odious and obscure,
Both law and physic are for petty wits;
Divinity is basest of the three,
Unpleasant, harsh, contemptible, and vile:
'Tis magic, magic that hath ravished me.
Then, gentle friends, aid me in this attempt;
And I that have with concise syllogisms
Gravelled the pastors of the German church,
And made the flowering pride of Wittenberg
Swarm to my problems, as the infernal spirits
On sweet Musæus, when he came to hell,
Will be as cunning as Agrippa was,
Whose shadows made all Europe honor him.

VALD. Faustus, these books, thy wit, and our experience
Shall make all nations to canònize us.
As Indian Moors obey their Spanish lords,
So shall the spirits of every element

Be always serviceable to us three;
Like lions shall they guard us when we please;
Like Almain rutters with their horsemen's staves
Or Lapland giants, trotting by our sides;
Sometimes like women or unwedded maids,
Shadowing more beauty in their airy brows
Than have the white breasts of the queen of love:
From Venice shall they drag huge argosies,
And from America the golden fleece
That yearly stuffs old Philip's treasury;
If learnèd Faustus will be resolute.

FAUST. Valdes, as resolute am I in this
As thou to live; therefore object it not.

CORN. The miracles that magic will perform
Will make thee vow to study nothing else.
He that is grounded in astrology,
Enriched with tongues, well seen in minerals,
Hath all the principles magic doth require.
Then doubt not, Faustus, but to be renowned,
And more frequented for this mystery
Than heretofore the Delphian Oracle.
The spirits tell me they can dry the sea,
And fetch the treasure of all foreign wracks,
Ay, all the wealth that our forefathers hid
Within the massy entrails of the earth;
Then tell me, Faustus, what shall we three want?

FAUST. Nothing, Cornelius! O, this cheers my soul!
Come show me some demonstrations magical,
That I may conjure in some lusty grove,
And have these joys in full possession.

VALD. Then haste thee to some solitary grove,
And bear wise Bacon's and Albanus' works,
The Hebrew Psalter and New Testament;
And whatsoever else is requisite
We will inform thee ere our conference cease.

CORN. Valdes, first let him know the words of art;
And then, all other ceremonies learned,
Faustus may try his cunning by himself.

VALD. First I'll instruct thee in the rudiments,
And then wilt thou be perfecter than I.

FAUST. Then come and dine with me, and after meat,
We'll canvass every quiddity thereof;

For ere I sleep I'll try what I can do:
This night I'll conjure tho' I die therefore.

> *Exeunt*

SCENE II

Before FAUSTUS' *house*

> *Enter two* SCHOLARS

1 SCHOL. I wonder what's become of Faustus that was wont to make our schools ring with *sic probo?*

2 SCHOL. That shall we know, for see here comes his boy.

> *Enter* WAGNER

1 SCHOL. How now, sirrah! Where's thy master?

WAG. God in heaven knows!

2 SCHOL. Why, dost not thou know?

WAG. Yes, I know. But that follows not.

1 SCHOL. Go to, sirrah! leave your jesting, and tell us where he is.

WAG. That follows not necessary by force of argument, that you, being licentiate, should stand upon't: therefore acknowledge your error, and be attentive.

2 SCHOL. Why, didst thou not say thou knewest?

WAG. Have you any witness on't?

1 SCHOL. Yes, sirrah, I heard you.

WAG. Ask my fellow if I be a thief.

2 SCHOL. Well, you will not tell us?

WAG. Yes, sir, I will tell you; yet if you were not dunces, you would never ask me such a question; for is not he *corpus naturale?* and is not that *mobile?* then wherefore should you ask me such a question? But that I am by nature phlegmatic, slow to wrath, and prone to lechery (to love, I would say), it were not for you to come within forty feet of the place of execution, although I do not doubt to see you both hanged the next sessions. Thus having triumphed over you, I will set my countenance like a precisian, and begin to speak thus: Truly, my dear brethren, my master is within at dinner, with Valdes and Cornelius, as this wine, if it could speak, would inform your worships; and so the Lord bless you, preserve you, and keep you, my dear brethren, my dear brethren.

> *Exit*

1 SCHOL. Nay, then. I fear he has fallen into that damned art, for which they two are infamous through the world.

2 SCHOL. Were he a stranger, and not allied to me, yet should I grieve for him. But come, let us go and inform the rector, and see if he by his grave counsel can reclaim him.

1 SCHOL. O, but I fear me nothing can reclaim him.
2 SCHOL. Yet let us try what we can do.
    Exeunt

SCENE III

    Enter FAUSTUS *to conjure in a grove*
FAUST. Now that the gloomy shadow of the earth
Longing to view Orion's drizzling look,
Leaps from the antarctic world unto the sky,
And dims the welkin with her pitchy breath,
Faustus, begin thine incantations,
And try if devils will obey thy hest,
Seeing thou hast prayed and sacrificed to them.
Within this circle is Jehovah's name,
Forward and backward anagrammatized,
The breviated names of holy saints,
Figures of every adjunct to the heavens,
And characters of signs and erring stars,
By which the spirits are enforced to rise:
Then fear not, Faustus, but be resolute,
And try the uttermost magic can perform.

    *Sint mihi dei Acherontis propitii! Valeat numen triplex Jehovæ!
Ignei, aerii, aquatani spiritus, salvete! Orientis princeps Belzebub,
inferni ardentis monarcha, et Demogorgon, propitiamus vos, ut ap-
pareat et surgate Mephistophilis. Quid tu moraris? per Jehovam,
Gehennam, et consecratam aquam quam nunc spargo, signumque
crucis quod nunc facio, et per vota nostra, ipse nunc surgat nobis
dicatus Mephistophilis!*

    Enter MEPHISTOPHILIS, *a devil*
I charge thee to return and change thy shape;
Thou are too ugly to attend on me.
Go, and return an old Franciscan friar;
That holy shape becomes a devil best.

    Exit DEVIL
I see there's virtue in my heavenly words;
Who would not be proficient in this art?
How pliant is this Mephistophilis,
Full of obedience and humility!
Such is the force of magic and my spells:
Now, Faustus, thou are conjuror laureat,
That canst command great Mephistophilis:
Quin regis Mephistophilis fratris imagine.

Enter MEPHISTOPHILIS *like a Franciscan Friar*

MEPH. Now, Faustus, what would'st thou have me to do?

FAUST. I charge thee wait upon me whilst I live,
To do whatever Faustus shall command,
Be it to make the moon drop from her sphere,
Or the ocean to overwhelm the world.

MEPH. I am a servant to great Lucifer,
And may not follow thee without his leave:
No more than he commands must we perform.

FAUST. Did not he charge thee to appear to me?

MEPH. No, I came thither of mine own accord.

FAUST. Did not my conjuring speeches raise thee? Speak.

MEPH. That was the cause, but yet *per accidens;*
For when we hear one rack the name of God,
Abjure the Scriptures and his Saviour Christ,
We fly in hope to get his glorious soul;
Nor will we come, unless he use such means
Whereby he is in danger to be damned:
Therefore the shortest cut for conjuring
Is stoutly to abjure the Trinity,
And pray devoutly to the Prince of Hell.

FAUST. So Faustus hath
Already done; and holds this principle,
There is no chief, but only Belzebub,
To whom Faustus doth dedicate himself.
This word "damnation" terrifies not him,
For he confounds hell in Elysium;
His ghost be with the old philosophers!
But, leaving these vain trifles of men's souls,
Tell me what is that Lucifer thy lord?

MEPH. Arch-regent and commander of all spirits.

FAUST. Was not that Lucifer an angel once?

MEPH. Yes, Faustus, and most dearly loved of God.

FAUST. How comes it then that he is prince of devils?

MEPH. O, by aspiring pride and insolence;
For which God threw him from the face of heaven.

FAUST. And what are you that live with Lucifer?

MEPH. Unhappy spirits that fell with Lucifer,
Conspired against our God with Lucifer,
And are for ever damned with Lucifer.

FAUST. Where are you damned?

MEPH. In hell.

FAUST. How comes it then that thou are out of hell?

MEPH. Why this is hell, nor am I out of it:
Think'st thou that I who saw the face of God,
And tasted the eternal joys of heaven,
Am not tormented with ten thousand hells,
In being deprived of everlasting bliss?
O Faustus! leave these frivolous demands,
Which strike a terror to my fainting soul.

FAUST. What, is great Mephistophilis so passionate
For being deprivèd of the joys of heaven?
Learn thou of Faustus' manly fortitude,
And scorn those joys thou never shalt possess.
Go bear these tidings to great Lucifer:
Seeing Faustus hath incurred eternal death
By desperate thoughts against Jove's deity,
Say he surrenders up to him his soul,
So he will spare him four and twenty years,
Letting him live in all voluptuousness;
Having thee ever to attend on me;
To give me whatsoever I shall ask,
To tell me whatsoever I demand,
To slay mine enemies, and aid my friends,
And always be obedient to my will.
Go and return to mighty Lucifer,
And meet me in my study at midnight,
And then resolve me of thy master's mind.

MEPH. I will, Faustus.
Exit

FAUST. Had I as many souls as there be stars,
I'd give them all for Mephistophilis.
By him I'll be great Emperor of the world,
And make a bridge thorough the moving air,
To pass the ocean with a band of men:
I'll join the hills that bind the Afric shore,
And make that country continent to Spain,
And both contributory to my crown.
The Emperor shall not live but by my leave,
Nor any potentate of Germany.
Now that I have obtained what I desire,
I'll live in speculation of this art
Till Mephistophilis return again.
Exit

SCENE IV

Before FAUSTUS' *house*

Enter WAGNER *and* CLOWN

WAG. Sirrah, boy, come hither.

CLOWN. How, boy! Swowns, boy! I hope you have seen many boys with such pickadevaunts as I have; boy, quotha.

WAG. Tell me, sirrah, hast thou any comings in?

CLOWN. Ay, and goings out too. You may see else.

WAG. Alas, poor slave! see how poverty jesteth in his nakedness! The villain is bare and out of service, and so hungry that I know he would give his soul to the Devil for a shoulder of mutton though 'twere blood-raw.

CLOWN. How? My soul to the Devil for a shoulder of mutton, though 'twere blood-raw! Not so, good friend. By'r-lady, I had need have it well roasted and good sauce to it, if I pay so dear.

WAG. Well, wilt thou serve me, and I'll make thee go like *Qui mihi discipulus?*

CLOWN. How, in verse?

WAG. No, sirrah; in beaten silk and stavesacre.

CLOWN. How, how, Knave's acre! Ay, I thought that was all the land his father left him. Do you hear? I would be sorry to rob you of your living.

WAG. Sirrah, I say in stavesacre.

CLOWN. Oho! Oho! Stavesacre! Why then belike if I were your man I should be full of vermin.

WAG. So thou shalt, whether thou beest with me or no. But sirrah, leave your jesting, and bind yourself presently unto me for seven years, or I'll turn all the lice about thee into familiars, and they shall tear thee in pieces.

CLOWN. Do you hear, sir? You may save that labor: they are too familiar with me already: swowns! they are as bold with my flesh as if they had paid for their meat and drink.

WAG. Well, do you hear, sirrah? Hold, take these guilders.

Gives money

CLOWN. Gridirons! what be they?

WAG. Why, French crowns.

CLOWN. Mass, but in the name of French crowns, a man were as good have as many English counters. And what should I do with these?

Wag. Why, now, sirrah, thou art at an hour's warning, whensoever and wheresoever the Devil shall fetch thee.

Clown. No, no. Here, take your gridirons again.

Wag. Truly I'll none of them.

Clown. Truly but you shall.

Wag. Bear witness I give them him.

Clown. Bear witness I give them you again.

Wag. Well, I will cause two devils presently to fetch thee away— Baliol and Belcher!

Clown. Let your Baliol and your Belcher come here, and I'll knock them, they were never so knocked since they were devils! Say I should kill one of them, what would folks say? "Do you see yonder tall fellow in the round slop—he has killed the devil." So I should be called Kill-devil all the parish over.

Enter two Devils; *the* Clown *runs up and down crying*

Wag. Baliol and Belcher! Spirits, away!

Exeunt Devils

Clown. What, are they gone? A vengeance on them, they have vile long nails! There was a he-devil, and a she-devil! I'll tell you how you shall know them; all he-devils has horns, and all she-devils has clifts and cloven feet.

Wag. Well, sirrah, follow me.

Clown. But, do you hear—if I should serve you, would you teach me to raise up Banios and Belcheos?

Wag. I will teach thee to turn thyself to anything; to a dog, or a cat, or a mouse, or a rat, or anything.

Clown. How! a Christian fellow to a dog or a cat, a mouse or a rat! No, no, sir. If you turn me into anything, let it be in the likeness of a little pretty frisking flea, that I may be here and there and everywhere. O, I'll tickle the pretty wenches' plackets; I'll be amongst them, i' faith.

Wag. Well, sirrah, come.

Clown. But, do you hear, Wagner?

Wag. How! Baliol and Belcher!

Clown. O Lord! I pray, sir, let Banio and Belcher go sleep.

Wag. Villain—call me Master Wagner, and let thy eye be diametarily fixed upon my right heel, with *quasi vestigiis nostris insistere.*

Exit

Clown. God forgive me, he speaks Dutch fustian. Well, I'll follow him: I'll serve him, that's flat.

Exit

SCENE V

Enter FAUSTUS *in his study*

FAUST. Now, Faustus, must
Thou needs be damned, and canst thou not be saved:
What boots it then to think of God or heaven?
Away with such vain fancies, and despair;
Despair in God, and trust in Belzebub;
Now go not backward: no, Faustus, be resolute:
Why waver'st thou? O, something soundeth in mine ears
"Abjure this magic, turn to God again!"
Ay, and Faustus will turn to God again.
To God?—He loves thee not—
The God thou serv'st is thine own appetite,
Wherein is fixed the love of Belzebub;
To him I'll build an altar and a church,
And offer lukewarm blood of new-born babes.

Enter GOOD ANGEL *and* EVIL

G. ANG. Sweet Faustus, leave that execrable art.
FAUST. Contrition, prayer, repentance! What of them?
G. ANG. O, they are means to bring thee unto heaven.
E. ANG. Rather, illusions—fruits of lunacy,
That makes men foolish that do trust them most.
G. ANG. Sweet Faustus, think of heaven and heavenly things.
E. ANG. No, Faustus, think of honor and of wealth.

Exeunt ANGELS

FAUST. Of wealth!
Why the signiory of Embden shall be mine.
When Mephistophilis shall stand by me,
What God can hurt thee? Faustus, thou are safe:
Cast no more doubts. Come, Mephistophilis,
And bring glad tidings from great Lucifer;
Is't not midnight? Come, Mephistophilis;
Veni, veni, Mephistophile!

Enter MEPHISTOPHILIS

Now tell me, what says Lucifer, thy lord?
MEPH. That I shall wait on Faustus whilst he lives,
So he will buy my service with his soul.
FAUST. Already Faustus hath hazarded that for thee.
MEPH. But, Faustus, thou must bequeath it solemnly,
And write a deed of gift with thine own blood,

For that security craves great Lucifer.
If thou deny it, I will back to hell.

FAUST. Stay, Mephistophilis! and tell me what good
Will my soul do thy lord.

MEPH. Enlarge his kingdom.

FAUST. Is that the reason why he tempts us thus?

MEPH. *Solamen miseris socios habuisse doloris.*

FAUST. Why, have you any pain that tortures others?

MEPH. As great as have the human souls of men.
But tell me, Faustus, shall I have thy soul?
And I will be thy slave, and wait on thee,
And give thee more than thou hast wit to ask.

FAUST. Ay, Mephistophilis, I give it thee.

MEPH. Then, Faustus, stab thine arm courageously,
And bind thy soul that at some certain day
Great Lucifer may claim it as his own;
And then be thou as great as Lucifer.

FAUST. [*stabbing his arm*] Lo, Mephistophilis, for love of thee,
I cut mine arm, and with my proper blood
Assure my soul to be great Lucifer's,
Chief lord and regent of perpetual night!
View here the blood that trickles from mine arm,
And let it be propitious for my wish.

MEPH. But, Faustus, thou must
Write it in manner of a deed of gift.

FAUST. Ay, so I will. [*Writes*] But, Mephistophilis,
My blood congeals, and I can write no more.

MEPH. I'll fetch thee fire to dissolve it straight.
        Exit

FAUST. What might the staying of my blood portend?
Is it unwilling I should write this bill?
Why streams it not that I may write afresh?
Faustus gives to thee his soul. Ah, there it stayed.
Why should'st thou not? Is not thy soul thine own?
Then write again, *Faustus gives to thee his soul.*

        Enter MEPHISTOPHILIS *with a chafer of coals*

MEPH. Here's fire. Come, Faustus, set it on.

FAUSTUS. So now the blood begins to clear again;
Now will I make an end immediately.
        Writes

MEPH. O, what will not I do to obtain his soul.
        Aside

FAUST. *Consummatum est:* this bill is ended,
And Faustus hath bequeathed his soul to Lucifer.
But what is this inscription on mine arm?
Homo, fuge! Whither should I fly?
If unto God, he'll throw me down to hell.
My senses are deceived; here's nothing writ—
I see it plain; here in this place is writ
Homo, fuge! Yet shall not Faustus fly.

 MEPH. I'll fetch him somewhat to delight his mind.
  Exit
  Enter MEPHISTOPHILIS *with* DEVILS, *giving crowns and rich*
  apparel to FAUSTUS, *and dance, and then depart*
 FAUST. Speak, Mephistophilis, what means this show?
 MEPH. Nothing, Faustus, but to delight thy mind withal,
And to show thee what magic can perform.
 FAUST. But may I raise up spirits when I please?
 MEPH. Ay, Faustus, and do greater things than these.
 FAUST. Then there's enough for a thousand souls.
Here, Mephistophilis, receive this scroll,
A deed of gift of body and of soul:
But yet conditionally that thou perform
All articles prescribed between us both.
 MEPH. Faustus, I swear by hell and Lucifer
To effect all promises between us made.
 FAUST. Then hear me read them: *On these conditions following.*
First, that Faustus may be a spirit in form and substance. Secondly,
that Mephistophilis shall be his servant, and at his command. Thirdly,
that Mephistophilis shall do for him and bring him whatsoever.
Fourthly, that he shall be in his chamber or house invisible. Lastly
that he shall appear to the said John Faustus, at all times, in what
form or shape soever he please. I, John Faustus, of Wittenberg, Doc-
tor, by these presents do give both body and soul to Lucifer, Prince of
the East, and his minister, Mephistophilis: and furthermore grant
unto them, that twenty-four years being expired, the articles above
written inviolate, full power to fetch or carry the said John Faustus,
body and soul, flesh, blood, or goods, into their habitation whereso-
ever. By me.

         JOHN FAUSTUS.
 MEPH. Speak, Faustus, do you deliver this as your deed?
 FAUST. Ay, take it, and the Devil give thee good on't!
 MEPH. Now, Faustus, ask what thou wilt.
 FAUST. First will I question with thee about hell.
Tell me where is the place that men call hell?

MEPH. Under the heavens.

FAUST. Ay, but whereabout?

MEPH. Within the bowels of these elements,
Where we are tortured·and remain for ever;
Hell hath no limits, nor is circumscribed
In one self place; for where we are is hell,
And where hell is there must we ever be:
And, to conclude, when all the world dissolves,
And every creature shall be purified,
All places shall be hell that is not heaven.

FAUST. Come, I think hell's a fable.

MEPH. Ay, think so still, till experience change thy mind.

FAUST. Why, think'st thou then that Faustus shall be damned?

MEPH. Ay, of necessity, for here's the scroll
Wherein thou hast given thy soul to Lucifer.

FAUST. Ay, and body too; but what of that?
Think'st thou that Faustus is so fond to imagine
That, after this life, there is any pain?
Tush; these are trifles, and mere old wives' tales.

MEPH. But, Faustus, I am an instance to prove the contrary.
For I am damnèd, and am now in hell.

FAUST. How! now in hell?
Nay, an this be hell, I'll willingly be damned here;
What? walking, disputing, etc.?
But, leaving off this, let me have a wife,
The fairest maid in Germany;
For I am wanton and lascivious,
And cannot live without a wife.

MEPH. How—a wife?
I prithee, Faustus, talk not of a wife.

FAUST. Nay, sweet Mephistophilis, fetch me one, for I will have one.

MEPH. Well—thou wilt have one. Sit there till I come: I'll fetch
thee a wife in the Devil's name.

> *Exit*
>
> *Re-enter* MEPHISTOPHILIS *with a* DEVIL *dressed like a woman,
> with fireworks*

MEPH. Tell me, Faustus, how dost thou like thy wife?

FAUST. A plague on her for a hot whore!

MEPH. Tut, Faustus,
Marriage is but a ceremonial toy;
And if thou lovest me, think no more of it.
I'll cull thee out the fairest courtesans,

And bring them every morning to thy bed;
She whom thine eye shall like, thy heart shall have,
Be she as chaste as was Penelope,
And as wise as Saba, or as beautiful
As was bright Lucifer before his fall.
Here, take this book, peruse it thoroughly:
> *Gives a book*

The iterating of these lines brings gold;
The framing of this circle on the ground
Brings whirlwinds, tempests, thunder and lightning;
Pronounce this thrice devoutly to thyself,
And men in armor shall appear to thee,
Ready to execute what thou desir'st.

FAUST. Thanks, Mephistophilis; yet fain would I have a book wherein I might behold all spells and incantations, that I might raise up spirits when I please.

MEPH. Here they are, in this book.
> *There turn to them*

FAUST. Now would I have a book where I might see all characters and planets of the heavens, that I might know their motions and dispositions.

MEPH. Here they are too.
> *Turn to them*

FAUST. Nay, let me have one book more—and then I have done—wherein I might see all plants, herbs, and trees that grow upon the earth.

MEPH. Here they be.

FAUST. O, thou art deceived.

MEPH. Tut, I warrant thee.
> *Turn to them. Exeunt*

SCENE VI

Enter FAUSTUS *in his study, and* MEPHISTOPHILIS

FAUST. When I behold the heavens, then I repent,
And curse thee, wicked Mephistophilis,
Because thou hast deprived me of those joys.

MEPH. Why, Faustus,
Think'st thou heaven is such a glorious thing?
I tell thee 'tis not half so fair as thou,
Or any man that breathes on earth.

FAUST. How prov'st thou that?

MEPH. 'Twas made for man, therefore is man more excellent.

FAUST. If it were made for man, 'twas made for me; I will renounce this magic and repent.

Enter GOOD ANGEL *and* EVIL ANGEL

G. ANG. Faustus, repent; yet God will pity thee.

E. ANG. Thou art a spirit; God cannot pity thee.

FAUST. Who buzzeth in my ears I am a spirit?
Be I a devil, yet God may pity me;
Ay, God will pity me if I repent.

E. ANG. Ay, but Faustus never shall repent.

Exeunt ANGELS

FAUST. My heart's so hardened I cannot repent.
Scarce can I name salvation, faith, or heaven,
But fearful echoes thunder in mine ears
"Faustus, thou are damned!" Then swords and knives,
Poison, gun, halters, and envenomed steel
Are laid before me to dispatch myself,
And long ere this I should have slain myself,
Had not sweet pleasure conquered deep despair.
Have not I made blind Homer sing to me
Of Alexander's love and Œnon's death?
And hath not he that built the walls of Thebes
With ravishing sound of his melodious harp,
Made music with my Mephistophilis?
Why should I die then, or basely despair?
I am resolved: Faustus shall ne'er repent—
Come, Mephistophilis, let us dispute again,
And argue of divine astrology.
Tell me, are there many heavens above the moon?
Are all celestial bodies but one globe,
As is the substance of this centric earth?

MEPH. As are the elements, such are the spheres
Mutually folded in each other's orb,
And, Faustus,
All jointly move upon one axle-tree
Whose terminine is termed the world's wide pole;
Nor are the names of Saturn, Mars, or Jupiter
Feigned, but are erring stars.

FAUST. But tell me, have they all one motion both, *situ et tempore?*

MEPH. All jointly move from east to west in twenty-four hours upon the poles of the world; but differ in their motion upon the poles of the zodiac.

FAUST. Tush!

These slender trifles Wagner can decide;

Hath Mephistophilis no greater skill?

Who knows not the double motion of the planets?

The first is finished in a natural day;

The second thus: as Saturn in thirty years;

Jupiter in twelve; Mars in four; the Sun, Venus, and Mercury in a
year; the moon in twenty-eight days. Tush, these are freshmen's
suppositions.

But tell me, hath every sphere a dominion or *intelligentia?*

MEPH. Ay.

FAUST. How many heavens, or spheres, are there?

MEPH. Nine: the seven planets, the firmament, and the empyreal
heaven.

FAUST. Well, resolve me in this question: Why have we not con-
junctions, oppositions, aspects, eclipses, all at one time, but in some
years we have more, in some less?

MEPH. *Per inœqualem motum respectu totius.*

FAUST. Well, I am answered. Tell me who made the world.

MEPH. I will not.

FAUST. Sweet Mephistophilis, tell me.

MEPH. Move me not, for I will not tell thee.

FAUST. Villain, have I not bound thee to tell me anything?

MEPH. Ay, that is not against our kingdom; but this is.

Think thou on hell, Faustus, for thou art damned.

FAUST. Think, Faustus, upon God that made the world.

MEPH. Remember this.

> *Exit*

FAUST. Ay, go, accursèd spirit, to ugly hell.

'Tis thou hast damned distressèd Faustus' soul.

Is't not too late?

> *Enter* GOOD ANGEL *and* EVIL ANGEL

E. ANG. Too late.

G. ANG. Never too late, if Faustus can repent.

E. ANG. If thou repent, devils shall tear thee in pieces.

G. ANG. Repent, and they shall never raze thy skin.

> *Exeunt* ANGELS

FAUST. Ah, Christ my Saviour,

Seek to save distressèd Faustus' soul!

> *Enter* LUCIFER, BELZEBUB, *and* MEPHISTOPHILIS

LUC. Christ cannot save thy soul, for he is just;

There's none but I have interest in the same.

FAUST. O, who art thou that look'st so terrible?

LUC. I am Lucifer.

And this is my companion-prince in hell.

FAUST. O Faustus! they are come to fetch away thy soul!

LUC. We come to tell thee thou dost injure us;

Thou talk'st of Christ contrary to thy promise;

Thou should'st not think of God: think of the Devil.

BELZ. And his dam, too.

FAUST. Nor will I henceforth; pardon me in this,

And Faustus vows never to look to heaven,

Never to name God, or to pray to him,

To burn his Scriptures, slay his ministers,

And make my spirits pull his churches down.

LUC. Do so and we will highly gratify thee. Faustus, we are come 'from hell to show thee some pastime: sit down, and thou shalt see all the Seven Deadly Sins appear in their proper shapes.

FAUST. That sight will be as pleasing unto me,

As Paradise was to Adam the first day

Of his creation.

LUC. Talk not of Paradise nor creation, but mark this show: talk of the Devil, and nothing else: come away!

Enter the SEVEN DEADLY SINS

Now, Faustus, examine them of their several names and dispositions.

FAUST. What art thou—the first?

PRIDE. I am Pride. I disdain to have any parents. I am like to Ovid's flea: I can creep into every corner of a wench; sometimes, like a periwig, I sit upon her brow; or like a fan of feathers, I kiss her lips; indeed I do—what do I not? But, fie, what a scent is here! I'll not speak another word, except the ground were perfumed, and covered with cloth of arras.

FAUST. What art thou—the second?

COVET. I am Covetousness, begotten of an old churl in an old leathern bag; and, might I have my wish, I would desire that this house and all the people in it were turned to gold, that I might lock you up in my good chest. O, my sweet gold!

FAUST. What art thou—the third?

WRATH. I am Wrath. I had neither father nor mother; I leapt out of a lion's mouth when I was scarce half an hour old; and ever since I have run up and down the world with this case of rapiers, wounding myself when I had nobody to fight withal. I was born in hell; and look to it, for some of you shall be my father.

FAUST. What art thou—the fourth?

ENVY. I am Envy, begotten of a chimney-sweeper and an oyster-wife. I cannot read, and therefore wish all books were burnt. I am lean with seeing others eat. O, that there would come a famine through all the world, that all might die, and I live alone! then thou should'st see how fat I would be. But must thou sit and I stand! Come down with a vengeance!

FAUST. Away, envious rascal! What art thou—the fifth?

GLUT. Who, I, sir? I am Gluttony. My parents are all dead, and the devil a penny they have left me, but a bare pension, and that is thirty meals a day and ten bevers—a small trifle to suffice nature. O, I come of a royal parentage! My grandfather was a Gammon of Bacon, my grandmother was a Hogshead of Claret wine; my godfathers were these, Peter Pickle-herring, and Martin Martlemas-beef; O, but my godmother, she was a jolly gentlewoman, and well beloved in every good town and city; her name was Mistress Margery March-bee. Now, Faustus, thou hast heard all my progeny, wilt thou bid me to supper?

FAUST. No, I'll see thee hanged: thou wilt eat up all my victuals.

GLUT. Then the Devil choke thee!

FAUST. Choke thyself, glutton! Who art thou—the sixth?

SLOTH. I am Sloth. I was begotten on a sunny bank, where I have lain ever since; and you have done me great injury to bring me from thence: let me be carried thither again by Gluttony and Lechery. I'll not speak another word for a king's ransom.

FAUST. What are you, Mistress Minx, the seventh and last?

LECHERY. Who, I, sir? I am the one that loves an inch of raw mutton better than an ell of fried stock-fish; and the first letter of my name begins with L.

LUC. Away to hell, to hell!

Exeunt the SINS

Now, Faustus, how dost thou like this?

FAUST. O, this feeds my soul!

LUC. Tut, Faustus, in hell is all manner of delight.

FAUST. O, might I see hell, and return again,
How happy were I then!

LUC. Thou shalt; I will send for thee at midnight.
In meantime take this book; peruse it thoroughly,
And thou shalt turn thyself into what shape thou wilt.

FAUST. Great thanks, mighty Lucifer!
This will I keep as chary as my life.

LUC. Farewell, Faustus, and think on the Devil.

FAUST. Farewell, great Lucifer! Come, Mephistophilis.

Exeunt omnes

Enter WAGNER *solus*

WAG. Learned Faustus,
To know the secrets of astronomy,
Graven in the book of Jove's high firmament,
Did mount himself to scale Olympus' top,
Being seated in a chariot burning bright,
Drawn by the strength of yoky dragons' necks.
He now is gone to prove cosmography,
And, as I guess, will first arrive at Rome,
To see the Pope the manner of his court,
And take some part of holy Peter's feast,
That to this day is highly solemnized.

　　Exit WAGNER

SCENE VII

The privy chamber of the Pope

Enter FAUSTUS *and* MEPHISTOPHILIS

FAUST. Having now, my good Mephistophilis,
Passed with delight the stately town of Trier,
Environed round with airy mountain tops,
With walls of flint, and deep entrenchèd lakes,
Not to be won by any conquering prince;
From Paris next, coasting the realm of France,
We saw the river Maine fall into Rhine,
Whose banks are set with groves of fruitful vines;
Then up to Naples, rich Campania,
Whose buildings fair and gorgeous to the eye,
The streets straight forth, and paved with finest brick,
Quarter the town in four equivalents:
There saw we learned Maro's golden tomb,
The way he cut, an English mile in length,
Thorough a rock of stone in one night's space;
From thence to Venice, Padua, and the rest,
In one of which a sumptuous temple stands,
That threats the stars with her aspiring top.
Thus hitherto has Faustus spent his time:
But tell me, now, what resting-place is this?
Hast thou, as erst I did command,
Conducted me within the walls of Rome?

MEPH. Faustus, I have; and because we will not be unprovided, I
have taken up his Holiness' privy chamber for our use.

FAUST. I hope his Holiness will bid us welcome.

MEPH. Tut, 'tis no matter, man, we'll be bold with his good cheer.
And now, my Faustus, that thou may'st perceive
What Rome containeth to delight thee with,
Know that this city stands upon seven hills
That underprop the groundwork of the same:
Just through the midst runs flowing Tiber's stream,
With winding banks that cut it in two parts:
Over the which four stately bridges lean,
That make safe passage to each part of Rome:
Upon the bridge called Ponte Angelo
Erected is a castle passing strong,
Within whose walls such store of ordnance are,
And double cannons framed of carved brass,
As match the days within one complete year;
Besides the gates, and high pyramides,
Which Julius Cæsar brought from Africa.

FAUST. Now, by the kingdoms of infernal rule,
Of Styx, of Acheron, and the fiery lake
Of ever-burning Phlegethon, I swear
That I do long to see the monuments
And situation of bright-splendent Rome:
Come, therefore, let's away.

MEPH. Nay, Faustus, stay; I know you'd fain see the Pope,
And take some part of holy Peter's feast,
Where thou shalt see a troop of bald-pate friars,
Whose *summum bonum* is in belly-cheer.

FAUST. Well, I'm content to compass them some sport,
And by their folly make us merriment.
Then charm me, Mephistophilis, that I
May be invisible, to do what I please
Unseen of any whilst I stay in Rome.

MEPHISTOPHILIS *charms him*

MEPH. So, Faustus, now
Do what thou wilt, thou shalt not be discerned.

Sound a sennet. Enter the POPE *and the* CARDINAL OF LORRAIN
to the banquet, with FRIARS *attending*

POPE. My Lord of Lorrain, wilt please you draw near?

FAUST. Fall to, and the devil choke you an you spare!

POPE. How now! Who's that which spake?—Friars, look about.

FRIAR. Here's nobody, if it like your Holiness.

POPE. My lord, here is a dainty dish was sent me from the Bishop of
Milan.

FAUST. I thank you, sir.
      Snatches it
POPE. How now! Who's that which snatched the meat from me?
Will no man look? My lord, this dish was sent me from the Cardinal of
Florence.
FAUST. You say true; I'll ha't.
      Snatches the dish
POPE. What, again! My lord, I'll drink to your grace.
FAUST. I'll pledge your grace.
      Snatches the cup
C. OF LOR. My lord, it may be some ghost newly crept out of pur-
gatory, come to beg a pardon of your Holiness.
POPE. It may be so. Friars, prepare a dirge to lay the fury of this
ghost. Once again, my lord, fall to.
      The POPE crosseth himself
FAUST. What, are you crossing of yourself?
Well, use that trick no more I would advise you.
      Cross again
Well, there's the second time. Aware the third,
I give you fair warning.
      *Cross again, and FAUSTUS hits him a box of the ear; and they
      all run away*
Come on, Mephistophilis, what shall we do?
MEPH. Nay, I know not. We shall be cursed with bell, book, and
candle.
FAUST. How! bell, book, and candle—candle, book, and bell,
Forward and backward to curse Faustus to hell!
Anon you shall hear a hog grunt, a calf bleat, and an ass bray,
Because it is Saint Peter's holiday.
      Enter all the FRIARS to sing the dirge
FRIAR. Come, brethren, let's about our business with good devotion.
      Sing this
Cursed be he that stole away his Holiness' meat from the table!
Maledicat Dominus!
Cursed be he that struck his Holiness a blow on the face! *Maledicat
Dominus!*
Cursed be he that took Friar Sandelo a blow on the pate! *Maledicat
Dominus!*
Cursed be he that disturbeth our holy dirge! *Maledicat Dominus!*
Cursed be he that took away his Holiness' wine! *Maledicat Dominus!*
Et omnes sancti! Amen!
      *MEPHISTOPHILIS and FAUSTUS beat the FRIARS, and fling
      fireworks among them: and so exeunt*

Enter CHORUS

CHORUS. When Faustus had with pleasure ta'en the view
Of rarest things, and royal courts of kings,
He stayed his course, and so returnèd home;
Where such as bear his absence but with grief,
I mean his friends, and near'st companions,
Did gratulate his safety with kind words,
And in their conference of what befell,
Touching his journey through the world and air,
They put forth questions of astrology,
Which Faustus answered with such learnèd skill,
As they admired and wondered at his wit.
Now is his fame spread forth in every land;
Amongst the rest the Emperor is one,
Carolus the Fifth, at whose palace now
Faustus is feasted 'mongst his noblemen.
What there he did in trial of his art,
I leave untold—your eyes shall see performed.
    Exit

SCENE VIII

An Inn-yard

Enter ROBIN *the Ostler with a book in his hand*

ROBIN. Oh, this is admirable! here I ha' stolen one of Doctor Faustus' conjuring books, and i' faith I mean to search some circles for my own use. Now will I make all the maidens in our parish dance at my pleasure, stark-naked before me; and so by that means I shall see more than e'er I felt or saw yet.

Enter RAFE *calling* ROBIN

RAFE. Robin, prithee, come away; there's a gentleman tarries to have his horse, and he would have his things rubbed and made clean: he keeps such a chafing with my mistress about it; and she has sent me to look thee out; prithee, come away.

ROBIN. Keep out, keep out, or else you are blown up; you are dismembered, Rafe: keep out, for I am about a roaring piece of work.

RAFE. Come, what dost thou with that same book? Thou canst not read.

ROBIN. Yes, my master and mistress shall find that I can read, he for his forehead, she for her private study; she's born to bear with me, or else my art fails.

RAFE. Why, Robin, what book is that?

ROBIN. What book! Why, the most intolerable book for conjuring that e'er was invented by any brimstone devil.

RAFE. Can'st thou conjure with it?

ROBIN. I can do all these things easily with it; first, I can make thee drunk with ippocras at any tabern in Europe for nothing; that's one of my conjuring works.

RAFE. Our Master Parson says that's nothing.

ROBIN. True, Rafe; and more, Rafe, if thou hast any mind to Nan Spit, our kitchen-maid, then turn her and wind her to thy own use as often as thou wilt, and at midnight.

RAFE. O brave Robin, shall I have Nan Spit, and to mine own use? On that condition I'd feed thy devil with horse-bread as long as he lives, of free cost.

ROBIN. No more, sweet Rafe: let's go and make clean our boots, which lie foul upon our hands, and then to our conjuring in the devil's name.

Exeunt

SCENE IX

The Same

Enter ROBIN *and* RAFE *with a silver goblet*

ROBIN. Come, Rafe, did not I tell thee we were for ever made by this Doctor Faustus' book? *ecce signum,* here's a simple purchase for horse-keepers; our horses shall eat no hay as long as this lasts.

RAFE. But, Robin, here comes the Vintner.

ROBIN. Hush! I'll gull him supernaturally.

Enter VINTNER

Drawer, I hope all is paid: God be with you; come, Rafe.

VINT. Soft, sir; a word with you. I must yet have a goblet paid from you, ere you go.

ROBIN. I, a goblet, Rafe; I, a goblet! I scorn you, and you are but a, etc. I, a goblet! search me.

VINT. I mean so, sir, with your favor.

Searches him

ROBIN. How say you now?

VINT. I must say somewhat to your fellow. You, sir!

RAFE. Me, sir! me, sir! search your fill. [*Vintner searches him*] Now, sir, you may be ashamed to burden honest men with a matter of truth.

VINT. Well, t'one of you hath this goblet about you.

ROBIN. You lie, drawer, 'tis afore me. [*Aside*] Sirrah you, I'll teach you to impeach honest men—stand by—I'll scour you for a goblet!—

stand aside you had best, I charge you in the name of Belzebub—look to the goblet, Rafe. [*Aside to* RAFE]

VINT. What mean you, sirrah?

ROBIN. I'll tell you what I mean. [*Reads from a book*] *Sanctobulorum Periphrasticon*—nay, I'll tickle you, Vintner. Look to the goblet, Rafe. [*Aside to* RAFE]

[*Reads*] *Polypragmos Belseborams framanto pacostiphos tostu, Mephistophilis, etc.*

> *Enter* MEPHISTOPHILIS, *sets squibs at their backs, and then exits. They run about*

VINT. *O nomine Domini!* what meanest thou, Robin? thou hast no goblet.

RAFE. *Peccatum peccatorum.* Here's thy goblet, good Vintner.

> *Gives the goblet to* VINTNER, *who exits*

ROBIN. *Misericordia pro nobis!* What shall I do? Good Devil, forgive me now, and I'll never rob thy library more.

> *Enter to them* MEPHISTOPHILIS

MEPH. Monarch of hell, under whose black survey
Great potentates do kneel with awful fear,
Upon whose altars thousand souls do lie,
How am I vexed with these villains' charms!
From Constantinople am I hither come
Only for pleasure of these damnèd slaves.

ROBIN. How, from Constantinople! You have had a great journey: will you take six-pence in your purse to pay for your supper, and begone?

MEPH. Well, villains, for your presumption I transform thee into an ape, and thee into a dog and so begone.

> *Exit*

ROBIN. How, into an ape: that's brave! I'll have fine sport with the boys. I'll get nuts and apples enow.

RAFE. And I must be a dog.

ROBIN. I'faith thy head will never be out of the pottage pot.

> *Exeunt*

SCENE X

The court

> *Enter* EMPEROR, FAUSTUS, *and a* KNIGHT *with* ATTENDANTS

EMP. Master Doctor Faustus, I have heard strange report of thy knowledge in the black art, how that none in my empire nor in the whole world can compare with thee for the rare effects of magic; they say thou hast a familiar spirit, by whom thou canst accomplish what thou list. This, therefore, is my request, that thou let me see some proof of thy skill, that mine eyes may be witnesses to confirm what mine ears have heard reported; and here I swear to thee by the honor of mine imperial crown, that, whatever thou doest, thou shalt be no ways prejudiced or endamaged.

KNIGHT. I'faith he looks much like a conjuror. [*Aside*]

FAUST. My gracious sovereign, though I must confess myself far inferior to the report men have published, and nothing answerable to the honor of your imperial majesty, yet for that love and duty binds me thereunto, I am content to do whatsoever your majesty shall command me.

EMP. Then, Doctor Faustus, mark what I shall say.
As I was sometimes solitary set
Within my closet, sundry thoughts arose
About the honor of mine ancestors,
How they had won by prowess such exploits,
Got such riches, subdued so many kingdoms
As we that do succeed, or they that shall
Hereafter possess our throne, shall
(I fear me) ne'er attain to that degree
Of high renown and great authority;
Amongst which kings is Alexander the Great,
Chief spectacle of the world's pre-eminence,
The bright shining of whose glorious acts
Lightens the world with his reflecting beams,
As when I hear but motion made of him
It grieves my soul I never saw the man.
If therefore thou by cunning of thine art
Canst raise this man from hollow vaults below,
Where lies entombed this famous conqueror,
And bring with him his beauteous paramour,
Both in their right shapes, gesture, and attire
They used to wear during their time of life,
Thou shalt both satisfy my just desire,
And give me cause to praise thee whilst I live.

FAUST. My gracious lord, I am ready to accomplish your request so far forth as by art, and power of my spirit, I am able to perform.

KNIGHT. I'faith that's just nothing at all. [*Aside*]

FAUST. But, if it like your grace, it is not in my ability to present before your eyes the true substantial bodies of those two deceased princes, which long since are consumed to dust.

KNIGHT. Ay, marry, Master Doctor, now there's a sign of grace in you, when you will confess the truth. [*Aside*]

FAUST. But such spirits as can lively resemble Alexander and his paramour shall appear before your grace in that manner that they best lived in, in their most flourishing estate; which I doubt not shall sufficiently content your imperial majesty.

EMP. Go to, Master Doctor, let me see them presently.

KNIGHT. Do you hear, Master Doctor? You bring Alexander and his paramour before the Emperor!

FAUST. How then, sir?

KNIGHT. I'faith that's as true as Diana turned me to a stag!

FAUST. No, sir, but when Actæon died, he left the horns for you. Mephistophilis, begone.

Exit MEPH.

KNIGHT. Nay an you go to conjuring, I'll begone.

Exit KNIGHT

FAUST. I'll meet with you anon for interrupting me so. Here they are, my gracious lord.

Enter MEPHISTOPHILIS *with* SPIRITS *in the shape of*
ALEXANDER *and his* PARAMOUR

EMP. Master Doctor, I heard this lady while she lived had a wart or mole in her neck: how shall I know whether it be so or no?

FAUST. Your highness may boldly go and see.

EMP. Sure these are no spirits, but the true substantial bodies of those two deceased princes.

Exeunt SPIRITS

FAUST. Will't please your highness now to send for the knight that was so pleasant with me here of late?

EMP. One of you call him forth!

Exit ATTENDANT

Enter the KNIGHT *with a pair of horns on his head*

How now, sir knight! why I had thought thou had'st been a bachelor, but now I see thou hast a wife, that not only gives thee horns, but makes thee wear them. Feel on thy head.

KNIGHT. Thou damnèd wretch and execrable dog,
Bred in the concave of some monstrous rock,
How darest thou thus abuse a gentleman?
Villain, I say, undo what thou hast done!

FAUST. O, not so fast, sir; there's no haste; but, good, are you remembered how you crossed me in my conference with the Emperor? I think I have met with you for it.

EMP. Good Master Doctor, at my entreaty release him; he hath done penance sufficient.

FAUST. My gracious lord, not so much for the injury he offered me here in your presence, as to delight you with some mirth, hath Faustus worthily requited this injurious knight; which, being all I desire, I am content to release him of his horns: and, sir knight, hereafter speak well of scholars. Mephistophilis, transform him straight. [MEPHISTOPHILIS *removes the horns*] Now, my good lord, having done my duty I humbly take my leave.

EMP. Farewell, Master Doctor; yet, ere you go,
Expect from me a bounteous reward.

Exit EMPEROR

SCENE XI

A green, then FAUSTUS' *house*

Enter FAUSTUS *and* MEPHISTOPHILIS

FAUST. Now, Mephistophilis, the restless course
That Time doth run with calm and silent foot,
Shortening my days and thread of vital life,
Calls for the payment of my latest years:
Therefore, sweet Mephistophilis, let us
Make haste to Wittenberg.

MEPH. What, will you go on horse-back or on foot?

FAUST. Nay, till I'm past this fair and pleasant green, I'll walk on foot.

Enter a HORSE-COURSER

HORSE-C. I have been all this day seeking one Master Fustian: mass, see where he is! God save you, Master Doctor!

FAUST. What, Horse-Courser! You are well met.

HORSE-C. Do you hear, sir? I have brought you forty dollars for your horse.

FAUST. I cannot sell him so: if thou likest him for fifty, take him.

HORSE-C. Alas, sir, I have no more.—I pray you speak for me.

MEPH. I pray you let him have him: he is an honest fellow, and he has a great charge, neither wife nor child.

FAUST. Well, come, give me your money. [HORSE-COURSER *gives* FAUSTUS *the money*] My boy will deliver him to you. But I must tell you one thing before you have him; ride him not into the water at any hand.

HORSE-C. Why, sir, will he not drink of all waters?

FAUST. O, yes, he will drink of all waters, but ride him not into the water: ride him over hedge or ditch, or where thou wilt, but not into the water.

Horse-C. Well, sir.—Now am I made man for ever: I'll not leave my horse for twice forty: if he had but the quality of hey-ding-ding, hey-ding-ding, I'd make a brave living on him: he has a buttock as slick as an eel. [*Aside*] Well, God buy, sir, your boy will deliver him me: but hark you, sir: if my horse be sick or ill at ease, if I bring his water to you, you'll tell me what it is?

Faust. Away, you villain; what, dost think I am a horse-doctor?

   Exit Horse-Courser

What are thou, Faustus, but a man condemned to die?
Thy fatal time doth draw to final end;
Despair doth drive distrust unto my thoughts:
Confound these passions with a quiet sleep:
Tush, Christ did call the thief upon the cross;
Then rest thee, Faustus, quiet in conceit. *Sleeps in his chair*

   Re-enter Horse-Courser, *all wet, crying*

Horse-C. Alas, alas! Doctor Fustian quotha? Mass, Doctor Lopus was never such a doctor. Has given me a purgation has purged me of forty dollars; I shall never see them more. But yet, like an ass as I was, I would not be ruled by him, for he bade me I should ride him into no water. Now I, thinking my horse had had some rare quality that he would not have had me known of, I, like a venturous youth, rid him into the deep pond at the town's end. I was no sooner in the middle of the pond, but my horse vanished away, and I sat upon a bottle of hay, never so near drowning in my life. But I'll seek out my Doctor, and have my forty dollars again, or I'll make it the dearest horse!—O, yonder is his snipper-snapper.—Do you hear? you hey-pass, where's your master?

Meph. Why, sir, what would you? You cannot speak with him.

Horse-C. But I will speak with him.

Meph. Why, he's fast asleep. Come some other time.

Horse-C. I'll speak with him now, or I'll break his glass windows about his ears.

Meph. I tell thee he has not slept this eight nights.

Horse-C. An he have not slept this eight weeks I'll speak with him.

Meph. See where he is, fast asleep.

Horse-C. Ay, this is he. God save you, Master Doctor, Master Doctor, Master Doctor Fustian!—Forty dollars, forty dollars for a bottle of hay!

Meph. Why, thou seest he hears thee not.

Horse-C. So-ho ho!—so-ho ho! [*Hollas in his ear*] No, will you not wake? I'll make you wake ere I go. [*Pulls him by the leg, and pulls it away*] Alas, I am undone! What shall I do?

FAUST. O, my leg, my leg! Help, Mephistophilis! call the officers. My leg, my leg!

MEPH. Come, villain, to the constable.

HORSE-C. O lord, sir, let me go, and I'll give you forty dollars more.

MEPH. Where be they?

HORSE-C. I have none about me. Come to my ostry and I'll give them you.

MEPH. Begone quickly.

HORSE-COURSER *runs away*

FAUST. What, is he gone? Farewell he! Faustus has his leg again, and the horse-courser, I take it, a bottle of hay for his labor. Well, this trick shall cost him forty dollars more.

Enter WAGNER

How now, Wagner, what's the news with thee?

WAG. Sir, the Duke of Vanholt doth earnestly entreat your company.

FAUST. The Duke of Vanholt! an honorable gentleman, to whom I must be no niggard of my cunning. Come, Mephistophilis, let's away to him.

Exeunt

SCENE XII

Court of the Duke

Enter the DUKE *and the* DUCHESS, FAUSTUS, *and* MEPHISTOPHILIS

DUKE. Believe me, Master Doctor, this merriment hath much pleased me.

FAUST. My gracious lord, I am glad it contents you so well.—But it may be, madam, you take no delight in this. I have heard that great bellied women do long for some dainties or other: what is it, madam? tell me, and you shall have it.

DUCHESS. Thanks, good Master Doctor; and for I see your courteous intent to pleasure me, I will not hide from you the thing my heart desires; and were it now summer, as it is January and the dead time of the winter, I would desire no better meat than a dish of ripe grapes.

FAUST. Alas, madam, that's nothing! Mephistophilis, begone. [*Exit* MEPHISTOPHILIS] Were it a greater thing than this, so it would content you, you should have it.

Enter MEPHISTOPHILIS *with the grapes*

Here they be, madam; wilt please you taste on them?

DUKE. Believe me, Master Doctor, this makes me wonder above the rest, that being in the dead time of winter, and in the month of January, how you should come by these grapes.

FAUST. If it like your grace, the year is divided into two circles over the whole world, that, when it is here winter with us, in the contrary circle it is summer with them, as in India, Saba, and farther countries in the East; and by means of a swift spirit that I have I had them brought hither, as you see.—How do you like them, madam; be they good?

DUCHESS. Believe me, Master Doctor, they be the best grapes that e'er I tasted in my life before.

FAUST. I am glad they content you so, madam.

DUKE. Come, madam, let us in, where you must well reward this learned man for the great kindness he hath showed to you.

DUCHESS. And so I will, my lord; and, whilst I live, rest beholding for this courtesy.

FAUST. I humbly thank your grace.

DUKE. Come, Master Doctor, follow us and receive your reward.

Exeunt

SCENE XIII

FAUSTUS' *study*

Enter WAGNER *solus*

WAG. I think my master means to die shortly,
For he hath given to me all his goods
And yet, methinks, if that death were [so] near,
He would not banquet, and carouse and swill
Amongst the students, as even now he doth,
Who are at supper with such belly-cheer
As Wagner ne'er beheld in all his life.
See where they come! belike the feast is ended.

Enter FAUSTUS, *with two or three* SCHOLARS *and* MEPHIS-
TOPHILIS

1 SCHOL. Master Doctor Faustus, since our conference about fair ladies, which was the beautifullest in all the world, we have determined with ourselves that Helen of Greece was the admirablest lady that ever lived: therefore, Master Doctor, if you will do us that favor, as to let us see that peerless dame of Greece, whom all the world admires for majesty, we should think ourselves much beholding unto you.

FAUST. Gentlemen,

For that I know your friendship is unfeignèd,
And Faustus' custom is not to deny
The just requests of those that wish him well,
You shall behold that peerless dame of Greece,
No otherways for pomp and majesty,
Than when Sir Paris crossed the seas with her,
And brought the spoils to rich Dardania.
Be silent, then, for danger is in words.

Music sounds and HELEN *passeth over the stage*

2 SCHOL. Too simple is my wit to tell her praise,
Whom all the world admires for majesty.

3 SCHOL. No marvel though the angry Greeks pursued
With ten years' war the rape of such a queen,
Whose heavenly beauty passeth all compare.

1 SCHOL. Since we have seen the pride of Nature's works,
And only paragon of excellence.

Enter an OLD MAN

Let us depart; and for this glorious deed
Happy and blest be Faustus evermore.

FAUST. Gentlemen, farewell—the same I wish to you.

Exeunt SCHOLARS *and* WAGNER

OLD MAN. Ah, Doctor Faustus, that I might prevail
To guide thy steps unto the way of life,
By which sweet path thou may'st attain the goal
That shall conduct thee to celestial rest!
Break heart, drop blood, and mingle it with tears,
Tears falling from repentant heaviness
Of thy most vile and loathsome filthiness,
The stench whereof corrupts the inward soul
With such flagitious crimes of heinous sins
As no commiseration may expel,
But mercy, Faustus, of thy Saviour sweet,
Whose blood alone must wash away thy guilt.

FAUST. Where art thou, Faustus? wretch, what hast thou done?
Damned art thou, Faustus, damned; despair and die!
Hell calls for right, and with a roaring voice
Says, "Faustus! come! thine hour is [almost] come!"
And Faustus now will come to do thee right.

MEPHISTOPHILIS *gives him a dagger*

OLD MAN. Ah stay, good Faustus, stay thy desperate steps!
I see an angel hovers o'er thy head,
And, with a vial full of precious grace,

Offers to pour the same into thy soul:
Then call for mercy, and avoid despair.

FAUST. Ah, my sweet friend, I feel
Thy words do comfort my distressèd soul.
Leave me a while to ponder on my sins.

OLD MAN. I go, sweet Faustus, but with heavy cheer,
Fearing the ruin of thy hopeless soul.

> *Exit*

FAUST. Accursèd Faustus, where is mercy now?
I do repent; and yet I do despair;
Hell strives with grace for conquest in my breast:
What shall I do to shun the snares of death?

MEPH. Thou traitor, Faustus, I arrest thy soul
For disobedience to my sovereign lord;
Revolt, or I'll in piecemeal tear thy flesh.

FAUST. Sweet Mephistophilis, entreat thy lord
To pardon my unjust presumption.
And with my blood again I will confirm
My former vow I made to Lucifer.

MEPH. Do it then quickly, with unfeignèd heart,
Lest greater danger do attend thy drift.

> FAUSTUS *stabs his arm and writes on a paper with his blood*

FAUST. Torment, sweet friend, that base and crookèd age,
That durst dissuade me from thy Lucifer,
With greatest torments that our hell affords.

MEPH. His faith is great: I cannot touch his soul;
But what I may afflict his body with
I will attempt, which is but little worth.

FAUST. One thing, good servant, let me crave of thee,
To glut the longing of my heart's desire—
That I might have unto my paramour
That heavenly Helen, which I saw of late,
Whose sweet embracings may extinguish clean
These thoughts that do dissuade me from my vow,
And keep mine oath I made to Lucifer.

MEPH. Faustus, this or what else thou shalt desire
Shall be performed in twinkling of an eye.

> *Enter* HELEN

FAUST. Was this the face that launched a thousand ships
And burnt the topless towers of Ilium?
Sweet Helen, make me immortal with a kiss.

> *Kisses her*

Her lips suck forth my soul; see where it flies!

Come, Helen, come, give me my soul again.
Here will I dwell, for heaven be in these lips,
And all is dross that is not Helena.
I will be Paris, and for love of thee,
Instead of Troy, shall Wittenberg be sacked
And I will combat with weak Menelaus,
And wear thy colors on my plumèd crest:
Yea, I will wound Achilles in the heel,
And then return to Helen for a kiss.
O, thou art fairer than the evening air
Clad in the beauty of a thousand stars;
Brighter art thou than flaming Jupiter
When he appeared to hapless Semele:
More lovely than the monarch of the sky
In wanton Arethusa's azured arms:
And none but thou shalt be my paramour!

Exeunt

Enter the OLD MAN

OLD MAN. Accursèd Faustus, miserable man,
That from thy soul exclud'st the grace of heaven,
And fly'st the throne of his tribunal seat!

Enter DEVILS

Satan begins to sift me with his pride:
As in this furnace God shall try my faith,
My faith, vile hell, shall triumph over thee.
Ambitious fiends! see how the heavens smile
At your repulse, and laugh your state to scorn!
Hence, hell! for hence I fly unto my God.

Exeunt

SCENE XIV

The same

Enter FAUSTUS *with the* SCHOLARS

FAUST. Ah, gentlemen!

1 SCHOL. What ails Faustus?

FAUST. Ah, my sweet chamber-fellow, had I lived with thee, then had I lived still! but now I die eternally. Look, comes he not, comes he not?

2 SCHOL. What means Faustus?

3 SCHOL. Belike he is grown into some sickness by being over solitary.

1 SCHOL. If it be so, we'll have physicians to cure him. 'Tis but a surfeit. Never fear, man.

FAUST. A surfeit of deadly sin that hath damned both body and soul.

2 SCHOL. Yet, Faustus, look up to heaven: remember God's mercies are infinite.

FAUST. But Faustus' offence can ne'er be pardoned: the serpent that tempted Eve may be saved, but not Faustus. Ah, gentlemen, hear me with patience, and tremble not at my speeches! Though my heart pants and quivers to remember that I have been a student here these thirty years, O, would I had never seen Wittenberg, never read book! And what wonders I have done, all Germany can witness, yea, all the world; for which Faustus hath lost both Germany and the world, yea heaven itself, heaven, the seat of God, the throne of the blessed, the kingdom of joy; and must remain in hell for ever, hell, ah, hell, for ever! Sweet friends! what shall become of Faustus being in hell for ever?

3 SCHOL. Yet, Faustus, call on God.

FAUST. On God, whom Faustus hath abjured! on God, whom Faustus hath blasphemed! Ah, my God, I would weep, but the Devil draws in my tears. Gush forth blood instead of tears! Yes, life and soul! O, he stays my tongue! I would lift up my hands, but see, they hold them, they hold them!

ALL. Who, Faustus?

FAUST. Lucifer and Mephistophilis. Ah, gentlemen, I gave them my soul for my cunning!

ALL. God forbid!

FAUST. God forbade it indeed; but Faustus hath done it: for vain pleasure of twenty-four years hath Faustus lost eternal joy and felicity. I writ them a bill with mine own blood: the date is expired; the time will come, and he will fetch me.

1 SCHOL. Why did not Faustus tell us of this before, that divines might have prayed for thee?

FAUST. Oft have I thought to have done so: but the Devil threatened to tear me in pieces if I named God; to fetch both body and soul if I once gave ear to divinity: and now 'tis too late. Gentlemen, away! lest you perish with me.

2 SCHOL. O, what shall we do to [save] Faustus?

FAUST. Talk not of me, but save yourselves, and depart.

3 SCHOL. God will strengthen me. I will stay with Faustus.

1 SCHOL. Tempt not God, sweet friend; but let us into the next room, and there pray for him.

FAUST. Ay, pray for me, pray for me! and what noise soever ye hear, come not unto me, for nothing can rescue me.

2 SCHOL. Pray thou, and we will pray that God may have mercy upon thee.

FAUST. Gentlemen, farewell: if I live till morning I'll visit you: if not—— Faustus is gone to hell.

ALL. Faustus, farewell.

Exeunt SCHOLARS

The clock strikes eleven

FAUST. Ah, Faustus,
Now hast thou but one bare hour to live,
And then thou must be damned perpetually!
Stand still, you ever-moving spheres of heaven,
That time may cease, and midnight never come;
Fair Nature's eye, rise, rise again and make
Perpetual day; or let this hour be but
A year, a month, a week, a natural day,
That Faustus may repent and save his soul!
O lente, lente, currite noctis equi!
The stars move still, time runs, the clock will strike,
The Devil will come, and Faustus must be damned.
Oh, I'll leap up to my God! Who pulls me down?
See, see where Christ's blood streams in the firmament!
One drop would save my soul—half a drop: ah, my Christ!
Ah, rend not my heart for naming of my Christ!
Yet will I call on him: O, spare me, Lucifer!—
Where is it now? 'tis gone; and see where God
Stretcheth out his arm, and bends his ireful brows!
Mountain and hills come, come and fall on me,
And hide me from the heavy wrath of God!
No! no!
Then will I headlong run into the earth;
Earth gape! O, no, it will not harbor me!
You stars that reigned at my nativity,
Whose influence hath allotted death and hell,
Now draw up Faustus like a foggy mist
Into the entrails of yon laboring clouds,
That when you vomit forth into the air,
My limbs may issue from their smoky mouths,
So that my soul may but ascend to heaven,

The clock strikes the half-hour

Ah, half the hour is past! 'twill all be past anon!

O God!
If thou wilt not have mercy on my soul,
Yet for Christ's sake whose blood hath ransomed me,
Impose some end to my incessant pain;
Let Faustus live in hell a thousand years—
A hundred thousand, and—at last—be saved!
O, no end is limited to damnèd souls!
Why wert thou not a creature wanting soul?
Or why is this immortal that thou hast?
Ah, Pythagoras' metempsychosis! were that true,
This soul should fly from me, and I be changed
Unto some brutish beast! all beasts are happy,
For, when they die,
Their souls are soon dissolved in elements;
But mine must live, still to be plagued in hell.
Curst be the parents that engendered me!
No, Faustus: curse thyself; curse Lucifer
That hath deprived thee of the joys of heaven.
> *The clock strikes twelve*
O, it strikes, it strikes! Now, body, turn to air,
Or Lucifer will bear thee quick to hell.
> *Thunder and lightning*
O soul, be changed into little water-drops,
And fall into the ocean—ne'er be found.
My God! my God! look not so fierce on me!
> *Enter* DEVILS
Adders and serpents, let me breathe awhile!
Ugly hell, gape not! come not, Lucifer!
I'll burn my books!—Ah Mephistophilis!
> *Exeunt with him*
> *Enter* CHORUS

CHO. Cut is the branch that might have grown full straight,
And burnèd is Apollo's laurel bough,
That sometime grew within this learnèd man.
Faustus is gone; regard his hellish fall,
Whose fiendful fortune may exhort the wise
Only to wonder at unlawful things,
Whose deepness doth entice such forward wits
To practise more than heavenly power permits.
> *Exit*
Terminat hora diem; terminat auctor opus.

THE DJINN BOTTLE

The idea of the decanted Devil, or djinn poured from the bottle, has a distinctly Eastern flavor, and there is more to it than at first meets the palate. It is, in fact, of the same vintage as the first spirituous ferment of civilization.

The word "djinn" is Arabian. And in this country where the jars were large enough to hold the forty thieves, the concept of an evil spirit in human form, bottled and neatly stoppered from further depredations, was a logical imaginative development. It only remained then for the storyteller at the bazaar or one of the Sultan's talkative ladyloves to reduce the size of the container for convenience in handling and transportation.

There has always been a mystic quality to the contents of a bottle. The message, the manuscript, the Devil (even the Demon Rum, an allusion worth noting), when bottled, take on a special significance.

Asmodeus (or Asmodi), who appears in Le Sage's satire of that title (selections from which are included here), makes his first appearance in our literature in the Book of Tobit in the Apocrypha. He is the lover of Sarah—a demon who has disposed of her seven previous husbands on their wedding nights, prior to the suit of Tobit.

The story may well have been added to Hebrew legend during the Babylonian exile, and, if so, it establishes one Eastern thread in the pattern woven around the Devil in Spain. Presumably, the other, the notion of the Devil-in-a-bottle, traveled from Arabia along the Mediterranean and came into Spain with the Moors. But whether the Tobit story came from Babylonia or from Egypt, authorities seem to agree that Asmodi derives from *Aeshma daeva,* a Persian spirit of evil, who later became (in the Talmud) the demon of lust. His fourteenth great-grandson, Asmodeus (called Mickey for short), appears as a young hellion suffering from rickets in the Stephen Vincent Benét short story, *Doc Mellhorn.*

Such genealogical (or should we say genie-ological?) details concerning Asmodi (or Asmodeus) may seem beside the point. Still, the symbolism of the love philter suggests itself in connection with him, and the element of sex is certainly not lacking in either Le Sage's bottled demon or John Collier's.

As for the concept of the Devil-in-a-bottle having become a peculiarly Spanish device, perhaps the legend itself was bottled on the Iberian peninsula, waiting for the modern world to pull the cork. Which is exactly what Mr. Collier accomplishes in *Bottle Party,* letting laughter and fresh air replace the Devil's phial humors.

And, if a further parallel suggests itself anent the Spanish political situation, the reader may make the most of it.

ASMODEUS; OR, THE DEVIL ON TWO STICKS

Alain René le Sage

A NIGHT in the month of October covered with its thick darkness the famous city of Madrid. Already the inhabitants, retired to their homes, had left the streets free for lovers who desired to sing their woes or their delights beneath the balconies of their mistresses; already had the tinkling of guitars aroused the care of fathers, or alarmed the jealousy of husbands; in short, it was near midnight, when Don Cleophas Leandro Perez Zambullo, a student of Alcala, suddenly emerged, by the skylight, from a house into which the incautious son of the Cytherean goddess had induced him to enter. He sought to preserve his life and his honor by endeavoring to escape from three or four hired assassins, who followed him closely, for the purpose of either killing him or compelling him to wed a lady with whom they had just surprised him.

Against such fearful odds he had for some time valiantly defended himself and had only flown, at last, on losing his sword in the combat. The bravos followed him for some time over the roofs of the neighboring houses, but, favored by the darkness, he evaded their pursuit; and, perceiving at some distance a light, which Love or Fortune had placed there to guide him through this perilous adventure, he hastened toward it with all his remaining strength. After having more than once endangered his neck, he at length reached a garret, whence the welcome rays proceeded, and without ceremony entered by the window, as much transported with joy as the pilot who safely steers his vessel into port when menaced with the horrors of shipwreck.

He looked cautiously around him; and, somewhat surprised to find nobody in the apartment, which was rather a singular domicile, he began to scrutinize it with much attention. A brass lamp was hanging from the ceiling; books and papers were heaped in confusion on the table; a globe and mariner's compass occupied one side of the room, and on the other were ranged phials and quadrants; all which made him conclude that he had found his way into the haunt of some astrologer, who, if he did not live there, was in the habit of resorting to this abode to make his observations.

He was reflecting on the dangers he had by good fortune escaped, and was considering whether he should remain where he was until the morning, or what other course he should pursue, when he heard a deep sigh very near him. He at first imagined it was a mere phantasy of his agitated mind, an illusion of the night; so, without troubling himself about the matter, he was in a moment again busied with his reflections.

But having distinctly heard a second sigh, he no longer doubted its reality; and, although he saw no one in the room, he nevertheless called out, Who the devil is sighing here? It is I, Signor Student, immediately answered a voice, in which there was something rather extraordinary; I have been for the last six months enclosed in one of these phials. In this house lodges a learned astrologer, who is also a magician: he it is who, by the power of his art, keeps me confined in this narrow prison. You are then a spirit? said Don Cleophas, somewhat perplexed by this new adventure. I am a demon, replied the voice; and you have come in the very nick of time to free me from slavery. I languish in idleness; for of all the devils in Hell, I am the most active and indefatigable.

These words somewhat alarmed Signor Zambullo; but, as he was naturally brave, he quickly recovered himself, and said in a resolute tone: Signor Diabolus, tell me, I pray you, what rank you may hold among your brethren. Are you an aristocrat, or a burgess? I am, replied the voice, a devil of importance, nay, the one of highest repute in this, as in the other world. Perchance, said Don Cleophas, you are the renowned Lucifer? Bah, replied the spirit; why, he is the mountebank's devil. Are you Uriel then? asked the Student. For shame! hastily interrupted the voice. No, he is the patron of tradesmen; of tailors, butchers, bakers, and other cheats of the middle classes. Well, perhaps you are Beelzebub? said Leandro. Are you joking? replied the spirit. He is the demon of duennas and footmen. That astonishes me, said Zambullo; I thought Beelzebub one of the greatest persons at your court. He is one of the meanest of its subjects, answered the Demon; I see you have no very clear notions of our Hell.

There is no doubt then, said Don Cleophas, that you are either Leviathan, Belphegor, or Ashtaroth. Ah! those three now, replied the voice, are devils of the first order, veritable spirits of diplomacy. They animate the councils of princes, create factions, excite insurrections, and light the torches of war. They are not such peddling devils as the others you have named. By the bye! tell me, interrupted the Scholar, what post is assigned to Flagel? He is the soul of special pleading, and the spirit of the bar. He composes the rules of court, invented the law of libel, and that for the imprisonment of insolvent debtors; in short, he inspires pleaders, possesses barristers, and besets even the judges.

For myself, I have other occupations: I make absurd matches; I marry graybeards with minors, masters with servants, girls with small fortunes with tender lovers who have none. It is I who introduced into this world luxury, debauchery, games of chance, and chemistry. I am the author of the first cookery book, the inventor of festivals, of dancing, music, plays, and of the newest fashions; in a word, I am ASMODEUS, surnamed the Devil on Two Sticks.

What do I hear, cried Don Cleophas; are you the famed Asmodeus, of whom such honorable mention is made by Agrippa and in the Clavicula Salamonis? Verily, you have not told me all your amusements; you have forgotten the best of all. I am well aware that you sometimes divert yourself by assisting unhappy lovers: by this token, last year only, a young friend of mine obtained, by your favor, the good graces of the wife of a doctor in our university, at Alcala. That is true, said the spirit; I reserved that for my last good quality. I am the Demon of voluptuousness, or, to express it more delicately, Cupid, the god of love; that being the name for which I am indebted to the poets, who, I must confess, have painted me in very flattering colors. They say I have golden wings, a fillet bound over my eyes; that I carry a bow in my hand, a quiver full of arrows on my shoulders, and have withal inexpressible beauty. Of this, however, you may soon judge for yourself, if you will but restore me to liberty.

Signor Asmodeus, replied Leandro Perez, it is, as you know, long since I have been devoted to you: the perils I have just escaped will prove to you how entirely. I am rejoiced to have an opportunity of serving you; but the vessel in which you are confined is undoubtedly enchanted, and I should vainly strive to open, or to break it: so I do not see clearly in what manner I can deliver you from your bondage.

I am not much used to these sorts of enchantments; and, between our-selves, if, cunning devil as you are, you know not how to gain your freedom, what probability is there that a poor mortal like myself can effect it? Mankind has this power, answered the Demon. The phial which encloses me is but a mere glass bottle, easy to break. You have only to throw it on the ground, and I shall appear before you in human form. In that case, said the Student, the matter is easier of accomplishment than I imagined. But tell me in which of the phials you are; I see a great number of them, and all so like one another, that there may be a devil in each, for aught I know. It is the fourth from the window, replied the spirit. There is the impress of a magical seal on its mouth; but the bottle will break, nevertheless. Enough, said Don Cleophas; I am ready to do your bidding. There is, however, one little difficulty which deters me: when I shall have rendered you the service you require, how know I that I shall not have to pay the magician, in my precious person, for the mischief I have done? No harm shall befall you, replied the Demon: on the contrary, I promise to content you with the fruits of my gratitude. I will teach you all you can desire to know; I will discover to you the shifting scenes of this world's great stage; I will exhibit to you the follies and the vices of mankind; in short, I will be your tutelary demon; and, more wise than the Genius of Socrates, I undertake to render you a greater sage than that un-fortunate philosopher. In a word, I am yours, with all my good and bad qualities; and they shall be to you equally useful.

Fine promises, doubtless, replied the Student; but if report speak truly, you devils are accused of not being religiously scrupulous in the performance of your undertakings. Report is not always a liar, said Asmodeus, and this is an instance to the contrary. The greater part of my brethren think no more of breaking their word than a minister of state; but for myself, not to mention the service you are about to render me, and which I can never sufficiently repay, I am a slave to my engagements; and I swear by all a devil holds sacred that I will not deceive you. Rely on my word, and the assurances I offer: and what must be peculiarly pleasing to you, I engage, this night, to avenge your wrongs on Donna Thomasa, the perfidious woman who had con-cealed within her house the four scoundrels who surprised you, that she might compel you to espouse her and patch up her damaged repu-tation.

The young Zambullo was especially delighted with this last promise. To hasten its accomplishment, he seized the phial and, without further thought on the event, he dashed it on the floor. It broke into a thou-sand pieces, inundating the apartment with a blackish liquor: this, evaporating by degrees, was converted into a thick vapor, which, suddenly dissipating, revealed to the astonished sight of the Student the figure of a man in a cloak, about two feet six inches high, and supported by two crutches. This little monster had the legs of a goat, a long visage, pointed chin, a dark sallow complexion, and a very flat nose; his eyes, to all appearance very small, resembled two burning coals; his enormous mouth was surmounted by a pair of red mustachios, and ornamented with two lips of unequaled ugliness.

The head of this graceful Cupid was enveloped in a sort of turban of red cape, relieved by a plume of cock's and peacock's feathers. Round his neck was a collar of yellow cloth, upon which were embroidered divers patterns of necklaces and earrings. He wore a short white satin gown, or tunic, encircled about the middle by a large band of parchment of the same color, covered with talismanic characters. On the gown, also, were painted various bodices, beautifully adapted for the display of the fair wearers' necks; scarves of different patterns, worked or colored aprons, and headdresses of the newest fashion—all so extravagant that it was impossible to admire one more than another.

But all this was nothing as compared with his cloak, the foundation of which was also white satin. Its exterior presented an infinity of figures delicately tinted in Indian ink, and yet with so much freedom and expression that you would have wondered who the devil could have painted it. On one side appeared a Spanish lady covered with her mantilla and leering at a stranger on the promenade; and on the other a Parisian grisette, who before her mirror was studying new airs to victimize a young *abbé,* at that moment opening the door. Here, the gay Italian was singing to the guitar beneath the balcony of his mistress; and there, the sottish German, with vest unbuttoned, stupefied with wine, and more begrimed with snuff than a French *petit-maître,* was sitting, surrounded by his companions, at a table covered with the filthy remnants of their debauch. In one place could be perceived a Turkish bashaw coming from the bath, attended by all the houris of his seraglio, each watchful for the handkerchief; and in another an English gentleman, who was gallantly presenting to his ladylove a pipe and a glass of porter.

Besides these there were gamesters, marvelously well portrayed; some, elated with joy, filling their hats with pieces of gold and silver; and others, who had lost all but their honor, and willing to stake on that, now turning their sacrilegious eyes to Heaven, and now gnawing the very cards in despair. In short, there were as many curious things to be seen on this cloak as on the admirable shield which Vulcan forged for Achilles, at the prayer of his mother Thetis; with this difference, however—the subjects on the buckler of the Grecian hero had no relation to his own exploits, while those on the mantle of Asmodeus were lively images of all that is done in this world at his suggestion.

☆   ☆   ☆

Upon perceiving that his appearance had not prepossessed the student very greatly in his favor, the Demon said to him, smiling: Well, Signor Don Cleophas Leandro Perez Zambullo, you behold the charming god of love, that sovereign master of the human heart. What think you of my air and beauty? Confess that the poets are excellent painters. Frankly, replied Don Cleophas, I must say they have a little flattered you. I fancy, it was not in this form that you won the love of Psyche. Certainly not, replied the Devil: I borrowed the graces of a little French marquis, to make her dote upon me. Vice must be hidden under a pleasing veil, or it wins not even woman. I take what shape best pleases me; and I could have discovered myself to you under the form of the Apollo Belvi, but that as I have nothing to disguise from you, I preferred you should see me under a figure more agreeable to the opinion which the world generally entertains of me. and my performances. I am not surprised, said Leandro, to find you rather ugly—excuse the phrase, I pray you; the transactions we are about to have with each other demand a little frankness: your features indeed almost exactly realize the idea I had formed of you. But tell me, how happens it that you are on crutches?

Why, replied the Demon, many years ago I had an unfortunate difference with Pillardoc, the spirit of gain, and the patron of pawn-brokers. The subject of our dispute was a stripling who came to Paris to seek his fortune. As he was capital game, a youth of promising talents, we contested the prize with a noble ardor. We fought in the regions of mid-air; and Pillardoc, who excelled me in strength, cast me on the earth after the mode in which Jupiter is related by the poets to have tumbled Vulcan. The striking resemblance of our mishaps gained me, from my witty comrades, the sobriquet of the Limping Devil, or the Devil on Two Sticks, which has stuck to me from that time to this. Nevertheless, limping as I am, I am tolerably quick in my movements; and you shall witness for my agility.

But, added he, a truce to idle talk; let us get out of this confounded garret. My friend, the magician, will be here shortly; as he is hard at work on rendering a handsome damsel, who visits him nightly, immortal. If he should surprise us, I shall be snug in a bottle in no time; and it may go hard but he finds one to fit you also. So let us away! But first to throw the pieces, of that which was once my prison, out of the window; for such "dead men" as these *do* tell tales.

What if your friend does find out that you are "missing"? What! hastily replied the Demon. I see you have never studied the Treatise on Compulsions. Were I hidden at the extremity of the earth, or in the region where dwells the fiery salamander; though I sought the murkiest cavern of the gnomes, or plunged in the most unfathomable depths of the ocean, I should vainly strive to evade the terrors of his wrath. Hell itself would tremble at the potency of his spells. In vain should I struggle: despite myself should I be dragged before my master, to feel the weight of his dreaded chains.

That being the case, said the Student, I fear that our intimacy will not be of long duration: this redoubtable necromancer will doubtless soon discover your flight. That is more than I know, replied the spirit; there is no foreseeing what may happen. What! cried Leandro Perez. A demon, and ignorant of the future! Exactly so, answered the Devil; and they are only our dupes who think otherwise. However, there are enough of them to find good employment for diviners and fortunetellers, especially among your women of quality; for those are always most eager about the future who have best reason to be contented with the present, which and the past are all we know or care for. I am ignorant, therefore, whether my master will soon discover my absence; but let us hope he will not: there are plenty of phials similar to the one in which I was enclosed, and he may never miss that. Besides, in his laboratory, I am something like a lawbook in the library of a financier. He never thinks of me; or if he does he would think he did me too great an honor if he condescended to notice me. He is the most haughty enchanter of my acquaintance: long as he has deprived me of my liberty, we have never exchanged a syllable.

That is extraordinary! said Don Cleophas. What have you done to deserve so much hatred or scorn? I crossed him in one of his projects, replied Asmodeus. There was a chair vacant in a certain Academy, which he had designed for a friend of his, a professor of necromancy; but which I had destined for a particular friend of my own. The magician set to work with one of the most potent talismans of the Cabala; but I knew better than that: I had placed my man in the service of the prime minister, whose word is worth a dozen talismans, with the Academicians, any day.

While the Demon was thus conversing, he was busily engaged in collecting every fragment of the broken phial; which having thrown out of the window, Signor Zambullo, said he, let us begone! Hold fast by the end of my mantle, and fear nothing. However perilous this appeared to Leandro Perez, he preferred the possible danger to the uncertainty of the magician's resentment; and, accordingly, he fastened himself as well as he could to the Demon, who in an instant whisked him out of the apartment.

☆   ☆   ☆

Cleophas found that Asmodeus had not vainly boasted of his agility. They darted through the air like an arrow from the bow, and were soon perched on the tower of San Salvador. Well, Signor Leandro, said the Demon as they alighted; what think you now of the justice of those who, as they slowly rumble in some antiquated vehicle, talk of a devilish bad carriage? I must, thereafter, think them most unreasonable, politely replied Zambullo. I dare affirm that his majesty of Castile has never traveled so easily; and then for speed, at your rate, one might travel round the world nor care to stretch a leg.

You are really too polite, replied the Devil; but, can you guess now why I have brought you here? I intend to show you all that is passing in Madrid; and as this part of the town is as good to begin with as any, you will allow that I could not have chosen a more appropriate situation. I am about, by my supernatural powers, to take away the roofs from the houses of this great city; and notwithstanding the darkness of the night, to reveal to your eyes whatever is doing within them. As he spake, he extended his right arm, the roofs disappeared, and the Student's astonished sight penetrated the interior of the surrounding dwellings as plainly as if the noonday sun shone over them. It was, says Luis Velez de Guevara, like looking into a pasty from which a set of greedy monks had just removed the crust.

The spectacle was, as you may suppose, sufficiently wonderful to rivet all the Student's attention. He looked amazedly around him, and on all sides were objects which most intensely excited his curiosity. At length the Devil said to him: Signor Don Cleophas, this confusion of objects, which you regard with an evident pleasure, is certainly very agreeable to look upon; but I must render useful to you what would be otherwise but a frivolous amusement. To unlock for you the secret chambers of the human heart, I will explain in what all these persons that you see are engaged. All shall be open to you; I will discover the hidden motives of their deeds, and reveal to you their unbidden thoughts.

Where shall we begin? See! do you observe this house to my right? Observe that old man, who is counting gold and silver into heaps. He is a miserly citizen. His carriage, which he bought for next to nothing at the sale of an alcalde of the Cortes, and which to save expense still sports the arms of its late owner, is drawn by a pair of worthless mules, which he feeds according to the law of the Twelve Tables; that is to say, he gives each, daily, one pound of barley: he treats them as the Romans treated their slaves—wisely, but not too well. It is now two years since he returned from the Indies, bringing with him innumerable bars of gold, which he has since converted into coin. Look at the old fool! with what satisfaction he gloats over his riches. And now, see what is passing in an adjoining chamber of the same house. Do you observe two young men with an old woman? Yes, replied Cleophas, they are probably his children. No, no! said the Devil. They are his nephews, and, what is better in their opinion, his heirs. In their anxiety for his welfare, they have invited a sorceress to ascertain when death will take from them their dear uncle, and leave to them the division of his spoil. In the next house there are a pair of pictures worth remarking. One is an antiquated coquette who is retiring to rest, after depositing on her toilet, her hair, her eyebrows and her teeth; the other is a gallant sexagenarian, who has just returned from a love campaign. He has already closed one eye, in its case, and placed his whiskers and peruke on the dressing table. His valet is now easing him of an arm and one leg, to put him to bed with the rest.

If I may trust my eyes, cried Zambullo, I see in the next room a tall young damsel, quite a model for an artist. What a lovely form and air! I see, said the Devil. Well! that young beauty is an elder sister of the gallant I have just described, and is a worthy pendant to the coquette who is under the same roof. Her figure, that you so much admire, is really good; but then she is indebted for it to an ingenious mechanist, whom I patronize. Her bust and hips are formed after my own patent; and it is only last Sunday that she generously dropped her bustle at the door of this very church, on the occasion of a charity sermon. Nevertheless, as she affects the juvenile, she has two cavaliers who ardently dispute her favor—nay, they have even come to blows on the occasion. Madmen! Two dogs fighting for a bone.

Prithee, laugh with me at an amateur concert which is performing in a neighboring mansion; an aftersupper offering to Apollo. They are singing cantatas. An old counselor has composed the air; and the words are by an alguazil, who does the amiable after that fashion among his friends—an ass who writes verses for his own pleasure, and for the punishment of others. A harpsichord and clarionet form the accompaniment; a lanky chorister, who squeaks marvelously, takes the treble, and a young girl with a hoarse voice the bass. What a delightful party! cried Don Cleophas. Had they tried expressly to get up a musical extravaganza, they could not have succeeded better.

Cast your eyes on that superb mansion, continued the Demon; and you will perceive a nobleman lying in a splendid apartment. He has, near his couch, a casket filled with billets-doux, in which he is luxu- riating, that the sweet nothings they contain may lull his senses gently to repose. They ought to be dear to him, for they are from a *signora* he adores, and who so well appreciates the value of her favors that she will soon reduce him to the necessity of soliciting the exile of a viceroyalty, for his own support. Let us leave them to watch the stir they are making in the next house to the left. Can you distinguish a lady in a bed with red damask furniture? Her name is Donna Fabula. She is of high rank, and is about to present an heir to her spouse, the aged Don Torribio, whom you see by her side, endeavoring to soothe the pangs of his lady until the arrival of the midwife. Is it not delightful to witness so much tenderness? The cries of his dear better half pierce him to the soul: he is overwhelmed with grief; he suffers as much as his wife. With what care—with what earnestness does he bend over her! Really, said Leandro, the man does appear deeply affected; but I perceive, in the room above, a youngster, apparently a domestic, who sleeps soundly enough; he troubles himself not for the event. And yet it ought to interest him, replied Asmodeus; for the sleeper is the first cause of his mistress's sufferings.

But see—a little beyond, continued the Demon: in that low room, you may observe an old wretch who is anointing himself with lard. He is about to join an assembly of wizards, which takes place tonight be- tween San Sebastian and Fontarabia. I would carry you thither in a moment, as it would amuse you; but that I fear I might be recognized by the devil who personates the goat.

That devil and you then, said the Scholar, are not good friends? No indeed! You are right, replied Asmodeus; he is that same Pillar- doc of whom I told you. The scoundrel would betray me, and soon inform the magician of my flight. You have perhaps had some other squabble with this gentleman? Precisely so, said the Demon: some ten years ago we had a second difference about a young Parisian who was thinking of commencing life. He wanted to make him a banker's clerk; and I, a lady-killer. Our comrades settled the dispute by making him a wretched monk. This done, they reconciled us: we embraced; and from that time have been mortal foes.

But, have done with this *belle assemblée*, said Don Cleophas; I am not at all curious to witness it: let us continue our scrutiny into what is before us. What is the meaning of those sparks of fire which issue from yonder cellar? They proceed from one of the most absurd occu- pations of mankind, replied the Devil. The grave personage whom

you behold near the furnace is an alchemist; and the flames are gradually consuming his rich patrimony, never to yield him what he seeks
in return. Between ourselves, the philosopher's stone is a chimera that
I myself invented to amuse the wit of man, who ever seeks to pass
those bounds which the laws of nature have prescribed for his intelligence. The alchemist's neighbor is an honest apothecary, who you
perceive is still at his labors, with his aged wife and assistant. You
would never guess what they are about. The apothecary is com-
pounding a progenerative pill for an old advocate who is to be married tomorrow; the assistant is mixing a laxative potion; and the old
lady is pounding astringent drugs in a mortar.

I perceive, in the house facing the apothecary's, said Zambullo, a
man who has just jumped out of bed, and is hastily dressing. Pshaw!
replied the spirit, he need not hurry himself. He is a physician; and
has been sent for by a prelate who since he has retired to rest—about
an hour—has absolutely coughed two or three times.

But look a little further, in a garret on the right, and try if you cannot distinguish a man half dressed, who is walking up and down the
room, dimly lighted by a single lamp. I see, said the Student; and so
clearly that I would undertake to furnish you with an inventory of his
chattels—to wit, a truckle bed, a three-legged stool, and a deal table;
the walls seem to be daubed all over with black paint. That exalted
personage, said Asmodeus, is a poet; and what appears to you black
paint are tragic verses with which he has ornamented his apartment,
being obliged, for want of paper, to commit his effusions to the wall.
By his agitation and frenzied air, I conclude he is now busily engaged
on some work of importance, said Don Cleophas. You are not far out,
replied the Devil: he only yesterday completed the last act of an
interesting tragedy, entitled *The Universal Deluge*. He cannot be reproached with having violated the unity of place, at all events, as the
entire action is limited to Noah's ark.

I can assure you it is a first-rate drama: all the animals talk as
learnedly as professors. It of course must have been a dedication,
upon which he has been laboring for the last six hours; and he is, at
this moment, turning the last period. It will be indeed a masterpiece
of adulatory composition: every social and political virtue; every
grace that can adorn; all that tends to render man illustrious, either
by his own deeds, or those of his ancestors, are attributed to its object—never was praise more lavishly bestowed, never was incense
burnt more liberally. For whom, then, of all the world, is so magnificent an apotheosis intended? Why, replied the Demon, the poet himself has not yet determined that; he has put in everything but the name.

However, he hopes to find some vain noble who may be more liberal than those to whom he has dedicated his former productions; although the purchasers of imaginary virtues are becoming every day more rare. It is not my fault that it is so; for it is a fault corrected in the wealthy patrons of literature, and a great benefit rendered to the public, who were certain to be deluged by trash from the Swiss of the press, so long as books were written merely for the produce of their dedications.

Apropos of this subject, added the Demon, I will relate to you a curious anecdote. It is not long since an illustrious lady accepted the honor of a dedication from a celebrated novelist, who, by the bye, writes so much in praise of other women that he thinks himself at liberty to abuse the one peculiarly his own. The lady in question was anxious to see the address before it was printed; and not finding herself described to her taste, she wisely undertook the task, and gave herself all those inconvenient virtues which the world so much admires. She then sent it to the author, who of course had weighty reasons for adopting it.

Hollo! cried Leandro. Surely those are robbers who are entering that house by the balcony. Precisely so, said Asmodeus; they are brigands, and the house is a banker's. Watch them! You will be amused. See! They have opened the safe and are ferreting everywhere; but the banker has been before them. He set out yesterday for Holland and has taken with him the contents of his coffers for fear of accidents. They may make a merit of their visit by informing his unfortunate depositors of their loss.

There is another thief, said Zambullo, mounting by a silken ladder into a neighboring dwelling. You are mistaken there, replied the Devil; at all events it is not gold he seeks. He is a marquis, who would rob a young maiden of the name, of which, however, she is not unwilling to part. Never was "stand and deliver" more graciously received: he of course has sworn he will marry her, and she of course believes him; for a marquis's "promises" have unlimited credit upon Love's Exchange.

I am curious to learn, interrupted the Student, what that man in a nightcap and dressing gown is about. He is writing very studiously, and near him is a little black figure, who occasionally guides his hand. He is a registrar of the civil courts, replied the Demon; and to oblige a guardian, is, for a consideration, altering a decree made in favor of the ward: the gentleman in black, who seems enjoying the sport, is Griffael, the registrars' devil. Griffael, then, said Don Cleophas, is a sort of deputy to Flagel; for, as he is the spirit of the bar, the registrars are doubtless included in his department. Not so, replied As-modeus; the registrars have been thought deserving of their peculiar demon, and I assure you they find him quite enough to do.

Near the registrar's house, you will perceive a young lady on the first floor. She is a widow; and the man, whom you see in the same room, is her uncle, who lodges in an apartment over hers. Admire the bashfulness of the dame! She is ashamed to put on her chemise before her aged relative, so modestly seeks the assistance of her lover, who is hidden in her dressing room.

In the same house with the registrar lives a stout graduate, who has been lame from his birth, but who has not his equal in the world for pleasantry. Volumnius, so highly spoken of by Cicero for his delicate yet pungent wit, was a fool to him. He is known through-out Madrid as "the bachelor Donoso," or "the facetious graduate"; and his company is sought by old and young, at the court and in the town: in short, wherever there is, or should be, conviviality, he is so much the rage that he has discharged his cook, as he never dines at home; to which he seldom returns until long after midnight. He is at present with the marquis of Alcazinas, who is indebted for this visit to chance only. How, to chance? interrupted Leandro. Why, replied the Demon, this morning, about noon, the graduate's door was be-sieged by at least half-a-dozen carriages, each sent for the especial honor of securing his society. The bachelor received the assembled pages in his apartment, and, displaying a pack of cards, thus ad-dressed them: My friends, as it is impossible for me to dine in six places at one time, and as it would not appear polite to show an undue preference, these cards shall decide the matter. Draw! I will dine with the king of clubs.

What object, said Don Cleophas, has yonder cavalier, who is sitting at a door on the other side of the street? Is he waiting for some pretty waiting-woman to usher him to his lady's chamber? No, no, answered Asmodeus; he is a young Castilian, whose modesty exceeds his love; so, after the fashion of the gallants of antiquity, he has come to pass the night at his mistress's portal. Listen to the twang of that wretched guitar, with which he accompanies his tender strains! On the second floor you may behold his inamorata: she is weeping as she hears him —but it is for the absence of his rival.

You observe that new building, which is divided into two wings. One is occupied by the proprietor, the old gentleman whom you see, now pacing the apartment, now throwing himself into an easy chair. Zambullo: who is he? If one may judge by the splendor which is dis-played in his mansion, he is a grandee of the first order. Nevertheless, said Asmodeus, he is but an ancient clerk of the treasury, who has grown old in such lucrative employment as to enable him to amass four millions of reals. As he has some compunctions of conscience for the means by which all this wealth has been acquired, and as he expects shortly to be called upon to render his account in another world, where bribery is impracticable, he is about to compound for his sins in this, by building a monastery; which done, he flatters himself that peace will revisit his heart. He has already obtained the necessary permission; but, as he has resolved that the establishment shall consist of monks who are extremely chaste, sober, and of the most Christian humility, he is much embarrassed in the selection. He need not build a very extensive convent.

The other wing is inhabited by a fair lady, who has just retired to rest after the luxury of a milk bath. This voluptuary is widow of a knight of the order of St. James, who left her at his death her title only; but fortunately her charms have secured for her valuable friends in the persons of two members of the council of Castile, who generously divide her favors and the expenses of her household.

Hark! cried the Student. Surely I hear the cries of distress. What dreadful misfortune has occurred? A very common one, said the Demon: two young cavaliers have been gambling in a hell (the name is a scandal on the infernal regions), which you perceive so brilliantly illuminated. They quarreled upon an interesting point of the game, and naturally drew their swords to settle it: unluckily they were equally skillful with their weapons, and are both mortally wounded. The elder is married, which is unfortunate; and the younger an only son. The wife and father have just come in time to receive their last sighs; and it is their lamentations that you hear. Unhappy boy, cries the fond parent over the still-breathing body of his son, how often have I conjured thee to renounce this dreadful vice!—how often have I warned thee it would one day cost thee thy life! Heaven is my witness that the fault is none of mine! Men, added the Demon, are always selfish, even in their griefs. Meanwhile the wife is in despair. Although her husband has dissipated the fortune she brought him on their marriage; although he has sold, to maintain his shameful excesses, her jewels, and even her clothes, not a word of reproach escapes her lips. She is inconsolable for her loss. Her grief is vented in frantic exclamations, mixed with curses on the cards, and the devil who invented them; on the place in which her husband fell, and on the people who surround her, and to whom she fondly attributes his ruin.

How much to be lamented, interrupted the Student, is the love of gaming which possesses so large a portion of mankind; in what an awful state of excitement does it plunge its victims. Heaven be praised! I am not included in their legion. You are in high feather, replied the Demon, in another, whose exploits are not much more ennobling, and scarcely less dangerous. Is the conquest of a courtesan a glory worth achievement? Is the possession of charms common to a whole city worth the peril of a life? Man is an amusing animal! The vision of a mole would enable him to discover the vices of his fellows, while that of the vulture could scarce detect a folly of his own. But let us turn to another affecting spectacle. You can discern, in the house just beyond the one we have been contemplating, a fat old man extended on a bed: he is a canon, who is now in a fit of apoplexy. The two persons, whom you see in his room, are said to be his nephew and niece: they are too much affected by his situation to be able to assist him, so are securing his valuable effects. By the time this is accomplished, he will be dead; and they will be sufficiently recovered, and at leisure, to weep over his remains.

Close by, you may perceive the funeral of two brothers, who, seized with the same disorder, took equally successful but different means of ensuring its fatality. One of them had the most utter confidence in his apothecary; the other eschewed the aid of medicine: the first died because he took all the trash his doctor sent him; the last because he would take nothing. Well! that is very perplexing, said Leandro; what is a poor sick devil to do? Why, replied Asmodeus, that is more than the one who has the honor of addressing you can determine. I know, for certain, that there are remedies for most ills; but I am not so sure that there are good physicians to administer them when necessary.

And now I have something more amusing to unriddle. Do you not hear a frightful din in the next street? A widow of sixty was married this morning to an Adonis of seventeen; and all the merry fellows of that part of town have assembled to celebrate the wedding by a concert of pots and pans, marrow bones and cleavers. You told me, said the Student, that these matches were under your control: at all events you had no hand in this. No, truly, answered the Demon, not I. Had I been free, I should not have meddled with them. The widow had her scruples, and has married for no better reason than that she may enjoy, without remorse, the pleasures she so dearly loves. These are not the unions I care to form; I prefer troubling people's consciences to setting them at rest.

Notwithstanding this charming serenade, said Zambullo, it seems to me that it is not the only concert performing in the neighborhood. No, said the Cripple; in a tavern in the same street, a lusty Flemish

captain, a chorister of the French opera, and an officer of the German
guard are singing a trio. They have been drinking since eight in the
morning; and each deems it a duty to his country to see the others
under the table.

Look for a moment on the house which stands by itself, nearly opposite to that of the apoplectic canon: you will see three very pretty
but very notorious courtesans enjoying themselves with as many young
courtiers. They are, indeed, lovely! exclaimed Don Cleophas. I am
not surprised that they should be notorious: happy are the lovers who
possess them! They seem, however, very partial to their present companions: I envy them their good fortune. Why, you are very green!
replied the Demon: their faces are not disguised with greater skill
than are their hearts. However prodigal of their caresses, they have
not the slightest tenderness for their foolish swains; their affection is
bounded to the purses of their lovers. One of them has just secured the
promise of a liberal establishment; and the others are prepared with
settlements which they are in expectation of securing ere they part. It
is the same with them all. Men vainly ruin themselves for the sex; gold
buys not love. The well-paid mistress soon treats her lover as a husband: that is a rule which I found necessary to establish in my code of
intrigue. But we will leave these fools to taste the pleasures they so
dearly purchase, while their valets, who are waiting in the street,
console themselves with the pleasing anticipation of enjoying them
gratis.

The Demon now directed the Student's attention to another part
of the city. You see, he continued, that house which is directly under
us; it contains something curious enough—a man loaded with debt
and sleeping profoundly. Of course then, said Leandro, he is a person
of distinction? Precisely so, answered Asmodeus: he is a marquis, possessed of a hundred thousand ducats per annum, but whose expenses,
nevertheless, exceed his income. His table and his mistresses require
that he should support them with credit, but that causes him no anxiety; on the contrary, when he opens an account with a tradesman, he
thinks that the latter is indebted to him. It is you, said he the other
day to a draper, it is you that I shall henceforth trust with the execution of my orders; it is a preference which you owe to my esteem.

While the marquis enjoys so tranquilly the sweet repose of which
he deprives his creditors, look at a man who—— Stay, Signor Asmodeus, interrupted Don Cleophas hastily; I perceive a carriage in
the street, and cannot let it pass without asking what it contains.

Hush! said the Cripple, lowering his voice, as though he feared he should be heard—learn that that vehicle conceals one of the most dignified personages in this kingdom, a president, who is going to amuse himself with an elderly lady of Asturia, who is devoted to his pleasures. That he may not be known, he has taken the precaution of imitating Caligula, who on a similar occasion disguised himself in a wig.

But—to return to the picture I was about to present to your sight when you interrupted me—observe, in the very highest part of the mansion, where sleeps the marquis, a man who is writing in a chamber filled with books and manuscripts. He is probably, said Zambullo, the steward, laboring to devise some means for discharging his master's obligations. Excellent! exclaimed the Devil; that, indeed, forms a great part of the amusement of such gentry in the service of noblemen! They seek rather to profit from derangement of their master's affairs than to put them in order. He is not, then, the steward whom you see; he is an author: the marquis keeps him in his house, to obtain the reputation of a patron of literature. This author, replied Don Cleophas, is apparently a man of eminence. Judge for yourself! replied the Demon. He is surrounded by a thousand volumes, and is composing one, on Natural History, in which there will not be a line of his own. He pillages these books and manuscripts without mercy; and, although he does nothing but arrange and connect his larcenies, he has more vanity than the most original writer upon earth.

You are not aware, continued the spirit, who lives three doors from this mansion: it is La Chichona, the very lady who acted so honorable a part in the story of the Count de Belflor. Ah! said Leandro. I am delighted to behold her. The dear creature, so considerate for youth, is doubtless one of the two old ladies whom I perceive in that room. One of them is leaning with both her elbows on the table, looking attentively at the other, who is counting out some money. Which of them is La Chichona? Not the one who is counting, said the Demon; her name is La Pebrada, and she is a distinguished member of the same profession: they are, indeed, partners; and are at this moment dividing the profits of an adventure which, by their assistance, has terminated favorably.

La Pebrada is the more successful of the two: she has among her clients several rich widows, who subscribe to her daily register. What do you mean by her register? interrupted the Student. Why, replied Asmodeus, it contains the names of all handsome foreigners, and particularly Frenchmen, who come to Madrid. The instant La Pebrada hears of an arrival, away she posts to the hotel of the newcomer, to learn every particular as to his country, birth, parentage, and education—his age, form, and appearance, all which are duly reported to her subscribers; and if, on reflection, the heart of any of her widows is inclined to an acquaintance, she adroitly manages a speedy interview with the stranger.

That is extremely convenient, replied Zambullo, smiling, and in some sort very proper; for, in truth, without these kind ladies and their agents, the youthful foreigner, who comes without introductions to Madrid, would lose an immense deal of time in gaining them. But tell me, are there in other countries widows as generous and women as intriguing? Capital! exclaimed the Devil—if there are? Why! can you doubt it? I should be unworthy of my demonship if I neglected to provide all large towns with them in plenty.

Cast your eyes upon Chichona's neighbor—yon printer, who is working at his press, alone. He has dismissed the devils in his employ these three hours; and he is now engaged for the night, on a work which he is printing privately. Ah! what may it be? said Leandro. It treats of insults, replied the Demon; and endeavors to prove that Religion is preferable to Honor; and that it is better to pardon than to avenge an affront. Oh! the scoundrel! exclaimed the Student. Well may he print in secret his infamous book. Its author had better not acknowledge his production: I would be one of the first to answer it with a horsewhip. What! can religion forbid the preservation of one's honor?

Let us not discuss that point, interrupted Asmodeus with a malicious smile. It appears that you have made the most of the lectures on morality you listened to at Alcala; and I give you joy of the result. You may say what you please, interrupted Cleophas in his turn, and so may the writer of this wretched absurdity: but though his reasonings were clear as the noonday sun, I should despise him and them. I am a Spaniard, and nothing is to me so delightful as revenge; and, by the bye, since you have pledged yourself to satisfy me for the perfidy of my mistress, I call on you at once to keep your promise.

I yield with pleasure, replied the Demon, to the wrath which agitates your breast. Oh! how I love those noble spirits who follow without scruple the dictates of their passions! I will obey your will at once; and indeed, the hour to avenge your wrongs is come: but first I wish to shew you something which will amuse you vastly. Look beyond the printing office, and observe with attention what is passing in an apartment, hung with drab cloth. I perceive, said Leandro, five or six women, who are with eagerness offering phials of something to a sort of valet, and they appear desperately agitated.

They are, replied Asmodeus, devotees, who have great reason to be agitated. There is in the next room a sick inquisitor. This venerable personage, who is about thirty-five years old, is attended by two of his dearest penitents, with untiring watchfulness. One is concocting his gruel, while the other at his pillow is employed in keeping his head warm, and is covering his stomach with a kind of blanket made of at least fifty lambskins. What on earth is the matter with him, then? asked Zambullo. He has a cold in his head, answered the Devil; and there is danger lest the disorder should extend to his lungs.

The ladies whom you see in his antechamber have hastened, on the alarm of his indisposition, with all sorts of remedies. One brings, to allay his apprehended cough, syrups of jujubes, mallows, coral, and coltsfoot; another, to preserve the said lungs of his reverence, syrups of long life, speedwell, amaranth, and the *elixir vitae;* this one, to fortify his brain and stomach, has brought balm, cinnamon, and treacle waters, besides *guttae vitae,* and the essences of nutmegs and ambergris; that offers anacardine and bezoardic confections; while a fifth carries tinctures of cloves, gillyflowers, sunflowers, and of coral and emeralds. All these zealous penitents are boasting to the valet of the virtues of the medicines they offer; and each by turns, drawing him aside, and slipping a ducat in his hand, whispers in his ear: Laurence, my dear Laurence, manage so, I beg of you, that what I bring for the dear man may have the preference.

By Jupiter! cried Don Cleophas, it must be allowed that inquisitors —even sick inquisitors—are happy mortals. I can answer for that, replied Asmodeus; I almost envy them their lot, myself, and like the son of Philip of Macedon, who once said that he would have been Diogenes, if he had not been Alexander, I can unhesitatingly say that, if I were not a devil, I would be an inquisitor.

But, Signor Student, continued he, let us go! Let us away, to punish the ingrate who so ill-requited your tenderness. Zambullo instantly seized the end of the Demon's cloak, and a second time was whirled with him through the air, until they alighted on the house of Donna Thomasa.

This frail damsel was seated at table, with the four gentlemen who, a few hours before, had so eagerly sought the acquaintance of Don Cleophas on the roof of her house. He trembled with rage, as he beheld them feasting on a brace of partridges and a rabbit, which, with some choice wine, he had sent to the traitress for his own supper; and, to add to his mortification, he perceived that joy reigned in the repast; and that it was evident, by the deportment of the lady, that the company of these scoundrels was much more agreeable to her than that of himself. Oh! the wretches! he cried, in a perfect fury, to see them enjoying themselves at my expense! Vastly pleasant, is it not?

Why, I must confess, replied the Demon, that you have witnessed spectacles more pleasing; but he who rejoices in the favors of such fair ones must expect to share them. This sort of thing has happened a thousand times, especially in France, among the abbés, the gentlemen of the long robe, and the financiers. If I had a sword, though, said Leandro, I would fall upon the villains, and spoil their sport for them. You would be hardly matched, replied the Demon—what were one among so many? Leave your revenge to me! I will manage it better than you could. I will soon set them together by the ears, in inspiring each of them with a fit of tenderness for your mistress; their swords will be out in no time, and you will be delighted with the uproar.

Asmodeus had no sooner spoken than he breathed forcibly, and from his mouth issued a violet-colored vapor which descended tortuously, like a fiery serpent, and spread itself round the table of Donna Thomasa. In an instant, one of her guests, more inflammable than his companions, rose from his seat, and, approaching the lady, embraced her amorously, when the others, in whom the spirit had begun to work, hastened together to snatch from him the dainty prize. Each claimed a preference: words ensued; a jealous rage possessed them; blows succeeded, and, as the Devil had foretold, they drew their weapons and commenced a furious combat. In the meanwhile Donna Thomasa exerted her lungs, and the neighborhood was speedily alarmed by her cries. They call for the police; the police arrive; they break open the door and find two of the hectors extended on the floor. They seize upon the others and take them with the Helen of the party to prison. In vain did she weep; in vain did she tear her locks, and exclaim in despair—the tears of unfortunate beauty had no more effect on the cavaliers who conducted her than they had on her former knight Zambullo, who almost died with laughter, in which the god of love most unnaturally joined him.

Well! said the Demon to the Student, are you content? No, no! replied Don Cleophas. To satisfy me in full, place me upon the prison, that I may have the pleasure of beholding in her dungeon the miserable who trifled with my love. I feel for her, now, a hatred which exceeds even the affection with which she formerly inspired me. Be it so! said the Devil. You shall ever find me a slave to your will, though it interfered with mine and my interests—provided always that it is safe to indulge you.

They flew through the air and were on the prison before the officers arrived with their captives. The two assassins were at once consigned to one of its lowest deeps, while Thomasa was led to a bed of straw, which she was to share with three or four other abandoned women, who had fallen into the hands of justice the same day, and with whom she was destined to be transported to the colonies, which a grateful mother country generally endows with this description of female inhabitants.

I am satisfied, said Zambullo; I have tasted a delicious revenge; my dear Thomasa will not pass the night quite so pleasantly as she had anticipated.

☆　　　☆　　　☆

Were you, this moment, at the Gate of the Sun, said the Devil, you would be horror-stricken at the spectacle which is now exhibiting. Through the negligence of a domestic, a mansion is on fire, which in its rage has already reduced to ashes the magnificent furniture it contains, and threatens to consume the whole building; but great as might be his loss, Don Pedro de Escolano, to whom the house belongs, would not regret it for a moment, could he but save his only daughter, Seraphina, who is likely to perish in the flames.

Don Cleophas expressing the greatest anxiety to see this fire, the Cripple transported him in an instant to the Gate of the Sun, and placed him in a house exactly opposite to that which was burning.

In the street beneath them nothing was to be heard but a confused noise, arising from cries of fire from one half of the crowd, and the more appropriate one of water from the other. As soon as Leandro was able to comprehend the scene, he saw that the grand staircase, which led to the principal apartments of Don Pedro's mansion, was all in flames, which also were issuing, with clouds of smoke, from every window in the house.

The fire is at its height, said the Demon: it has just reached the roof, and its thousand tongues are spitting in the air millions of brilliant sparks. It is a magnificent sight; so much so that the persons who have flocked from all parts around it, to assist in extinguishing the flames, are awed into helpless amazement. You may discern in the crowd of spectators an old man in a dressing gown: it is the Signor de Escolano. Do you not hear his cries and lamentations? He is addressing the men who surround him, and conjuring them to rescue his child. But in vain does he implore them—in vain does he offer all his wealth—none dares expose his life to save the ill-fated lady, who is only sixteen, and whose beauty is incomparable. The old man is in despair: he accuses them of cowardice; he tears his hair and beard;

he beats his breast; the excess of his grief has made him almost mad. Seraphina, poor girl, abandoned by her attendants, has just swooned with terror in her own apartment, where, in a few minutes, a dense smoke will stifle her. She is lost to him forever: no mortal can save her.

Ah! Signor Asmodeus, exclaimed Leandro Perez, prompted by feelings of generous compassion, if you love me, yield to the pity which desolates my heart: reject not my humble prayer when I entreat you to save this lovely girl from the horrid death which threatens her. I demand it, as the price of the service I rendered but now to you. Do not, this time, oppose yourself to my desires: I shall die with grief if you refuse me.

The Devil smiled on witnessing the profound emotion of the Student. The fire warms you, Signor Zambullo, said he. Verily! you would have made an exquisite knight-errant: you are courageous, compassionate for the sufferings of others, and particularly prompt in the service of sorrowing damsels. You would be just the man, now, to throw yourself in the midst of the furnace yonder, like an Amadis, to attempt the deliverance of the beauteous Seraphina, and to restore her safe and sound to her disconsolate father. Would to Heaven, replied Don Cleophas, that it were possible. I would undertake the task without hesitation. Pity that your death, resumed the Cripple, would be the sole reward of so noble an exploit! I have already told you that human courage can avail nothing on the occasion. Well! I suppose, to gratify you, I must meddle in the matter; so observe how I shall set about it: you can watch from hence all my operations.

He had no sooner spoken these words than, borrowing the form of Leandro Perez, to the great astonishment of the Student, he alighted unobserved amid the crowd, which he elbowed without ceremony and, quickly passing through it, rushed into the fire as into his natural element. The spectators who beheld him, alarmed at the apparent madness of the attempt, uttered a cry of horror. What insanity! said one. Is it possible that interest can blind a man to such an extent as this? None but a downright idiot could have been tempted by any proffered recompense to dare such certain death. The rash youth, said another, must be the lover of Don Pedro's daughter; and in the desperation of his grief has resolved to save his mistress or to perish with her.

In short, they predicted for him the fate of Empedocles, when, a minute afterward, they saw him emerge from the flames with Seraphina in his arms. The air resounded with acclamations, and the people were loud in their praises of the brave cavalier who had performed so noble a feat. When rashness ends in success, critics are silent; and so this prodigy now appeared to the assembled multitude as a very natural result of a Spaniard's daring.

As the lady was still insensible, her father did not dare to give himself up to joy: he feared that, although thus miraculously delivered from the fire, she would die before his eyes, from the terrible impression made upon her mind by the peril she had encountered. He was, however, soon reassured, when, recovering from her swoon, her eyes opened, and looking on the old man, she said to him with an affectionate voice: Signor, I should have had more occasion for affliction than rejoicing at the preservation of my life, were not yours also in safety. Ah! my child, replied her father, embracing her, nothing is lost since you are saved. But let us thank, exclaimed he, presenting to her the double of Cleophas—let us testify our gratitude to this young cavalier. He is your preserver; it is to him you owe your life. How can we repay that debt? Not all that I possess would suffice to cancel the obligation he has conferred upon us.

To these observations the Devil replied, with an air which would have done Don Cleophas credit: Signor, I am noble, and a Castilian. I seek no other reward for the service I have had the happiness to render you than the pleasure of having dried your tears, and of having saved from the flames the lovely object which they threatened to devour—surely such a service is its own reward.

The disinterestedness and generosity of their benefactor raised for him the highest feelings of admiration and esteem in the breast of the Signor de Escolano, who entreated him to call upon them, and offered him his warmest friendship. The Devil replied in fitting terms to the frank advances of the old man; and, after many other compliments had passed, the father and daughter retired to a small building, which remained uninjured, at the bottom of the garden. The Demon then rejoined the Student, who, seeing him return under his former guise, said to him: Signor Asmodeus, have my eyes deceived me? Were you not but now in my shape and figure? Excuse the liberty, replied the Cripple; and I will tell you the motive for this metamorphosis. I have formed a grand design: I intend that you should marry Seraphina, and, under your form, I have already inspired her with a violent passion for your lordship. Don Pedro, also, is highly satisfied with you, because I told him that in rescuing his daughter I had no other object than to render them both happy, and that the honor of having happily terminated so perilous an adventure was a sufficient reward for a Spanish gentleman. The good man has a noble soul, and will not easily be outdone in generosity; and he is at this moment deliberating within himself whether he shall not give you his daughter, as the most worthy return he can make to you for having saved her life.

Why, what's the matter now? exclaimed the Student. What wonderful emotion agitates you thus, and chains your willing tongue? Ah! Signor Leandro, answered the Demon with tremulous voice, what misery for me! The magician who kept me prisoned in my bottle has discovered that I am absent without leave, and prepares e'en now such mighty spiritings, to call me back to his laboratory, as I must fain obey. Alas! exclaimed Zambullo, quite affected, I am mortified beyond expression! What a loss am I about to suffer! Must we, then, my dear Asmodeus, separate forever?

I trust not, replied the Devil. The magician may require some office of my ministry; and if I have the fortune to assist him in his projects, perhaps, out of gratitude, he may restore me to liberty. Should that arrive, as I hope it may, rely on my rejoining you at once; on condition, however, that you reveal not to mortal ears what has this night passed between us. Should you be weak enough to confide this to anyone, I warn you, continued Asmodeus emphatically, that you will never see me more.

I have one consolation in leaving you, he resumed, which is, that at least I have made your fortune. You will marry the lovely Seraphina, into whose bosom it has been my business to instil a doting passion for your lordship. The Signor Don Pedro de Escolano, too, has made up his mind to bestow her hand upon you; and do you take care not to let so splendid a gift escape your own. But, mercy on me, he concluded, I hear already the potent master who constrains me; all Hell resounds with the echoes of the fearful words pronounced by this redoubtable magician: I dare not stay a moment longer. Farewell, my dear Zambullo! We may meet again. As he ceased, he embraced Don Cleophas, and, after having dropped the Student in his own apartment on his way to the laboratory, disappeared.

Upon the retreat of Asmodeus, the Student, feeling fatigued at having passed all the night upon his legs, and by the extraordinary bustle in which he had been occupied, undressed himself and went to bed. Agitated as his mind may be supposed to have been, it is no wonder that he lay for some time restless; but at last, paying with compound interest to Morpheus the tribute which all mortals owe to his somber majesty, he fell into a deathlike sleep, in which he passed the whole of that day and the following night.

Twenty-four hours had he been thus lost to the world, when Don Luis de Lujana, a young cavalier whom he numbered among his friends, entered his chamber, singing out lustily, Hollo! Signor Don Cleophas, get up with you! At this salutation, Zambullo awoke. Are you aware, said Don Luis to him, that you have been in bed since yesterday morning? Impossible! exclaimed Leandro. Not the less true for that, replied his friend; twice have you slept the clock's dull round. All the inmates of the house assure me of this fact.

The Student, astonished at the trance from which he emerged, feared at first that his adventures with Asmodeus were but an illusion. He could not, however, persist in this belief; and when he recalled to himself certain circumstances of his intercourse with the Demon, he soon ceased to doubt of its reality. But, to make assurance doubly sure, he rose, dressed himself quickly, and went out with Don Luis, whom he took, without saying why, in the direction of the Gate of the Sun. Arrived there, and perceiving the mansion of Don Pedro almost reduced to ashes, Don Cleophas feigned surprise. What do I behold? he cried. What dreadful ravages has fire made here! To whom did this unlucky house belong, and when was it thus consumed?

Don Luis de Lujana, having replied to these two questions, thus continued: This fire is less spoken of in the town on account of the great damage it has done than for a circumstance which attended it, and of which I will tell you. The Signor Don Pedro de Escolano has an only daughter, who is lovely as the day: they say that she was in a room all filled with fire and smoke, in which it seemed certain she must perish; but that nevertheless her life was saved by a youthful cavalier, whose name I have not heard—it forms the subject of conversation throughout Madrid. The young man's daring is lauded to the skies; and it is believed that, as a reward for his success, however humble my gentleman may be, he may well hope to gain a life interest in the daughter of the Don.

Leandro Perez listened to Don Luis without appearing to take the slightest interest in what he heard; then getting rid of his friend, under some specious pretext, he gained the Prado, where, seating himself beneath a tree, he was soon plunged in a profound reverie. The Devil first came flitting through his mind. Ah! my dear Asmodeus, he exclaimed, I cannot too much regret you. You, in a moment, would have borne me round the world; and, with you, should I have journeyed without any of the usual devilries of traveling: gentle spirit, you are a loss indeed! But, he added a moment afterward, my loss, perhaps, is not quite irreparable: why should I despair of seeing the Demon again? It may fall out, as he himself suggested, that the magician will shortly restore him to freedom and to me. As the Devil left his mind the lady entered it; upon which he resolved at once to seek Don Pedro in his temporary abode, moved principally by curiosity to see the lovely Seraphina.

As soon as he appeared before Don Pedro, that signor rushed toward him with open arms and, embracing him, exclaimed: Welcome! generous cavalier. I began to feel angry at your absence. What! said I, Don Cleophas, after the pressing invitation which I gave him to my house, still to shun my sight! He ill indeed repays the impatience of my soul to testify for him the friendship and esteem which fill it.

Zambullo bowed respectfully at this kindly objurgation; and, in order to excuse his seeming coldness, replied to the old man that he had feared to incommode him in the confusion which the event of the preceding day must have occasioned. I cannot listen to such an excuse, resumed Don Pedro; you can never be unwelcome in a house which but for your noble conduct would have been a house of mourning indeed. But, he added, follow me, if you please; you have other thanks than mine to receive. And taking the Student's hand, he led him to the apartment of Seraphina.

My child, said Don Pedro, as he entered the room where this lady was reposing from the noonday heat, I present to you the gentleman who so courageously saved your life. Show to him now, if you can, how deeply sensible you are of the obligation he conferred, since the danger from which he rescued you deprived you of the power to do so on the spot. On this, the Signora Seraphina, opening a mouth of roses to express the gratitude of her heart to Leandro Perez, paid him in compliments so warm and graceful as would charm my readers as much as they did this blushing object, could I repeat each honeyed word; but as they have not been faithfully reported, I think it better to omit them altogether, than chance to spoil them by my own imperfect knowledge in such matters.

I will only say that Don Cleophas thought he beheld and listened to some bright divinity, and that he was at once the victim of his eyes and ears. To say that he loved her is a thing of course; but, far from regarding the beauteous form before him as a possession to which he might aspire, his heart foreboded, despite all that the Demon had assured him, that they would never pay at such a price the service they imagined him to have rendered. As her charms increased in their effect upon his mind, doubts, teasing doubts, came threatening to destroy the infant hope, first-cherished child of Love.

What completed his mystification on the subject was that Don

Pedro, during the lengthened conversation which ensued, not once e'en touched upon the tender theme, but contented himself with loading him with civilities, without hinting in the slightest degree that he had any desire for the honor of his relationship. Seraphina too, as polite as her father, while she did not fail in expressions of the deepest gratitude, dropped no one word whose magic charm would serve Zambullo to conjure visions of wedding joys; so that our Student left the Signor Escolano and his daughter with love as his companion, but leaving hope behind him.

Asmodeus, my friend, he muttered as he walked along, as though the Devil still were by his side, when you assured me that Don Pedro was disposed to adopt me as his son-in-law, and that Seraphina burned with passion lighted in her heart by you for me, it must have pleased you to make merry at my cost, or else you know as little of the present time as of that which is to come.

He now regretted that he had ever seen the dangerous beauty; and looking on the love which filled his breast as an unhappy passion which he ought to stifle in its infancy, he resolved to set about it in earnest. He even reproached himself for having desired to gain his point, supposing he had found the father all disposed to give his daughter to him, and represented to himself that it would have been disgraceful to have owed his happiness to a deception like that he had projected.

He was yet occupied with these reflections, when Don Pedro, having sent to seek him on the following day, said to him: Signor Leandro Perez, it is time I proved to you by deeds that in obliging me you have not to do with one of those who repay a benefit in courtly phrases. You saved my daughter: and I wish that she, herself, should recompense the peril you encountered for her sake. I have consulted Seraphina thereupon, and find her ready to obey my will; nay, I can say with pride, I recognized her for my child indeed when I proposed that she should give her hand to him who saved her life. She showed her joy by transports which at once convinced my soul her generosity responds to mine. It is settled, therefore, that you shall marry with my daughter.

After having spoken thus, the good Signor de Escolano, who reasonably expected that Don Cleophas would have gone down on his knees to thank him for so great a boon, was sufficiently surprised to find him speechless, and displaying an evident embarrassment. Speak, Zambullo! he at length exclaimed. What am I to infer from the confusion which my proposition to you has occasioned? What possible objection can you have? What! a private gentleman—although respectable—to refuse an alliance which a noble would have courted! Has then the honor of my house some blemish of which I am ignorant?

Signor, replied Leandro, I know too well the space that Heaven has set between us. Why then, returned Don Pedro, seem you to care so little for a marriage which does you so much honor? Confess! Don Cleophas, you love some maiden, and have pledged your faith; and it is your honor now which bars your road to fortune. Had I, replied the Student, a mistress to whom my vows had bound my future fate, it is not fortune that should bid me break them; but it is no such tie that now compels me to reject your proffered bounty. Honor, it is true, compels me to renounce the glorious destiny that you would tempt me with; but, far from seeking to abuse your kindness, I am about to undeceive you to my own undoing. I am not the deliverer of Seraphina.

What do I hear! exclaimed Don Pedro, in utter astonishment. It was not you who rescued Seraphina from the flames which threatened her with instant death! It was not Don Cleophas who had the courage to risk his life to save her! No, signor, replied Zambullo; mortal man would have vainly essayed to shield her from her fate; learn that it was a devil to whom you owe your daughter's life.

These words only increased the astonishment of Don Pedro, who, not conceiving that he was to understand them literally, entreated the Student to explain himself. Upon which, Leandro, regardless of the loss of the Demon's friendship, related all that had passed between Asmodeus and himself. Having finished, the old man resumed and said to Don Cleophas: The confidence you have reposed in me confirms me in my design of giving you my daughter. You were her chief deliverer. Had you not thus entreated the Devil whom you speak of to snatch her from the death which menaced her, it is clear he would have suffered her to perish. It is you then who preserved the life of Seraphina, which cannot be better devoted than to the happiness of your own. You deserve her; and I again offer you her hand with the half of my estate.

Leandro Perez, at these words, which removed all his conscientious scruples, threw himself at the feet of Don Pedro to thank him for his generosity. In a few weeks, the marriage was celebrated with a magnificence suitable to the espousal of the heir of the Signor de Escolano, and to the great satisfaction of the relations of our Student, who was thus amply repaid for the few hours' freedom he had procured for the Devil on Two Sticks.

BOTTLE PARTY

John Collier

FRANKLIN FLETCHER dreamed of luxury in the form of tiger skins and beautiful women. He was prepared, at a pinch, to forego the tiger skins. Unfortunately the beautiful women seemed equally rare and inaccessible. At his office and at his boardinghouse the girls were mere mice, or were puddingy girls, or swarthy, or had insufficiently read the advertisements. He met no others. At thirty-five he gave up and decided he must console himself with a hobby, which is a very miserable second-best.

He prowled about in odd corners of the town, looking in at the windows of antique dealers and junk shops, wondering what on earth he might collect. He came upon a poor shop, in a poor alley, in whose dusty window stood a single object: it was a full-rigged ship in a bottle. Feeling rather like that himself, he decided to go in and ask the price.

The shop was small and bare. Some shabby racks were ranged about the walls, and these racks bore a large number of bottles of every shape and size, containing a variety of objects which were interesting only because they were in bottles. While Franklin still looked about, a little door opened, and out shuffled the proprietor, a wizened old man in a smoking cap, who seemed mildly surprised and mildly pleased to have a customer.

He showed Franklin bouquets, and birds of paradise, and the Battle of Gettysburg, and miniature Japanese gardens, and even a shrunken human head, all stoppered up in bottles. "And what," said Frank, "are those, down there on the bottom shelf?"

"They are not much to look at," said the old man. "A lot of people think they are all nonsense. Personally, I like them."

He lugged out a few specimens from their dusty obscurity. One seemed to have nothing but a little dried-up fly in it; others contained what might have been horsehairs or straws, or mere wisps of Heaven knows what; some appeared to be filled with gray or opalescent smoke. "They are," said the old man, "various sorts of genii, jinns, sibyls, demons, and such things. Some of them, I believe, are much harder, even than a full-rigged ship, to get into a bottle."

"Oh, but come! This is New York," said Frank.

"All the more reason," said the old man, "to expect the most extraordinary jinns in bottles. I will show you. Wait a moment. The stopper is a little stiff."

"What is this one like?" asked Frank.

"This one," said the old man, desisting in his efforts and holding the bottle up to the light. "This one—— Good heavens! My eyes are getting weak. I very nearly undid the wrong bottle. A very ugly customer indeed. Dear me! It's just as well I didn't get that stopper undone. I'd better put him right back in the rack. I must remember he's in the back right-hand corner. I'll stick a label on him one of these days. Here's something more harmless."

"What's in that?" said Frank.

"Supposed to be the most beautiful girl in the world," said the old man. "All right if you like that sort of thing. Myself, I've never troubled to undo her. I'll find something more interesting."

"Well, from a scientific point of view," said Frank, "I——"

"No. No," said the old man. "Talking of science: look at this." He held up one which contained a tiny, mummified, insect-looking object, just visible through the grime. "Put your ear to it," he said.

Frank did so. He heard, in a sort of whistling nothing of a voice, the words, "Louisiana Lad, Saratoga, four-fifteen. Louisiana Lad, Saratoga, four-fifteen," repeated over and over again.

"What on earth is that?" said he.

"That," said the old man, "is the original Cumaean Sibyl. Very interesting. She's taken up racing."

"Very interesting," said Frank. "All the same, I'd just like to see that other. I adore beauty."

"A bit of an artist, eh?" said the old man. "Believe me, what you really want is a good, all-round, serviceable type. Here's one, for example. I recommend this little fellow from personal experience. He's practical. He can fix you anything."

"Well, if that's so," said Frank, "why haven't you got a palace, tiger skins, and all that?"

"I had all that," said the old man. "And he fixed it. Yes, this was my first bottle. All the rest came from him. First of all I had a palace, pictures, marbles, slaves. And, as you say, tiger skins. I had him put Cleopatra on one of them."

"What was she like?" cried Frank.

"All right," said the old man, "if you like that sort of thing. I got bored with it. I thought to myself, 'What I'd like, really, is a little shop, with all sorts of things in bottles.' So I had him fix it. He got me the sibyl. He got me the ferocious fellow there. In fact, he got me all of them."

"And now he's in there?" said Frank.

"Yes. He's in there," said the old man. "Listen to him."

Frank put his ear to the bottle. He heard, uttered in the most plaintive tones, "Let me out. Do let me out. Please let me out. I'll do anything. Let me out. I'm harmless. Please let me out. Just for a little while. Do let me out. I'll do anything. Please——"

Frank looked at the old man. "He's there all right," he said. "He's there."

"Of course he's there," said the old man. "I wouldn't sell you an empty bottle. What do you take me for? In fact, I wouldn't sell this one at all, for sentimental reasons, only I've had the shop a good many years now, and you're my first customer."

Frank put his ear to the bottle again. "Let me out. Let me out. Oh, please let me out. I'll——"

"I say," said Frank, "does he go on like that all the time?"

"Very probably," said the old man. "I can't say I listen. I prefer the radio."

"It seems rather tough on him," said Frank sympathetically.

"Maybe," said the old man. "They don't seem to like bottles. Personally, I do. They fascinate me. For example, I——"

"Tell me," said Frank, "is he really harmless?"

"Oh yes," said the old man. "Bless you, yes. Some say they're tricky —Eastern blood and all that—I never found him so. I used to let him out: he'd do his stuff, then back he'd go again. I must say, he's very efficient."

"He could get me something?"

"Absolutely anything."

"And how much do you want for him?" said Frank.

"Oh, I don't know," said the old man. "Ten million dollars, perhaps."

"I say! I haven't got that. Still, if he's as good as you say, I could pay you on the installment system."

"Don't worry. Give me five bucks. I've got all I want, really. Shall I wrap him up for you?"

Frank paid over his five bucks and hurried home with the precious bottle, terrified of breaking it. As soon as he was in his room he pulled out the stopper. Out flowed a prodigious quantity of greasy smoke, which immediately solidified into the figure of a gross and fleshy Oriental, six feet six in height, with rolls of fat, a hook nose, a wicked white to his eye, vast double chins, altogether like a film producer, only larger. Frank, striving desperately for something to say, ordered shashlik, kebab, and Turkish delight. These were immediately forth-coming.

Frank, having recovered his balance, noted that these modest offer-ings were of surpassing quality, and set upon dishes of solid gold, su-perbly engraved, and polished to a dazzling brightness. It is by little details of this description that one may recognize a really first-rate servant. Frank was delighted but restrained his enthusiasm. "Gold plates," said he, "are all very well. Let us, however, get down to brass tacks. I should like a palace."

"To hear," said his dusky henchman, "is to obey."

"It should," said Frank, "be of suitable size, suitably situated, suita-bly furnished, suitable pictures, suitable marbles, hangings, and all that. I should like there to be a large number of tiger skins. I am very fond of tiger skins."

"They shall be there," said the slave.

"I am," said Frank, "a bit of an artist, as your late owner remarked. My art, so to speak, demands the presence, upon these tiger skins, of a number of young women, some blonde, some brunette, some petite, some Junoesque, some languorous, some vivacious, all beautiful, and they need not be overdressed. I hate overdressing. It is vulgar. Have you got that?"

"I have," said the jinn.

"Then," said Frank, "let *me* have it."

"Condescend only," said his servant, "to close your eyes for the space of a single minute, and, opening them, you shall find yourself surrounded by the agreeable objects you have described."

"O.K.," said Frank. "But no tricks, mind!"

He closed his eyes as requested: a low, musical humming, whoosh-ing sound rose and fell about him. At the end of the minute he looked around: there were the arches, pillars, marbles, hangings, etc., of the most exquisite palace imaginable, and wherever he looked he saw a tiger skin, and on every tiger skin there reclined a young woman of surpassing beauty, who was certainly not vulgarly overdressed.

Our good Frank was, to put it mildly, in an ecstasy. He darted to and fro like a honeybee in a florist's shop. He was received everywhere with smiles sweet beyond description and with glances of an open or a veiled responsiveness. Here were blushes and lowered lids. Here was the flaming face of ardor. Here was a shoulder turned, but by no means a cold shoulder. Here were open arms, and such arms! Here was love dissembled, but vainly dissembled. Here was love triumphant. "I must say," said Frank at a later hour, "I have spent a really delight-ful afternoon. I have enjoyed it thoroughly."

"Then may I crave," said the jinn, who was at that moment serving him his supper, "may I crave the boon of being allowed to act as your butler, and as general minister to your pleasures, instead of being returned to that abominable bottle?"

"I don't see why not," said Frank. "It certainly seems rather tough that, after having fixed all this up, you should be crammed back into the bottle again. Very well, act as my butler, but understand, whatever the convention may be, I wish you never to enter a room without knocking. And above all—no tricks."

The jinn, with a soapy smile of gratitude, withdrew, and Frank shortly retired to his harem, where he passed the evening as pleasantly as he had passed the afternoon.

Some weeks went by, entirely filled with these agreeable pastimes, till Frank, in obedience to a law which not even the most efficient of jinns can set aside, found himself growing a little overparticular, a little blasé, a little inclined to criticize and find fault.

"These," said he to his jinn, "are very pretty young creatures, if you like that sort of thing, but I imagine they can hardly be first-rate, or I should feel more interest in them. I am, after all, a connoisseur: nothing can please me but the very best. Take them away. Roll up all the tiger skins but one."

"It shall be done," said the jinn. "Behold, it is accomplished."

"And on that remaining tiger skin," said Frank, "put me Cleopatra herself."

The next moment Cleopatra was there, looking, it must be admitted, absolutely superb. "Hullo!" she said. "Here I am, on a tiger skin again!"

"Again!" cried Frank, suddenly reminded of the old man in the shop. "Here! Take her back. Bring me Helen of Troy."

Next moment Helen of Troy was there. "Hullo!" she said. "Here I am, on a tiger skin again!"

"Again!" cried Frank. "Damn that old man! Take her away. Bring me Queen Guinevere."

Guinevere said exactly the same thing; so did Madame la Pompadour, Lady Hamilton, and every other famous beauty that Frank could think of. "No wonder," said he, "that that old man was such an extremely wizened old man! The old fiend! The old devil! He has properly taken the gilt off all the gingerbread. Call me jealous if you like; I will not play second fiddle to that ugly old rascal. Where shall I find a perfect creature, worthy of the embraces of such a connoisseur as I am?"

"If you are deigning to address that question to me," said the jinn, "let me remind you that there was, in that shop, a little bottle which my late master had never unstoppered, because I supplied him with it after he had lost interest in matters of this sort. Nevertheless, it has the reputation of containing the most beautiful girl in the whole world."

"You are right," cried Frank. "Get me that bottle without delay."

In a few seconds the bottle lay before him. "You may have the afternoon off," said Frank to the jinn.

"Thank you," said the jinn. "I will go and see my family in Arabia. I have not seen them for a long time." With that he bowed and withdrew. Frank turned his attention to the bottle, which he was not long in unstoppering.

Out came the most beautiful girl you can possibly imagine. Cleopatra and all that lot were hags and frumps compared with her. "Where am I?" said she. "What is this beautiful palace? What am I doing on a tiger skin? Who is this handsome young prince?"

"It's me!" cried Frank in a rapture. "It's me!"

The afternoon passed like a moment in Paradise. Before Frank knew it the jinn was back, ready to serve up supper. Frank must sup with his charmer, for this time it was love, the real thing. The jinn, entering with the viands, rolled up his wicked eyes at the sight of so much beauty.

It happened that Frank, all love and restlessness, darted out into the garden between two mouthfuls to pluck his beloved a rose. The jinn, on the pretense of serving her wine, edged up very closely. "I don't know if you remember me," said he in a whisper. "I used to be in the next bottle to you. I have often admired you through the glass."

"Oh yes," said she. "I remember you to perfection."

At that moment Frank returned. The jinn could say no more, but he stood about the room, inflating his monstrous chest and showing off his plump and dusky muscles. "You need not be afraid of him," said Frank. "He is only a jinn. Pay no attention to him. Tell me if you really love me."

"Of course I do," said she.

"Well, say so," said he. "Why don't you say so?"

"I have said so," said she. "Of course I do. Isn't that saying so?"

This vague, evasive reply dimmed all Frank's happiness, as if a cloud had come over the sun. Doubt sprang up in his mind and entirely ruined moments of exquisite bliss.

"What are you thinking of?" he would say.

"I don't know," she would reply.

"Well, you ought to know," he would say, and then a quarrel would begin.

Once or twice he even ordered her back into her bottle. She obeyed with a malicious and secretive smile.

"Why should she give that sort of smile?" said Frank to the jinn, to whom he confided his distress.

"I cannot tell," replied the jinn. "Unless she has a lover concealed in there."

"Is it possible?" cried Frank in consternation.

"It is surprising," said the jinn, "how much room there is in one of these bottles."

"Come out!" cried Frank. "Come out at once!"

His charmer obediently emerged. "Is there anyone else in that bottle?" cried Frank.

"How could there be?" she asked with a look of rather overdone innocence.

"Give me a straight answer," said he. "Answer me yes or no."

"Yes or no," she replied maddeningly.

"Hell and fury!" cried Frank. "I'll go and find out for myself. If I find anybody, God help him and you!"

With that, and with an intense effort of the will, he flowed himself into the bottle. He looked all around: there was no one. Suddenly he heard a sound above him. He looked up, and there was the stopper being thrust in.

"What are you doing?" cried he.

"We are putting in the stopper," said the jinn.

Frank cursed, begged, prayed, and implored. "Let me out!" he cried. "Let me out. Please let me out. Do let me out. I'll do anything. Let me out, do."

The jinn, however, had other matters to attend to. Frank had the infinite mortification of beholding these other matters through the glassy walls of his prison. Next day he was picked up, whisked through the air, and deposited in the dirty little shop, among the other bottles, from which this one had never been missed.

There he remained for an interminable period, covered all over with dust, and frantic with rage at the thought of what was going on in his exquisite palace between his jinn and his faithless charmer. In the end some sailors happened to drift into the shop, and, hearing this bottle contained the most beautiful girl in the world, they bought it up by general subscription of the fo'c'sle. When they unstoppered him at sea and found it was only poor Frank, their disappointment knew no bounds, and they used him with the utmost barbarity.

THE DEVIL QUOTES SCRIPTURE

THE DEVIL quotes Scripture to his own ends; he is no mean theologian. Theology is to him an open book; he was there. He was the first war correspondent, reporting the progress of his own war. Had a saint the slightest quaver of doubt in the course of history, Satan appeared to record it. Had a pope an afterthought concerning some divine command, Satan hastened to the council chambers of the Vatican. But the Devil was a slow starter.

He did not come into his own in the Western world until the Middle Ages. Then witch burnings reddened the sky from the Danube to the English Channel. Nor did the tight little island neglect this most incredible of all mass hysterias; England and Scotland contributed their full measure of native fuel to the fire.

Charles Mackay, in that engaging and erudite tome, *Extraordinary Popular Delusions and the Madness of Crowds,* traces the witch mania back to a misinterpretation of the old Mosaic law, "Thou shalt not suffer a witch to live." "In the time of Moses," writes Dr. Mackay, "it is evident that there were impostors who trafficked upon the credulity of mankind, and insulted the supreme majesty of the true God by pretending to the power of divination. Hence the law which Moses, by divine command, promulgated against these criminals."

The Devil, in any event, made the most of it. He had been sold to the populace by the monks in their early miracle plays in which he always figured. And, at the same time, he had been sold to the intelligentsia through the writings of a long line of saints before whom he made as many personal appearances as the most ubiquitous Hollywood star.

At the beginning of the Christian era the Devil's stock was low. Dr. Paul Carus, in his *History of the Devil,* calls attention to the fact that Satan, as *a proper name signifying the Devil,* appears in only five incidents in the Old Testament, although Satan, as a translation of "enemy," is to be found frequently. In the Book of Job, Satan, "going to and fro in the earth and walking up and down in it," is the adversary of man rather than of the Deity. This Satan is a servant of Yahweh. Snide and malicious, he is nonetheless welcome whenever the "sons of God" present themselves before the Lord.

H. G. Wells noticed this unusual relationship between God and the Devil in the Book of Job and used it to good effect in *The Undying Fire,* a novel published just after World War I. Transcending time and space with his customary fluency, Mr. Wells in his opening chapter presents the Deity and Satan as opponents in an eternal (but friendly) game of chess.

The play, according to Mr. Wells, is far more intricate than in "the little ingenious game that originated in India." Satan can never win, but neither can he lose as long as he can prevent the appearance of any reasoned scheme. It is his duty to inject "a slight inexplicable inaccuracy into each move."

But it is the description of the Devil himself that is the most arresting. Satan, says the author, has the compact alertness of habitual travel. He brings a flavor of initiative and even bustle to a scene that would otherwise be one of serene perfection. Even his halo has a slightly traveled look, and his labels are still upon him. And, commenting on the duality of good and evil, Mr. Wells writes: "If God is omnipresent by a calm necessity, Satan is everywhere by an infinite activity."

The Devil of the wandering tribes of Israel was a figure of many contradictions. In Leviticus (although not in the King James version) the duality of the supreme power is expressed in double sacrifice: Aaron is instructed to cast lots upon two goats, one to be slain for Yahweh and one (the scapegoat) to be sent alive into the desert as an offering to Azazel. Dr. Carus believes this to be a lingering vestige in Hebrew custom from a period when the power of evil received an equal share of worship with the power of good.

Azazel seems to have been only one of the many pagan gods who were replaced by Satan in the New Testament, and it requires no special theological discernment to mark the Devil's upward progress from the beginning of the Christian era. Satan is a very real person when he tempts Jesus in the Gospels; he reaches magnificence in the rolling periods of St. John the Divine: "And the great dragon was cast out, that old serpent, called the Devil, and Satan, which deceiveth the whole world."

From the ludicrous and slightly slapstick picture of St. Dunstan searing the Devil's nose with his red-hot pincers to the solemn discussion of demonic possession in the Dialogues of Gregory the Great, the Devil permeates the history of the Church. St. Augustine assigns seven reasons why devils can foresee the future, among them the rapidity with which they can travel, the fact that they know more than we do, and finally that they understand better than men the writings of the Prophets and hence can more accurately interpret them.

Albert Reville writes in *The Devil, His Origin, Greatness and Decadence:* "There was not a saint to whom the Devil did not at least appear once under human form." He recounts the legend of St. Theophilus in the sixth century who, in a moment of wounded pride, made himself over formally to Satan (see the Faust legend) and then, being devoured by remorse, persuaded the Virgin Mary to recover the fatal document for him. He reports a remark of the Abbot Richalmus who lived in Franconia some seven hundred years ago. The good abbot once turned to his acolyte, saying, "Just look at my lip; for twenty years has an imp clung to it, just to make it hang down."

In fact, a familiarity with the Devil during the Middle Ages gradually led to numerous legends in which the saints treated him with little more than contempt, frequently outwitting the Devil and turning his talents to their own account. Reville comments further in this connection: "Had he not, for instance, been such a simpleton as to get architects out of hobbles by supplying them with splendid plans for the cathedrals of Aix-la-Chappelle and Cologne? It is true that at Aix he had bargained for the soul of the first person that entered the church, and at Cologne for that of the architect himself; but then he was outwitted, after all. At Aix a wolf was goaded into the newly finished church; at Cologne, the architect, having got possession of the promised plan, instead of giving Satan a proper deed by which his soul was made over, suddenly draws from under his gown a bone of one of the eleven thousand virgins, which he thrusts in the evil one's face, who makes off with a thousand oaths."

In the three stories included in this section, the Devil wins his round in Alphonse Daudet's *The Three Low Masses,* gluttony having always been an easy mark for the chief cook of the world's greatest kitchen. He loses the other two.

Richard Garnett's story, *The Demon Pope,* seems to stem in part from an account of Sylvester II written by William of Malmesbury, an English Benedictine monk. This Pope's secular name was Gerbert, and he is supposed to have studied magic in Spain. The Devil in Malmesbury's detailed and circumstantial revelations appears in the form of a magic head constructed by the Pope to answer questions beyond his own powers of divination. However, Sylvester's magic head triumphs while Mr. Garnett's Devil is no match for either the Pope or the College of Cardinals.

In *The Screwtape Letters* even the fastest theological footwork of Uncle S. is not sufficient to net the soul of his nephew's patient, and so the Devil loses once again.

Still, no one would question the virtuosity of Uncle Screwtape. He fully appreciates the value of Scripture. He knows only too well how the Devil has quoted it throughout the course of history.

THE THREE LOW MASSES

A CHRISTMAS STORY

Alphonse Daudet

"Two truffled turkeys, Garrigou?"

"Yes, your reverence, two magnificent turkeys, stuffed with truffles. I should know something about it, for I myself helped to fill them. One would have said their skin would crack as they were roasting, it is that stretched. . . ."

"Jesu-Maria! I who like truffles so much! . . . Quick, give me my surplice, Garrigou. . . . And have you seen anything else in the kitchen besides the turkeys?"

"Yes, all kinds of good things. . . . Since noon we have done nothing but pluck pheasants, hoopoes, barn fowls, and woodcocks. Feathers were flying about all over. . . . Then they have brought eels, gold carp, and trout out of the pond, besides. . . ."

"What size were the trout, Garrigou?"

"As big as that, your reverence. . . . Enormous!"

"Oh heavens! I think I see them. . . . Have you put the wine in the vessels?"

"Yes, your reverence, I have put the wine in the vessels. . . . But la! it is not to be compared to what you will drink presently, when the midnight Mass is over. If you only saw that in the dining hall of the château! The decanters are all full of wines glowing with every color! . . . And the silver plate, the chased epergnes, the flowers, the lusters! . . . Never will such another midnight repast be seen. The noble marquis has invited all the lords of the neighborhood. At least forty of you will sit down to table, without reckoning the farm bailiff and the notary. . . . Oh, how lucky is your reverence to be one of them! . . . After a mere sniff of those fine turkeys, the scent of truffles follows me everywhere. . . . Yum!"

"Come now, come now, my child. Let us keep from the sin of gluttony, on the night of the Nativity especially. . . . Be quick and light the wax tapers and ring the first bell for the Mass, for it's nearly midnight and we must not be behind time."

This conversation took place on a Christmas night in the year of grace one thousand six hundred and something, between the Reverend Dom Balaguère (formerly Prior of the Barnabites, now paid chaplain of the Lords of Trinquelague) and his little clerk Garrigou, or at least him whom he took for his little clerk Garrigou, for you must know that the Devil had on that night assumed the round face and soft features of the young sacristan, in order the more effectually to lead the reverend father into temptation and make him commit the dreadful sin of gluttony. Well, then, while the supposed Garrigou (hum!) was with all his might making the bells of the baronial chapel chime out, his reverence was putting on his chasuble in the little sacristy of the château, and with his mind already agitated by all these gastronomic descriptions, he kept saying to himself as he was robing: "Roasted turkeys . . . golden carp . . . trout as big as that! . . ."

Out of doors the soughing night wind was carrying abroad the music of the bells, and, with this, lights began to make their appearance on the dark sides of Mount Ventoux, on the summit of which rose the ancient towers of Trinquelague. The lights were borne by the families of the tenant farmers, who were coming to hear the midnight Mass at the château. They were scaling the hill in groups of five or six together and singing, the father in front carrying a lantern, and the women wrapped up in large brown cloaks, beneath which their little children snuggled and sheltered. In spite of the cold and the lateness of the hour these good folks were marching blithely along, cheered by the thought that after the Mass was over there would be, as always in former years, tables set for them down in the kitchens. Occasionally the glass windows in some lord's carriage, preceded by torchbearers, would glisten in the moonlight on the rough ascent; or perhaps a mule would jog by with tinkling bells, and by the light of the misty lanterns the tenants would recognize their bailiff and would salute him as he passed with:

"Good evening, Master Arnoton."

"Good evening. Good evening, my friend."

The night was clear, and the stars were twinkling with frost; the north wind was nipping, and at times a fine small hail that slipped off one's garments without wetting them faithfully maintained the tradition of Christmas being white with snow. On the summit of the hill, as the goal toward which all were wending, gleamed the château, with its enormous mass of towers and gables, and its chapel steeple rising into the blue-black sky. A multitude of little lights were twinkling, coming, going, and moving about at all the windows; they looked like the sparks one sees running about in the ashes of burnt paper.

After you had passed the drawbridge and the postern gate, it was necessary, in order to reach the chapel, to cross the first court, which was full of carriages, footmen, and sedan chairs, and was quite illuminated by the blaze of torches and the glare of the kitchen fires. Here were heard the click of turnspits, the rattle of saucepans, the clash of glasses and silver plate in the commotion attending the preparation of the feast, while over all rose a warm vapor smelling pleasantly of roast meat, piquant herbs, and complex sauces, and which seemed to say to the farmers, as well as to the chaplain and to the bailiff and to everybody:

"What a good midnight repast we are going to have after the Mass!"

2

Ting-a-ring!—a—ring!

The midnight Mass is beginning in the chapel of the château, which is a cathedral in miniature, with groined and vaulted roofs, oak woodwork as high as the walls, expanded draperies, and tapers all aglow. And what a lot of people! What grand dresses! First of all, seated in the carved stalls that line the choir, is the Lord of Trinquelague in a coat of salmon-colored silk, and about him are ranged all the noble lords who have been invited.

On the opposite side, on velvet-covered praying stools, the old dowager marchioness in flame-colored brocade and the youthful Lady of Trinquelague, wearing a lofty headdress of plaited lace in the newest fashion of the French court, have taken their places. Lower down, dressed in black, with punctilious wigs and shaven faces, like two grave notes among the gay silks and the figured damasks, are seen the bailiff, Thomas Arnoton, and the notary, Master Ambroy. Then come the stout major-domos, the pages, the horsemen, the stewards, Dame Barbara, with all her keys hanging at her side on a real silver ring. At the end, on the forms, are the lower class, the female servants, the cotter farmers and their families; and lastly, down there near the door, which they open and shut very carefully, are messieurs the scullions, who enter in the interval between two sauces to take a little whiff of Mass, and these bring the smell of the repast with them into the church, which now is in high festival and warm from the number of lighted tapers.

Is it the sight of their little white caps that so distracts the celebrant? Is it not rather Garrigou's bell? That mad little bell which is shaken at the altar foot with an infernal impetuosity that seems all the time to be saying: "Come, let us make haste, make haste. . . . The sooner we shall have finished, the sooner shall we be at table." The fact is that every time this Devil's bell tinkles the chaplain forgets his Mass and thinks of nothing but the midnight repast. He fancies he sees the cooks bustling about, the stoves glowing with forgelike fires, the two magnificent turkeys, filled, crammed, marbled with truffles. . . .

Then again he sees, passing along, files of little pages carrying dishes enveloped in tempting vapors, and with them he enters the great hall now prepared for the feast. Oh, delight! There is the immense table all laden and luminous, peacocks adorned with their feathers, pheasants spreading out their reddish-brown wings, ruby-colored decanters, pyramids of fruit glowing amid green boughs, and those wonderful fish Garrigou (ah well, yes, Garrigou!) had mentioned laid on a couch of fennel, with their pearly scales gleaming as if they had just come out of the water, and bunches of sweet-smelling herbs in their monstrous snouts. So clear is the vision of these marvels that it seems to Dom Balaguère that all these wondrous dishes are served before him on the embroidered altar cloth, and two or three times, instead of the *Dominus vobiscum,* he finds himself saying the *Benedicite.* Except for these slight mistakes, the worthy man pronounces the service very conscientiously, without skipping a line, without omitting a genuflection, and all goes tolerably well until the end of the first Mass, for you know that on Christmas Day the same officiating priest must celebrate three consecutive Masses.

"That's one done!" says the chaplain to himself with a sigh of relief; then, without losing a moment, he motioned to his clerk, or to him whom he supposed to be his clerk, and . . .

"Ting-a-ring . . . Ting-a-ring, a-ring!"

Now the second Mass is beginning, and with it begins also Dom Balaguère's sin. "Quick, quick, let us make haste," Garrigou's bell cries out to him in its shrill little voice, and this time the unhappy celebrant, completely given over to the demon of gluttony, fastens upon the missal and devours its pages with the eagerness of his overexcited appetite. Frantically he bows down, rises up, merely indicates the sign of the cross and the genuflections, and curtails all his gestures in order to get sooner finished. Scarcely has he stretched out his arms at the Gospel, before he is striking his breast at the Confiteor. It is a contest between himself and the clerk as to who shall mumble the faster. Versicles and responses are hurried over and run one into another. The words, half pronounced, without opening the mouth, which would take up too much time, terminate in unmeaning murmurs.

"*Oremus ps . . . ps . . . ps . . .*"

"*Mea culpa . . . pa . . . pa . . .*"

Like vintagers in a hurry pressing grapes in the vat, these two paddle in the Mass Latin, sending splashes in every direction.

"*Dom . . . scum! . . .*" says Balaguère.

". . . *Stutuo! . . .*" replies Garrigou, and all the time the cursed little bell is tinkling there in their ears, like the jingles they put on post horses to make them gallop fast. You may imagine at that speed a low Mass is quickly disposed of.

"That makes two," says the chaplain, quite panting; then without taking time to breathe, red and perspiring, he descends the altar steps and . . .

"Ting-a-ring! . . . Ting-a-ring! . . ."

Now the third Mass is beginning. There are but a few more steps to be taken to reach the dining hall; but, alas! the nearer the midnight repast approaches, the more does the unfortunate Balaguère feel himself possessed by mad impatience and gluttony. The vision becomes more distinct; the golden carps, the roasted turkeys are there, there! . . . He touches them . . . he . . . Oh heavens! The dishes are smoking; the wines perfume the air, and with furiously agitated clapper the little bell is crying out to him:

"Quick, quick, quicker yet!"

But how could he go quicker? His lips scarcely move. He no longer pronounces the words . . . unless he were to impose upon Heaven outright and trick it out of its Mass. . . . And that is precisely what he does, the unfortunate man! . . . From temptation to temptation; he begins by skipping a verse, then two. Then the Epistle is too long—he does not finish it, skims over the Gospel, passes before the Credo without going into it, skips the Pater, salutes the Preface from a distance, and by leaps and bounds thus hurls himself into eternal damnation, constantly followed by the vile Garrigou (*vade retro, Satanas!*), who seconds him with wonderful skill, sustains his chasuble, turns over the leaves two at a time, elbows the reading desks, upsets the vessels, and is continually sounding the little bell louder and louder, quicker and quicker.

You should have seen the scared faces of all who were present, as they were obliged to follow this Mass by mere mimicry of the priest, without hearing a word; some rise when others kneel, and sit down when the others are standing up, and all the phases of this singular service are mixed up together in the multitude of different attitudes presented by the worshipers on the benches. . . .

"The *abbé* goes too fast. . . . One can't follow him," murmured the old dowager, shaking her headdress in confusion. Master Arnoton, with great steel spectacles on his nose, is searching in his prayer book to find where the dickens they are. But at heart all these good folks, who themselves are thinking about feasting, are not sorry that the Mass is going on at this posthaste; and when Dom Balaguère with radiant face turns toward those present and cries with all his might: "*Ite, missa est,*" they all respond to him a "*Deo gratias*" in but one voice, and that as joyous and enthusiastic as if they thought themselves already seated at the midnight repast and drinking the first toast.

3

Five minutes afterward the crowd of nobles were sitting down in the great hall, with the chaplain in the midst of them. The château, illuminated from top to bottom, was resounding with songs, with shouts, with laughter, with uproar; and the venerable Dom Balaguère was thrusting his fork into the wing of a fowl and drowning all remorse for his sin in streams of regal wine and the luscious juices of the viands. He ate and drank so much, the dear, holy man, that he died during the night of a terrible attack, without even having had time to repent; and then in the morning when he got to Heaven, I leave you to imagine how he was received.

He was told to withdraw on account of his wickedness. His fault was so grievous that it effaced a whole lifetime of virtue. . . . He had robbed them of a midnight Mass. . . . He should have to pay for it with three hundred, and he should not enter into Paradise until he had celebrated in his own chapel these three hundred Christmas Masses in the presence of all those who had sinned with him and by his fault. . . .

. . . And now this is the true legend of Dom Balaguère as it is related in the olive country. At the present time the château of Trinquelague no longer exists, but the chapel still stands on the top of Mount Ventoux, amid a cluster of green oaks. Its decayed door rattles in the wind, and its threshold is choked up with vegetation; there are birds' nests at the corners of the altar and in the recesses of the lofty windows, from which the stained glass has long ago disappeared. It seems, however, that every year at Christmas a supernatural light wanders amid these ruins, and the peasants, in going to the Masses and to the midnight repasts, see this phantom of a chapel illuminated by invisible tapers that burn in the open air, even in snow and wind. You may laugh at it if you like, but a vine dresser of the place, named Garrigue—doubtless a descendant of Garrigou—declared to me that one Christmas night, when he was a little tipsy, he lost his way on the hill of Trinquelague, and this is what he saw: Till eleven o'clock, nothing. All was silent, motionless, inanimate. Suddenly, about midnight, a chime sounded from the top of the steeple, an old, old chime, which seemed as if it were ten leagues off. Very soon Garrigue saw lights flitting about and uncertain shadows moving in the road that climbs the hill. They passed on beneath the chapel porch and murmured:

"Good evening, Master Arnoton!"

"Good evening, good evening, my friends!"

When all had entered, my vine dresser, who was very courageous, silently approached, and when he looked through the broken door, a singular spectacle met his gaze. All those he had seen pass were seated round the choir and in the ruined nave, just as if the old seats still existed. Fine ladies in brocade, with lace headdresses; lords adorned from head to foot; peasants in flowered jackets such as our grandfathers had; all with an old, faded, dusty, tired look. From time to time the night birds, the usual inhabitants of the chapel, who were aroused by all these lights, would come and flit round the tapers, the flames of which rose straight and ill-defined, as if they were burning behind a veil; and what amused Garrigue very much was a certain personage with large steel spectacles, who was ever shaking his tall black wig, in which one of these birds was quite entangled and kept itself upright by noiselessly flapping its wings. . . .

At the farther end a little old man of childish figure was on his knees in the middle of the choir, desperately shaking a clapperless and soundless bell, while a priest, clad in ancient gold, was coming and going before the altar, reciting prayers of which not a word was heard. . . . Most certainly this was Dom Balaguère in the act of saying his third low Mass.

THE DEMON POPE

Richard Garnett

"So you won't sell me your soul?" said the Devil.

"Thank you," replied the student, "I had rather keep it myself, if it's all the same to you."

"But it's not all the same to me. I want it very particularly. Come, I'll be liberal. I said twenty years. You can have thirty."

The student shook his head.

"Forty!"

Another shake.

"Fifty!"

As before.

"Now," said the Devil. "I know I'm going to do a foolish thing, but I cannot bear to see a clever, spirited young man throw himself away. I'll make you another kind of offer. We don't have any bargain at present, but I will push you on in the world for the next forty years. This day forty years I come back and ask you for a boon; not your soul, mind, or anything not perfectly in your power to grant. If you give it, we are quits; if not, I fly away with you. What say you to this?"

The student reflected for some minutes. "Agreed," he said at last.

Scarcely had the Devil disappeared, which he did instantaneously, ere a messenger reined in his smoking steed at the gate of the University of Cordova (the judicious reader will already have remarked that Lucifer could never have been allowed inside a Christian seat of learning) and, inquiring for the student Gerbert, presented him with the Emperor Otho's nomination to the Abbacy of Bobbio, in consideration, said the document, of his virtue and learning, well-nigh miraculous in one so young. Such messengers were frequent visitors during Gerbert's prosperous career. Abbot, bishop, archbishop, cardinal, he was ultimately enthroned Pope on April 2, 999, and assumed the appellation of Silvester the Second. It was then a general belief that the world would come to an end in the following year, a catastrophe which to many seemed the more imminent from the election of a chief pastor whose celebrity as a theologian, though not inconsiderable, by no means equaled his reputation as a necromancer.

The world, notwithstanding, revolved scatheless through the dreaded twelvemonth, and early in the first year of the eleventh century Gerbert was sitting peacefully in his study, perusing a book of magic. Volumes of algebra, astrology, alchemy, Aristotelian philosophy, and other such light reading filled his bookcase, and on a table stood an improved clock of his invention, next to his introduction of the arabic numerals his chief legacy to posterity. Suddenly a sound of wings was heard, and Lucifer stood by his side.

"It is a long time," said the fiend, "since I have had the pleasure of seeing you. I have now called to remind you of our little contract, concluded this day forty years."

"You remember," said Silvester, "that you are not to ask anything exceeding my power to perform."

"I have no such intention," said Lucifer. "On the contrary, I am about to solicit a favor which can be bestowed by you alone. You are Pope; I desire that you would make me a cardinal."

"In the expectation, I presume," returned Gerbert, "of becoming Pope on the next vacancy."

"An expectation," replied Lucifer, "which I may most reasonably entertain, considering my enormous wealth, my proficiency in intrigue, and the present condition of the Sacred College."

"You would doubtless," said Gerbert, "endeavor to subvert the foundations of the Faith, and, by a course of profligacy and licentiousness, render the Holy See odious and contemptible."

"On the contrary," said the fiend, "I would extirpate heresy, and all learning and knowledge as inevitably tending thereunto. I would suffer no man to read but the priest, and confine his reading to his breviary. I would burn your books together with your bones on the first convenient opportunity. I would observe an austere propriety of conduct and be especially careful not to loosen one rivet in the tremendous yoke I was forging for the minds and consciences of mankind."

"If it be so," said Gerbert, "let's be off!"

"What!" exclaimed Lucifer. "You are willing to accompany me to the infernal regions!"

"Assuredly, rather than be accessory to the burning of Plato and Aristotle and give place to the darkness against which I have been contending all my life."

"Gerbert," replied the demon, "this is arrant trifling. Know you not that no good man can enter my dominions? That, were such a thing possible, my empire would become intolerable to me and I should be compelled to abdicate?"

"I do know it," said Gerbert, "and hence I have been able to receive your visit with composure."

"Gerbert," said the Devil, with tears in his eyes, "I put it to you— is this fair; is this honest? I undertake to promote your interests in the world; I fulfill my promise abundantly. You obtain through my instrumentality a position to which you could never otherwise have aspired. Often have I had a hand in the election of a pope, but never before have I contributed to confer the tiara on one eminent for virtue and learning. You profit by my assistance to the full and now take advantage of an adventitious circumstance to deprive me of my reasonable guerdon. It is my constant experience that the good people are much more slippery than the sinners and drive much harder bargains."

"Lucifer," answered Gerbert, "I have always sought to treat you as a gentleman, hoping that you would approve yourself such in return. I will not inquire whether it was entirely in harmony with this character to seek to intimidate me into compliance with your demand by threatening me with a penalty which you well knew could not be enforced. I will overlook this little irregularity and concede even more than you have requested. You have asked to be a cardinal. I will make you Pope——"

"Ha!" exclaimed Lucifer, and an internal glow suffused his sooty hide, as the light of a fading ember is revived by breathing upon it.

"For twelve hours," continued Gerbert. "At the expiration of that time we will consider the matter further; and if, as I anticipate, you are more anxious to divest yourself of the papal dignity than you were to assume it, I promise to bestow upon you any boon you may ask within my power to grant, and not plainly inconsistent with religion or morals."

"Done!" cried the demon. Gerbert uttered some cabalistic words, and in a moment the apartment held two Pope Silvesters, entirely indistinguishable save by their attire and the fact that one limped slightly with the left foot.

"You will find the pontifical apparel in this cupboard," said Gerbert, and, taking his book of magic with him, he retreated through a masked door to a secret chamber. As the door closed behind him he chuckled and muttered to himself, "Poor old Lucifer! Sold again!"

If Lucifer was sold he did not seem to know it. He approached a large slab of silver which did duty as a mirror and contemplated his personal appearance with some dissatisfaction.

"I certainly don't look half so well without my horns," he soliloquized, "and I am sure I shall miss my tail most grievously."

A tiara and a train, however, made fair amends for the deficient appendages, and Lucifer now looked every inch a pope. He was about to call the master of the ceremonies and summon a consistory, when the door was burst open, and seven cardinals, brandishing poniards, rushed into the room.

"Down with the sorcerer!" they cried as they seized and gagged him.

"Death to the Saracen!"

"Practices algebra and other devilish arts!"

"Knows Greek!"

"Talks Arabic!"

"Reads Hebrew!"

"Burn him!"

"Smother him!"

"Let him be deposed by a general council," said a young and inexperienced cardinal.

"Heaven forbid!" said an old and wary one, *sotto voce*.

Lucifer struggled frantically, but the feeble frame he was doomed to inhabit for the next eleven hours was speedily exhausted. Bound and helpless, he swooned away.

"Brethren," said one of the senior cardinals, "it hath been delivered by the exorcists that a sorcerer or other individual in league with the demon doth usually bear upon his person some visible token of his infernal compact. I propose that we forthwith institute a search for this stigma, the discovery of which may contribute to justify our proceedings in the eyes of the world."

"I heartily approve of our Brother Anno's proposition," said another, "the rather as we cannot possibly fail to discover such a mark, if, indeed, we desire to find it."

The search was accordingly instituted and had not proceeded far ere a simultaneous yell from all the seven cardinals indicated that their investigation had brought more light than they had ventured to expect.

The Holy Father had a cloven foot!

For the next five minutes the cardinals remained utterly stunned, silent, and stupefied with amazement. As they gradually recovered their faculties it would have become manifest to a nice observer that the Pope had risen very considerably in their good opinion.

"This is an affair requiring very mature deliberation," said one.

"I always feared that we might be proceeding too precipitately," said another.

"It is written, 'the devils believe,' " said a third: "the Holy Father, therefore, is not a heretic at any rate."

"Brethren," said Anno, "this affair, as our Brother Benno well remarks, doth indeed call for mature deliberation. I therefore propose that, instead of smothering His Holiness with cushions, as originally contemplated, we immure him for the present in the dungeon adjoining hereunto and, after spending the night in meditation and prayer, resume the consideration of the business tomorrow morning."

"Informing the officials of the palace," said Benno, "that His Holiness has retired for his devotions and desires on no account to be disturbed."

"A pious fraud," said Anno, "which not one of the fathers would for a moment have scrupled to commit."

The cardinals accordingly lifted the still-insensible Lucifer and bore him carefully, almost tenderly, to the apartment appointed for his detention. Each would fain have lingered in hopes of his recovery, but each felt that the eyes of his six brethren were upon him: and all, therefore, retired simultaneously, each taking a key of the cell.

Lucifer regained consciousness almost immediately afterward. He had the most confused idea of the circumstances which had involved him in his present scrape and could only say to himself that if they were the usual concomitants of the papal dignity, these were by no means to his taste, and he wished he had been made acquainted with them sooner. The dungeon was not only perfectly dark but horribly cold, and the poor Devil in his present form had no latent store of infernal heat to draw upon. His teeth chattered; he shivered in every limb and felt devoured with hunger and thirst. There is much probability in the assertion of some of his biographers that it was on this occasion that he invented ardent spirits; but, even if he did, the mere conception of a glass of brandy could only increase his sufferings. So the long January night wore wearily on, and Lucifer seemed likely to expire from inanition, when a key turned in the lock, and Cardinal Anno cautiously glided in, bearing a lamp, a loaf, half a cold roast kid, and a bottle of wine.

"I trust," he said, bowing courteously, "that I may be excused any slight breach of etiquette of which I may render myself culpable from the difficulty under which I labor of determining whether, under present circumstances, 'your holiness' or 'your infernal majesty' be the form of address most befitting me to employ."

"Bub-ub-bub-boo," went Lucifer, who still had the gag in his mouth.

"Heavens!" exclaimed the cardinal. "I crave your infernal holiness's forgiveness. What a lamentable oversight!"

And, relieving Lucifer from his gag and bonds, he set out the refection, upon which the demon fell voraciously.

"Why the devil, if I may so express myself," pursued Anno, "did not your holiness inform us that you *were* the Devil? Not a hand would then have been raised against you. I have myself been seeking all my life for the audience now happily vouchsafed me. Whence this mistrust of your faithful Anno, who has served you so loyally and zealously these many years?"

Lucifer pointed significantly to the gag and fetters.

"I shall never forgive myself," protested the cardinal, "for the part I have borne in this unfortunate transaction. Next to ministering to your majesty's bodily necessities, there is nothing I have so much at heart as to express my penitence. But I entreat your majesty to remember that I believed myself to be acting in your majesty's interest by overthrowing a magician who was accustomed to send your majesty upon errands and who might at any time enclose you in a box and cast you into the sea. It is deplorable that your majesty's most devoted servants should have been thus misled."

"Reasons of State," suggested Lucifer.

"I trust that they no longer operate," said the cardinal. "However, the Sacred College is now fully possessed of the whole matter: it is therefore unnecessary to pursue this department of the subject further. I would now humbly crave leave to confer with your majesty, or rather, perhaps, your holiness, since I am about to speak of spiritual things, on the important and delicate point of your holiness's successor. I am ignorant how long your holiness proposes to occupy the apostolic chair; but of course you are aware that public opinion will not suffer you to hold it for a term exceeding that of the pontificate of Peter. A vacancy, therefore, must one day occur; and I am humbly to represent that the office could not be filled by one more congenial than myself to the present incumbent, or on whom he could more fully rely to carry out in every respect his views and intentions."

And the cardinal proceeded to detail various circumstances of his past life, which certainly seemed to corroborate his assertion. He had not, however, proceeded far ere he was disturbed by the grating of another key in the lock, and had just time to whisper impressively, "Beware of Benno," ere he dived under a table.

Benno was also provided with a lamp, wine, and cold viands. Warned by the other lamp and the remains of Lucifer's repast that some colleague had been beforehand with him, and not knowing how many more might be in the field, he came briefly to the point as regarded the Papacy and preferred his claim in much the same manner as Anno. While he was earnestly cautioning Lucifer against this cardinal as one who could and would cheat the very Devil himself, another key turned in the lock, and Benno escaped under the table, where Anno immediately inserted his fingers into his right eye. The little squeal consequent upon this occurrence Lucifer successfully smothered by a fit of coughing.

Cardinal No. 3, a Frenchman, bore a Bayonne ham and exhibited the same disgust as Benno on seeing himself forestalled. So far as his requests transpired, they were moderate, but no one knows where he would have stopped if he had not been scared by the advent of Cardinal No. 4. Up to this time he had only asked for an inexhaustible purse, power to call up the Devil *ad libitum,* and a ring of invisibility to allow him free access to his mistress, who was unfortunately a married woman.

Cardinal No. 4 chiefly wanted to be put into the way of poisoning

Cardinal No. 5, and Cardinal No. 5 preferred the same petition as respected Cardinal No. 4.

Cardinal No. 6, an Englishman, demanded the reversion of the archbishoprics of Canterbury and York, with the faculty of holding them together and of unlimited non-residence. In the course of his harangue he made use of the phrase *non obstantibus,* of which Lucifer immediately took a note.

What the seventh cardinal would have solicited is not known, for he had hardly opened his mouth when the twelfth hour expired, and Lucifer, regaining his vigor with his shape, sent the Prince of the Church spinning to the other end of the room and split the marble table with a single stroke of his tail. The six crouched and huddling cardinals cowered, revealed to one another, and at the same time enjoyed the spectacle of His Holiness darting through the stone ceiling, which yielded like a film to his passage and closed up afterward as if nothing had happened. After the first shock of dismay they unanimously rushed to the door but found it bolted on the outside. There was no other exit and no means of giving an alarm. In this emergency the demeanor of the Italian cardinals set a bright example to their ultramontane colleagues. *"Bisogna pazienzia,"* they said as they shrugged their shoulders. Nothing could exceed the mutual politeness of Cardinals Anno and Benno, unless that of the two who had sought to poison each other. The Frenchman was held to have gravely derogated from good manners by alluding to this circumstance, which had reached his ears while he was under the table, and the Englishman swore so outrageously at the plight in which he found himself that the Italians then and there silently registered a vow that none of his nation should ever be Pope, a maxim which, with one exception, has been observed to this day.

Lucifer, meanwhile, had repaired to Silvester, whom he found arrayed in all the insignia of his dignity, of which, as he remarked, he thought his visitor had probably had enough.

"I should think so indeed," replied Lucifer. "But at the same time I feel myself fully repaid for all I have undergone by the assurance of the loyalty of my friends and admirers and the conviction that it is needless for me to devote any considerable amount of personal attention to ecclesiastical affairs. I now claim the promised boon, which it will be in no way inconsistent with thy functions to grant, seeing that it is a work of mercy. I demand that the cardinals be released and that their conspiracy against thee, by which I alone suffered, be buried in oblivion."

"I hoped you would carry them all off," said Gerbert with an expression of disappointment.

"Thank you," said the Devil. "It is more to my interest to leave them where they are."

So the dungeon door was unbolted, and the cardinals came forth, sheepish and crestfallen. If, after all, they did less mischief than Lucifer had expected from them, the cause was their entire bewilderment by what had passed and their utter inability to penetrate the policy of Gerbert, who henceforth devoted himself even with ostentation to good works. They could never quite satisfy themselves whether they were speaking to the Pope or to the Devil, and when under the latter impression habitually emitted propositions which Gerbert justly stigmatized as rash, temerarious, and scandalous. They plagued him with allusions to certain matters mentioned in their interviews with Lucifer, with which they naturally but erroneously supposed him to be conversant, and worried him by continual nods and titterings as they glanced at his nether extremities. To abolish this nuisance, and at the same time silence sundry unpleasant rumors which had somehow got abroad, Gerbert devised the ceremony of kissing the Pope's feet, which, in a grievously mutilated form, endures to this day. The stupefaction of the cardinals on discovering that the Holy Father had lost his hoof surpasses all description, and they went to their graves without having obtained the least insight into the mystery.

SELECTIONS FROM THE SCREWTAPE LETTERS

C. S. Lewis

LETTER XX

My dear Wormwood,

I note with great pleasure that the Enemy has, for the time being, put a forcible end to your direct attacks on the patient's chastity. You ought to have known that He always does in the end, and you ought to have stopped before you reached that stage. For as things are, your man has now discovered the dangerous truth that these attacks don't last forever; consequently you cannot use again what is, after all, our best weapon—the belief of ignorant humans, that there is no hope of getting rid of us except by yielding. I suppose you've tried persuading him that chastity is unhealthy?

I haven't yet got a report from you on young women in the neighborhood. I should like it at once, for if we can't use his sexuality to make him unchaste we must try to use it for the promotion of a desirable marriage. In the meantime I would like to give you some hint about the type of woman—I mean the physical type—which he should be encouraged to fall in love with if "falling in love" is the best we can manage.

In a rough-and-ready way, of course, this question is decided for us by spirits far deeper down in the Lowerarchy than you and I. It is the business of these great masters to produce in every age a general misdirection of what may be called sexual "taste." This they do by working through the small circle of popular artists, dressmakers, actresses, and advertisers who determine the fashionable type. The aim is to guide each sex away from those members of the other with whom spiritually helpful, happy, and fertile marriages are most likely. Thus we have now for many centuries triumphed over nature to the extent of making certain secondary characteristics of the male (such as the beard) disagreeable to nearly all the females—and there is more in that than you might suppose. As regards the male taste we have varied a good deal. At one time we have directed it to the statuesque and aristocratic type of beauty, mixing men's vanity with their desires and encouraging the race to breed chiefly from the most arrogant and prodigal women. At another, we have selected an exaggeratedly feminine type, faint and languishing, so that folly and cowardice, and all the general falseness and littleness of mind which go with them, shall be at a premium. At present we are on the opposite tack. The age of jazz has succeeded the age of the waltz, and we now teach men to like women whose bodies are scarcely distinguishable from those of boys. Since this is a kind of beauty even more transitory than most, we thus aggravate the female's chronic horror of growing old (with many excellent results) and render her less willing and less able to bear children. And that is not all. We have engineered a great increase in the license which society allows to the representation of the apparent nude (not the real nude) in art, and its exhibition on the stage or the bathing beach. It is all a fake, of course; the figures in the popular art are falsely drawn; the real women in bathing suits or tights are actually pinched in and propped up to make them appear firmer and more slender and more boyish than nature allows a full-grown woman to be. Yet at the same time, the modern world is taught to believe that it is being "frank" and "healthy" and getting back to nature. As a result we are more and more directing the desires of men to something which does not exist—making the role of the eye in sexuality more and more important and at the same time making its demands more and more impossible. What follows you can easily forecast!

That is the general strategy of the moment. But inside that framework you will still find it impossible to encourage your patient's desires in one of two directions. You will find, if you look carefully into any human's heart, that he is haunted by at least two imaginary women—a terrestrial and an infernal Venus—and that his desire differs qualitatively according to its object. There is one type for which his desire is such as to be naturally amenable to the Enemy—readily mixed with charity, readily obedient to marriage, colored all through with that golden light of reverence and naturalness which we detest; there is another type which he desires brutally, and desires to desire brutally, a type best used to draw him away from marriage altogether but which, even within marriage, he would tend to treat as a slave, an idol, or an accomplice. His love for the first might involve what the Enemy calls evil, but only accidentally; the man would wish that she was not someone else's wife and be sorry that he could not love her lawfully. But in the second type, the felt evil is what he wants; it is that "tang" in the flavor which he is after. In the face, it is the visible animality, or sulkiness, or craft, or cruelty which he likes, and in the body, something quite different from what he ordinarily calls Beauty, something he may even, in a sane hour, describe as ugliness, but which, by our art, can be made to play on the raw nerve of his private obsession.

The real use of the infernal Venus is, no doubt, as prostitute or mistress. But if your man is a Christian, and if he has been well trained in nonsense about irresistible and all-excusing "Love," he can often be induced to marry her. And that is very well worth bringing about. You will have failed as regards fornication and solitary vice, but there are other, and more indirect, methods of using a man's sexuality to his undoing. And, by the way, they are not only efficient, but delightful; the unhappiness produced is of a very lasting and exquisite kind.

Your affectionate uncle
SCREWTAPE

LETTER XXII

MY DEAR WORMWOOD,

So! Your man is in love—and in the worst kind he could possibly have fallen into—and with a girl who does not even appear in the report you sent me. You may be interested to learn that the little misunderstanding with the Secret Police which you tried to raise about some unguarded expressions in one of my letters has been tided over. If you were reckoning on that to secure my good offices, you will find yourself mistaken. You shall pay for that as well as for your other blunders. Meanwhile I enclose a little booklet, just issued, on the new House of Correction for Incompetent Tempters. It is profusely illustrated and you will not find a dull page in it.

I have looked up this girl's dossier and am horrified at what I find. Not only a Christian but such a Christian—a vile, sneaking, simpering, demure, monosyllabic, mouselike, watery, insignificant, virginal, bread-and-butter miss. The little brute. She makes me vomit. She stinks and scalds through the very pages of the dossier. It drives me mad, the way the world has worsened. We'd have had her to the arena in the old days. That's what her sort is made for. Not that she'd do much good there, either. A two-faced little cheat (I know the sort) who looks as if she'd faint at the sight of blood and then dies with a smile. A cheat every way. Looks as if butter wouldn't melt in her mouth and yet has a satirical wit. The sort of creature who'd find *ME* funny! Filthy, insipid little prude—and yet ready to fall into this booby's arms like any other breeding animal. Why doesn't the Enemy blast her for it, if He's so moonstruck by virginity—instead of looking on there, grinning?

He's a hedonist at heart. All those fasts and vigils and stakes and crosses are only a façade. Or only like foam on the seashore. Out at sea, out in His sea, there is pleasure, and more pleasure. He makes no secret of it; at His right hand are "pleasures for evermore." Ugh! I don't think He has the least inkling of that high and austere mystery to which we rise in the Miserific Vision. He's vulgar, Wormwood. He has a bourgeois mind. He has filled His world full of pleasures. There are things for humans to do all day long without His minding in the least—sleeping, washing, eating, drinking, making love, playing, praying, working. Everything has to be *twisted* before it's any use to us. We fight under cruel disadvantages. Nothing is naturally on our side. (Not that that excuses *you*. I'll settle with you presently. You have always hated me and been insolent when you dared.)

Then, of course, he gets to know this woman's family and whole circle. Could you not see that the very house she lives in is one that he ought never to have entered? The whole place reeks of that deadly odor. The very gardener, though he has only been there five years, is beginning to acquire it. Even guests, after a week-end visit, carry some of the smell away with them. The dog and the cat are tainted with it. And a house full of the impenetrable mystery. We are certain (it is a matter of first principles) that each member of the family must in some way be making capital out of the others—but we can't find out how. They guard as jealously as the Enemy Himself the secret of what really lies behind this pretense of disinterested love. The whole house and garden is one vast obscenity. It bears a sickening resemblance to the description one human writer made of Heaven: "the regions where there is only life and therefore all that is not music is silence."

Music and silence—how I detest them both! How thankful we should be that ever since our Father entered Hell—though longer ago than humans, reckoning in light years, could express—no square inch of infernal space and no moment of infernal time has been surrendered to either of those abominable forces, but all has been occupied by Noise—Noise, the grand dynamism, the audible expression of all that is exultant, ruthless, and virile—Noise which alone defends us from silly qualms, despairing scruples, and impossible desires. We will make the whole universe a noise in the end. We have already made great strides in this direction as regards the Earth. The melodies and silences of Heaven will be shouted down in the end. But I admit we are not yet loud enough, or anything like it. Research is in progress. Meanwhile *you*, disgusting little——

[*Here the MS. breaks off and is resumed in a different hand.*]

In the heat of composition I find that I have inadvertently allowed myself to assume the form of a large centipede. I am accordingly dictating the rest to my secretary. Now that the transformation is complete I recognize it as a periodical phenomenon. Some rumor of it has reached the humans, and a distorted account of it appears in the poet Milton, with the ridiculous addition that such changes of shape are a "punishment" imposed on us by the Enemy. A more modern writer— someone with a name like Pshaw—has, however, grasped the truth. Transformation proceeds from within and is a glorious manifestation of that Life Force which Our Father would worship if he worshiped anything but himself. In my present form I feel even more anxious to see you, to unite you to myself in an indissoluble embrace,

(*Signed*) TOADPIPE

For his Abysmal Sublimity Under Secretary
Screwtape, T.E., B.S., etc.

SATAN FINDS THE NEW WORLD

———————◆———————

THE NEW WORLD might have been explored at an earlier date had not Satan and his legions inhabited our shores. Brave sea captains fishing the banks for Lenten fish let their Gothic imaginations run riot before returning to French ports. The first French explorers mistook Indians in plumage for veritable devils. And Isles of Demons inspired the poetry of fear in simple Basque and Breton fishermen venturing north of Newfoundland.

Francis Parkman speaks of an old map which pictures these isles embellished with "devils rampant, with wings, horns, and tail. The passing voyager heard the din of their infernal orgies, and woe to the sailor or fisherman who ventured alone into the haunted woods."

These demons, like St. Elmo's fire in Shakespeare's *Tempest*, played about the mast in ghostly fashion. And with griffins, sea serpents, and curious creatures having "the body of a bear and the head of a man" held North America against the all-too-avid battalions of the Cross.

But the flower of France, ably seconded by priests in gray and priests in black, were soon to push their way up the St. Lawrence and the Ottawa on the northern route to the Great Lakes and finally the Mississippi. Exorcizing Okies, Manitous, and other assorted devils, and sprinkling holy water on the unwilling savages, these dedicated martyrs faced every imaginable hardship to clear the dark forests of Lucifer's inspired minions.

Sometimes a fiery cross would burn in the sky from the direction of the feared Iroquois. At other times angels of ethereal beauty danced on mountains of the quickened imagination. And many a twist of tobacco was silently cast into the waters of dangerous rapids as a propitiation to the Manitou before the frail canoes laden with beaver pelts were sent dancing through the twisting, foaming currents of the wilderness rivers.

Meanwhile, with whip and sword and slave chains the Spaniards were exploiting other regions of the Devil far to the south. And it was not long before a third front against Satan was opened by cavaliers and grim English Puritans.

Captain John Smith tells of Devil worship and the sacrifice of children among the Indians of sylvan Virginia:

There is yet in Virginia no place discouered to bee so Savage in which the savages haue not a religion, Deare, and Bow and Arrowes. All thinges that were able to do them hurt beyond their prevention they adore with their kinde of divine worship; as the fire, water, lightning, thunder, our ordinance peeces, horses, &c. But their chiefe God they worship is the Diuell. Him they call *Oke,* and serue him more of feare than loue. They say they haue conference with him and fashion themselues as neare to his shape as they can imagine. In their Temples they haue his image euill favouredly carued and then painted and adorned with chaines, copper, and beades, and couered with a skin in such manner as the deformity may well suit with such a God.

In some part of the Country, they haue yearely a sacrifice of children. Such a one was at *Quiyoughcohanock,* some 10 miles from *James* Towne, and thus performed.

Fifteene of the properest young boyes, betweene 10 and 15 yeares of age, they painted white. Hauing brought them forth, the people spent the fore-noone in dancing and singing about them with rattles.

In the afternoone, they put those children to the roote of a tree. By them, all the men stood in a guard, every one hauing a Bastinado in his hand, made of reeds bound together. This made a lane betweene them all along, through which there were appointed 5 young men to fetch these children. So every one of the fiue went through the guard, to fetch a child, each after other by turnes: the guard fearelessly beating them with their Bastinadoes, and they patiently enduring and receauing all; defend-ing the children with their naked bodies from the unmercifull blowes they pay them soundly, though the children escape. All this while, the women weepe and crie out very passionately; prouiding mats, skinnes, mosse, and drie wood, as things fitting their childrens funerals.

After the children were thus passed the guard, the guard tore down the tree, branches and boughs, with such violence, that they rent the body and made wreathes for their heads, or bedecked their haire with the leaues. What else was done with the children was not seene; but they were all cast on a heape in a valley, as dead: where they made a great feast for al the company.

The *Werowance* (chief) being demanded the meaning of this sacrifice, answered that the children were not all dead, but that the *Oke* or *Divell* did sucke the blood from their left breast (of those) who chanced to be his by lot, till they were dead. But the rest were kept in the wildernesse by the yong men till nine moneths were expired, during which time they must not conuerse with any: and of these, were made their Priests and Coniurers.

This sacrifice they held to bee so necessarie, that if they should omit it, their *Oke* or *Divell* and all their other *Quiyoughcosughes* (which are their other Gods) would let them haue no Deare, Turkies, Corne, nor fish: and yet besides, hee would make great slaughter amongst them.

And in this lamentable ignorance doe these poore soules sacrifice them-selues to the Diuell, not knowing their Creator.

Satan (but the medieval Christian Satan rather than his red-skinned American associate) most certainly sailed on the Mayflower, and some of his descendants have been bragging about it ever since. He also found his way to New Amsterdam and other beachheads from Maine to the Carolinas, engaging in his pay dispensers of firewater, slave traders, theologians, and other rascals with a fine disregard for race and creed.

The publicity he received from such hell's-fire-and-brimstone mongers as Cotton Mather and Jonathan Edwards has inspired cer-tain evangelists to this very day.

Mather, for instance, in his *The Wonders of the Invisible World,* justifies the burning of witches with the following unanswerable argument:

The New Englanders are a People of God settled in those, which were once the Devil's Territories; and it may easily be supposed that the Devil was exceedingly disturbed, when he perceived such a People here accom-plishing the Promise of old made unto our Blessed Jesus, That He should have the Utmost parts of the Earth for his Possession. There was not a greater Uproar among the Ephesians, when the Gospel was first brought among them, than there was among the Power of the Air (after whom those Ephesians walked) when first the Silver Trumpets of the Gospel here made the Joyful Sound. The Devil thus Irritated, immediately try'd all sorts of Methods to overturn this poor Plantation; and so much of the Church, as was Fled into this Wilderness, immediately found, the Serpent cast out of his Mouth a Flood for the carrying of it away.

I believe, that never were more Satanical Devices used for the Un-settling of any People under the Sun, than what have been Employ'd for the Extirpation of the Vine which God has here Planted, Casting out the Heathen, and preparing a Room before it, and causing it to take deep Root, and fill the Land, so that it sent its Boughs unto the Atlantic Sea Eastward, and its Branches into the Connecticut River Westward, and the Hills were covered with the shadow thereof.

But, All those Attempts of Hell, have hitherto been Abortive, many an Ebenezer has been Erected unto the Praise of God, by his Poor People here; and, Having obtained Help from God, we continued to this Day. Wherefore the Devil is now making one Attempt more upon us; an Attempt more Difficult, more Surprizing, more snarl'd with unintelligible Circumstances than any that we have hitherto Encountred; an Attempt so Critical, that if we get well through we shall soon Enjoy Halcyon Days with all the Vultures of Hell Trodden under our Feet. He has wanted his Incarnate Legions to Persecute us, as the People of God have in the other Hemisphere been Persecuted; he has therefore drawn forth his more Spiritual ones to make an Attacque upon us. We have been advised by some Credible Christians yet alive, that a Malefactor, accused of Witchcraft as well as Murder, and Executed in this place more than Forty Years ago, did then give Notice of, an Horrible Plot against the Country by Witchcraft, and a Foundation of Witchcraft then laid, which if it were not seasonably discovered, would probably Blow up, and pull down all the Churches in the Country. And we have now with Horror seen the Discovery of such a Witchcraft!

An Army of Devils is horribly broke in upon the place which is the Center, and after a sort, the First-born of our English Settlements; and the Houses of the Good People there are fill'd with the doleful Shrieks of their Children and Servants, Tormented by Invisible Hands, with Tortures altogether preternatural. After the Mischiefs there Endeavoured, and since in part Conquered, the terrible Plague of Evil Angels, hath made its Progress into some other places, where other Persons have been in like manner Diabolically handled. These our poor Afflicted Neighbours, quickly after they become Infected and Infested with these Daemons, arrive to a Capacity of Discerning those which they conceive the Shapes of their Troublers; and notwithstanding the Great and Just Suspicion, that the Daemons might Impose the Shapes of Innocent Persons in their Spectral Exhibitions upon the Sufferers (which may perhaps prove no small part of the Witch-Plot in the issue) yet many of the Persons thus Represented, being Examined, several of them have been Convicted of a very Damnable Witchcraft; yea, more than One Twenty have Confessed, that they have Signed unto a Book, which the Devil show'd them, and Engaged in his Hellish Design of Bewitching, and Ruining our Land.

We know not, at least I know not, how far the Delusions of Satan may be Interwoven into some Circumstances of the Confessions; but one would think, all the Rules of Understanding Humane Affairs are at an end, if after so many most Voluntary Harmonious Confessions, made by Intelligent Persons of all Ages, in sundry Towns, at several Times, we must not Believe the main strokes wherein those Confessions all agree; especially when we have a thousand preternatural Things every day before our eyes, wherein the Confessors do acknowledge their Concernment, and give Demonstration of their being so Concerned. If the Devils now can strike the minds of men with any Poisons of so fine a Composition and Operation, that Scores of Innocent People shall Unite, in Confessions of a Crime, which we see actually committed, it is a thing prodigious, beyond the

Wonders of the former Ages, and it threatens no less than a sort of Dissolution upon the World. Now, by these Confessions 'tis Agreed, That the Devil has made a dreadful Knot of Witches in the Country.

Meanwhile Jonathan Edwards, not to be outdone, pictured the flaming wrath of Hell in such appalling clarity that lakes of brimstone fairly lapped at the feet of the terrified sinners in his congregation. Religious tornadoes swept the new land from coast to wilderness. Log-college Evangelists, Methodists, and Baptists joined the hue and cry. And Satan was roundly abused at camp meetings, where psalm singing vied with corn liquor to raise the frontier birth rate to unprecedented levels.

Fortunately a more literate leaven had been added to the populace. Writers of distinction were beginning to realize that "Old Nick," or "Old Scratch" as he was known to his familiars, was a subject for delicate irony and satire, a useful tragicomic figure to utilize as a foil in pricking the bubble of human pretensions.

It is perhaps no coincidence that almost every major American humorist wrote at least one story about the Devil which will stand rereading. Washington Irving, Bret Harte, Mark Twain, and Eugene Field are but a few who tweaked Beelzebub's tail with seeming impunity.

Washington Irving obviously did not believe in the Prince of Usurers pictured in *The Devil and Tom Walker,* a fact which did not elude the editor of the *Eclectic Review,* who in 1825 published the following dire pronunciamento: "If Mr. Irving believes in the existence of Tom Walker's master, we can scarcely conceive how he can so earnestly jest about him; at all events, we would counsel him to beware lest his own spells should prove fatal to him."

Edgar Allan Poe, who should have been the Devil's finest publicist (since he shared so many of his moods and virtues), seems to have been curiously incapable of conjuring up Lucifer in his more chill-inspiring manifestations. If it were not *lese Satanic majesty* to suggest it, we might question Poe's infernal magic.

But Poe's description of the "finicky little personage" whom he identifies as Satan in *The Devil in the Belfry* is perhaps worth a moment's attention if only in contrast to Milton's Apostate Angel, "O Prince, O Chief of many Throned Powers." Poe's Lucifer is purely ludicrous:

His countenance was of a dark snuff-color, and he had a long hooked nose, pea eyes, a wide mouth, and an excellent set of teeth, which latter he seemed anxious of displaying, as he was grinning from ear to ear.

What with mustachios and whiskers, there was none of the rest of his face to be seen. His head was uncovered, and his hair neatly done up in *papillotes.* His dress was a tight-fitting swallow-tailed black coat (from one of whose pockets dangled a vast length of white handkerchief), black kerseymere knee-breeches, black stockings, and stumpy-looking pumps, with huge bunches of black satin ribbon for bows. Under one arm he carried a huge *chapeau-de-bras,* and under the other a fiddle nearly five times as big as himself. In his left hand was a gold snuff-box, from which, as he capered down the hill, cutting all manner of fantastic steps, he took snuff incessantly with an air of the greatest possible self-satisfaction.

The Devil was becoming a homely, comic, almost a friendly fellow, less dangerous by far than roaring Mike Fink (half horse and half alligator), who could outrun, outjump, outgouge, and outbrag ary a keelboatman on the Ohio River. Even in the folk tales of the Negroes, Satan is often curiously lacking in demoniac power. American laughter was at work exorcising evil.

Mark Twain's Satan in *The Mysterious Stranger* is an angelic nephew of Lucifer completely without evil (or rather above good and evil in an almost Nietzschean sense). Life was pictured as a vision, a fiction "hysterically insane—like all dreams."

Vernon L. Parrington remarks upon this bitter, late-found knowledge which was wormwood in Samuel Clemens' mouth: *"The Mysterious Stranger* is only *Tom Sawyer* retold in the midnight of his disillusion.

"What an ending for a child of the Gilded Age. In his youth a complete frontiersman . . . in the end . . . a solitary pioneer exploring the universe, seeking a homestead in an ironical cosmos, until, overwhelmed by the intolerable solitude, he made mock at all the gods. What a commentary on the Gilded Age."

Satan had run the gamut in America from master of the Witches' Sabbath in Cotton Mather's New England to a dream, a phantom, an ethereal figment of the eternal imagination in *The Mysterious Stranger.* Both laughter and philosophy had been used to exorcise his evil.

But these were mere stratagems. He had not yet been worsted in mortal battle until Stephen Vincent Benét pitted that all-American hero Dan'l Webster against Old Scratch in a duel for which Satan chose the weapons. No rough frontiersman, no matter what his homespun courage, could have thrown Blackstone at the Prince of Lawyers with such deft and legalistic accuracy; no American-bred controversialist had yet arisen so capable of matching Lucifer in quoting precedent.

In Dan'l Webster the Old World and the New fused to create a New Hampshire Gladstone who feared neither Calhoun nor the Devil.

Yankee ingenuity and American optimism had confounded the Prince of Evil.

THE DEVIL AND TOM WALKER

Washington Irving

A FEW MILES from Boston in Massachusetts there is a deep inlet, winding several miles into the interior of the country from Charles Bay and terminating in a thickly wooded swamp or morass. On one side of this inlet is a beautiful dark grove; on the opposite side the land rises abruptly from the water's edge into a high ridge, on which grow a few scattered oaks of great age and immense size. Under one of these gigantic trees, according to old stories, there was a great amount of treasure buried by Kidd the pirate. The inlet allowed a facility to bring the money in a boat secretly and at night to the very foot of the hill; the elevation of the place permitted a good lookout to be kept that no one was at hand, while the remarkable trees formed good landmarks by which the place might easily be found again. The old stories add, moreover, that the Devil presided at the hiding of the money and took it under his guardianship, but this, it is well known, he always does with buried treasure, particularly when it has been ill-gotten. Be that as it may, Kidd never returned to recover his wealth, being shortly after seized at Boston, sent out to England, and there hanged for a pirate.

About the year 1727, just at the time that earthquakes were prevalent in New England and shook many tall sinners down upon their knees, there lived near this place a meager, miserly fellow of the name of Tom Walker. He had a wife as miserly as himself: they were so miserly that they even conspired to cheat each other. Whatever the woman could lay hands on, she hid away; a hen could not cackle but she was on the alert to secure the new-laid egg. Her husband was continually prying about to detect her secret hoards, and many and fierce were the conflicts that took place about what ought to have been common property. They lived in a forlorn-looking house that stood alone and had an air of starvation. A few straggling savin trees, emblems of sterility, grew near it; no smoke ever curled from its chimney; no traveler stopped at its door. A miserable horse, whose ribs were as articulate as the bars of a gridiron, stalked about a field, where a thin carpet of moss, scarcely covering the ragged beds of pudding stone, tantalized and balked his hunger; and sometimes he would lean his head over the fence, look piteously at the passer-by, and seem to petition deliverance from this land of famine.

The house and its inmates had altogether a bad name. Tom's wife was a tall termagant, fierce of temper, loud of tongue, and strong of arm. Her voice was often heard in wordy warfare with her husband, and his face sometimes showed signs that their conflicts were not confined to words. No one ventured, however, to interfere between them. The lonely wayfarer shrank within himself at the horrid clamor and clapper-clawing, eyed the den of discord askance, and hurried on his way, rejoicing, if a bachelor, in his celibacy.

One day that Tom Walker had been to a distant part of the neighborhood he took what he considered a short cut homeward, through the swamp. Like most short cuts, it was an ill-chosen route. The swamp was thickly grown with great gloomy pines and hemlocks, some of them ninety feet high, which made it dark at noonday and a retreat for all the owls of the neighborhood. It was full of pits and quagmires, partly covered with weeds and mosses, where the green surface often betrayed the traveler into a gulf of black, smothering mud; there were also dark and stagnant pools, the abodes of the tadpole, the bullfrog, and the water snake, where the trunks of pines and hemlocks lay half drowned, half rotting, looking like alligators sleeping in the mire.

Tom had long been picking his way cautiously through this treacherous forest, stepping from tuft to tuft of rushes and roots, which afforded precarious footholds among deep sloughs, or pacing carefully, like a cat, along the prostrate trunks of trees, startled now and then by the sudden screaming of the bittern or the quacking of a wild duck rising on the wing from some solitary pool. At length he arrived at a firm piece of ground, which ran out like a peninsula into the deep bosom of the swamp. It had been one of the strongholds of the Indians during their wars with the first colonists. Here they had thrown up a kind of fort, which they had looked upon as almost impregnable and had used as a place of refuge for their squaws and children. Nothing remained of the old Indian fort but a few embankments, gradually sinking to the level of the surrounding earth and already overgrown in part by oaks and other forest trees, the foliage of which formed a contrast to the dark pines and hemlocks of the swamp.

It was late in the dusk of evening when Tom Walker reached the old fort, and he paused there awhile to rest himself. Anyone but he would have felt unwilling to linger in this lonely, melancholy place, for the common people had a bad opinion of it, from the stories handed down from the time of the Indian wars, when it was asserted that the savages held incantations here and made sacrifices to the evil spirit.

Tom Walker, however, was not a man to be troubled with any fears of the kind. He reposed himself for some time on the trunk of a fallen hemlock, listening to the boding cry of the tree toad and delving with his walking staff into a mound of black mold at his feet. As he turned up the soil unconsciously, his staff struck against something hard. He raked it out of the vegetable mold, and lo! a cloven skull, with an Indian tomahawk buried deep in it, lay before him. The rust on the weapon showed the time that had elapsed since this deathblow had been given. It was a dreary memento of the fierce struggle that had taken place in this last foothold of the Indian warriors.

"Humph!" said Tom Walker as he gave it a kick to shake the dirt from it.

"Let that skull alone!" said a gruff voice. Tom lifted up his eyes and beheld a great black man seated directly opposite him on the stump of a tree. He was exceedingly surprised, having neither heard nor seen anyone approach, and he was still more perplexed on observing, as well as the gathering gloom would permit, that the stranger was neither Negro nor Indian. It is true he was dressed in a rude half-Indian garb and had a red belt or sash swathed round his body, but his face was neither black nor copper color, but swarthy and dingy, and begrimed with soot, as if he had been accustomed to toil among fires and forges. He had a shock of coarse black hair that stood out from his head in all directions and bore an ax on his shoulder.

He scowled for a moment at Tom with a pair of great red eyes.

"What are you doing on my grounds?" said the black man with a hoarse, growling voice.

"Your grounds!" said Tom with a sneer. "No more your grounds than mine; they belong to Deacon Peabody."

"Deacon Peabody be d——d," said the stranger, "as I flatter myself he will be, if he does not look more to his own sins and less to those of his neighbors. Look yonder and see how Deacon Peabody is faring."

Tom looked in the direction that the stranger pointed and beheld one of the great trees, fair and flourishing without, but rotten at the core, and saw that it had been nearly hewn through, so that the first high wind was likely to blow it down. On the bark of the tree was scored the name of Deacon Peabody, an eminent man, who had waxed wealthy by driving shrewd bargains with the Indians. He now looked around and found most of the tall trees marked with the name of some great man of the colony, and all more or less scored by the ax. The one on which he had been seated, and which had evidently just been hewn down, bore the name of Crowninshield, and he recollected a mighty rich man of that name who made a vulgar display of wealth, which it was whispered he had acquired by buccaneering.

"He's just ready for burning!" said the black man with a growl of triumph. "You see I am likely to have a good stock of firewood for winter."

"But what right have you," said Tom, "to cut down Deacon Peabody's timber?"

"The right of a prior claim," said the other. "This woodland belonged to me long before one of your white-faced race put foot upon the soil."

"And pray, who are you, if I may be so bold?" said Tom.

"Oh, I go by various names. I am the wild huntsman in some countries; the black miner in others. In this neighborhood I am known by the name of the black woodsman. I am he to whom the red men consecrated this spot, and in honor of whom they now and then roasted a white man, by way of sweet-smelling sacrifice. Since the red men have been exterminated by you white savages, I amuse myself by presiding at the persecutions of Quakers and Anabaptists; I am the great patron and prompter of slave dealers and the grand master of the Salem witches."

"The upshot of all which is that, if I mistake not," said Tom sturdily, "you are he commonly called Old Scratch."

"The same, at your service!" replied the black man with a half-civil nod.

Such was the opening of this interview, according to the old story, though it has almost too familiar an air to be credited. One would think that to meet with such a singular personage in this wild, lonely place would have shaken any man's nerves, but Tom was a hard-minded fellow, not easily daunted, and he had lived so long with a termagant wife that he did not even fear the Devil.

It is said that after this commencement they had a long and earnest conversation together as Tom returned homeward. The black man told him of great sums of money buried by Kidd the pirate under the oak trees on the high ridge, not far from the morass. All these were under his command and protected by his power, so that none could find them but such as propitiated his favor. These he offered to place within Tom Walker's reach, having conceived an especial kindness for him, but they were to be had only on certain conditions. What these conditions were may be easily surmised, though Tom never disclosed them publicly. They must have been very hard, for he required time to think of them, and he was not a man to stick at trifles when money was in view. When they had reached the edge of the swamp the stranger paused. "What proof have I that all you have been telling me is true?" said Tom. "There's my signature," said the black man, pressing his finger on Tom's forehead. So saying, he turned off among the thickets of the swamp and seemed, as Tom said, to go down, down, down, into the earth, until nothing but his head and shoulders could be seen, and so on, until he totally disappeared.

When Tom reached home he found the black print of a finger burnt, as it were, into his forehead, which nothing could obliterate.

The first news his wife had to tell him was the sudden death of Absalom Crowninshield, the rich buccaneer. It was announced in the papers with the usual flourish that "a great man had fallen in Israel."

Tom recollected the tree which his black friend had just hewn down and which was ready for burning. "Let the freebooter roast," said Tom; "who cares!" He now felt convinced that all he had heard and seen was no illusion.

He was not prone to let his wife into his confidence, but as this was an uneasy secret, he willingly shared it with her. All her avarice was awakened at the mention of hidden gold, and she urged her husband to comply with the black man's terms and secure what would make them wealthy for life. However Tom might have felt disposed to sell himself to the Devil, he was determined not to do so to oblige his wife, so he flatly refused, out of the mere spirit of contradiction. Many and bitter were the quarrels they had on the subject, but the more she talked, the more resolute was Tom not to be damned to please her.

At length she determined to drive the bargain on her own account and, if she succeeded, to keep all the gain to herself. Being of the same fearless temper as her husband, she set off for the old Indian fort toward the close of a summer's day. She was many hours absent. When she came back she was reserved and sullen in her replies. She spoke something of a black man, whom she had met about twilight hewing at the root of a tall tree. He was sulky, however, and would not come to terms; she was to go again with a propitiatory offering, but what it was she forbore to say.

The next evening she set off again for the swamp, with her apron heavily laden. Tom waited and waited for her, but in vain; midnight came, but she did not make her appearance; morning, noon, night returned, but still she did not come. Tom now grew uneasy for her safety, especially as he found she had carried off in her apron the silver teapot and spoons and every portable article of value. Another night elapsed; another morning came, but no wife. In a word, she was never heard of more.

What was her real fate nobody knows, in consequence of so many pretending to know. It is one of those facts which have become confounded by a variety of historians. Some asserted that she lost her way among the tangled mazes of the swamp and sank into some pit or slough; others, more charitable, hinted that she had eloped with the household booty and made off to some other province, while others surmised that the tempter had decoyed her into a dismal quagmire, on the top of which her hat was found lying. In confirmation of this, it was said a great black man, with an ax on his shoulder, was seen late that very evening coming out of the swamp, carrying a bundle tied in a check apron, with an air of surly triumph.

The most current and probable story, however, observes that Tom Walker grew so anxious about the fate of his wife and his property that he set out at length to seek them both at the Indian fort. During a long summer's afternoon he searched about the gloomy place, but no wife was to be seen. He called her name repeatedly, but she was nowhere to be heard. The bittern alone responded to his voice as he flew screaming by, or the bullfrog croaked dolefully from a neighboring pool. At length, it is said, just in the brown hour of twilight, when the owls began to hoot and the bats to flit about, his attention was attracted by the clamor of carrion crows hovering about a cypress tree. He looked up and beheld a bundle tied in a check apron and hanging in the branches of the tree, with a great vulture perched hard by, as if keeping watch upon it. He leaped with joy, for he recognized his wife's apron and supposed it to contain the household valuables.

"Let us get hold of the property," said he consolingly to himself, "and we will endeavor to do without the woman."

As he scrambled up the tree the vulture spread its wide wings and sailed off, screaming, into the deep shadows of the forest. Tom seized the checked apron, but, woeful sight! found nothing but a heart and liver tied up in it!

Such, according to this most authentic old story, was all that was to be found of Tom's wife. She had probably attempted to deal with the black man as she had been accustomed to deal with her husband, but though a female scold is generally considered a match for the Devil, yet in this instance she appears to have had the worst of it. She must have died game, however, for it is said Tom noticed many prints of cloven feet deeply stamped about the tree and found handfuls of hair that looked as if they had been plucked from the coarse black shock of the woodsman. Tom knew his wife's prowess by experience. He shrugged his shoulders as he looked at the signs of a fierce clapper-clawing. "Egad," said he to himself, "Old Scratch must have had a tough time of it!"

Tom consoled himself for the loss of his property with the loss of his wife, for he was a man of fortitude. He even felt something like grati-tude toward the black woodsman, who, he considered, had done him a kindness. He sought, therefore, to cultivate a further acquaintance with him, but for some time without success; the old blacklegs played shy, for whatever people may think, he is not always to be had for calling for: he knows how to play his cards when pretty sure of his game.

At length, it is said, when delay had whetted Tom's eagerness to the quick and prepared him to agree to anything rather than not gain the promised treasure, he met the black man one evening in his usual woodsman's dress, with his ax on his shoulder, sauntering along the swamp and humming a tune. He affected to receive Tom's advances with great indifference, made brief replies, and went on humming his tune.

By degrees, however, Tom brought him to business, and they began to haggle about the terms on which the former was to have the pirate's treasure. There was one condition which need not be mentioned, being generally understood in all cases where the Devil grants favors, but there were others about which, though of less importance, he was in-flexibly obstinate. He insisted that the money found through his means should be employed in his service. He proposed, therefore, that Tom should employ it in the black traffic; that is to say, that he should fit out a slave ship. This, however, Tom resolutely refused: he was bad enough in all conscience, but the Devil himself could not tempt him to turn slave trader.

Finding Tom so squeamish on this point, he did not insist upon it but proposed, instead, that he should turn usurer, the Devil being ex-tremely anxious for the increase of usurers, looking upon them as his peculiar people.

To this no objections were made, for it was just to Tom's taste.

"You shall open a broker's shop in Boston next month," said the black man.

"I'll do it tomorrow, if you wish," said Tom Walker.

"You shall lend money at two per cent a month."

"Egad, I'll charge four!" replied Tom Walker.

"You shall extort bonds, foreclose mortgages, drive the merchants to bankruptcy——"

"I'll drive them to the D——l," cried Tom Walker.

"You are the usurer for my money!" said blacklegs with delight. "When will you want the rhino?"

"This very night."

"Done!" said the Devil.

"Done!" said Tom Walker. So they shook hands and struck a bargain.

A few days' time saw Tom Walker seated behind his desk in a countinghouse in Boston.

His reputation for a ready-moneyed man, who would lend money out for a good consideration, soon spread abroad. Everybody remembers the time of Governor Belcher, when money was particularly scarce. It was a time of paper credit. The country had been deluged with government bills; the famous Land Bank had been established; there had been a rage for speculating; the people had run mad with schemes for new settlements, for building cities in the wilderness; land jobbers went about with maps of grants, and townships, and Eldorados, lying nobody knew where, but which everybody was ready to purchase. In a word, the great speculating fever which breaks out every now and then in the country had raged to an alarming degree, and everybody was dreaming of making sudden fortunes from nothing. As usual, the fever had subsided; the dream had gone off, and the imaginary fortunes with it; the patients were left in doleful plight, and the whole country resounded with the consequent cry of "hard times."

At this propitious time of public distress did Tom Walker set up as usurer in Boston. His door was soon thronged by customers. The needy and adventurous, the gambling speculator, the dreaming land jobber, the thriftless tradesman, the merchant with cracked credit; in short, everyone driven to raise money by desperate means and desperate sacrifices hurried to Tom Walker.

Thus Tom was the universal friend of the needy and acted like a "friend in need"; that is to say, he always exacted good pay and good security. In proportion to the distress of the applicant was the hardness of his terms. He accumulated bonds and mortgages, gradually squeezed his customers closer and closer, and sent them at length, dry as a sponge, from his door.

In this way he made money hand over hand, became a rich and mighty man, and exalted his cocked hat upon 'Change. He built himself, as usual, a vast house, out of ostentation, but left the greater part of it unfinished and unfurnished, out of parsimony. He even set up a carriage in the fullness of his vainglory, though he nearly starved the horses which drew it; and as the ungreased wheels groaned and screeched on the axletrees, you would have thought you heard the souls of the poor debtors he was squeezing.

As Tom waxed old, however, he grew thoughtful. Having secured the good things of this world, he began to feel anxious about those of the next. He thought with regret on the bargain he had made with his black friend and set his wits to work to cheat him out of the conditions. He became, therefore, all of a sudden, a violent churchgoer. He prayed loudly and strenuously, as if Heaven were to be taken by force of lungs. Indeed, one might always tell when he had sinned most during the week, by the clamor of his Sunday devotion. The quiet Christians who had been modestly and steadfastly traveling Zionward were struck with self-reproach at seeing themselves so suddenly outstripped in their career by this new-made convert. Tom was as rigid in religious as in money matters; he was a stern supervisor and censurer of his neighbors and seemed to think every sin entered up to their account became a credit on his own side of the page. He even talked of the expediency of reviving the persecution of Quakers and Anabaptists. In a word, Tom's zeal became as notorious as his riches.

Still, in spite of all this strenuous attention to forms, Tom had a lurking dread that the Devil, after all, would have his due. That he might not be taken unawares, therefore, it is said he always carried a small Bible in his coat pocket. He had also a great folio Bible on his countinghouse desk and would frequently be found reading it when people called on business; on such occasions he would lay his green spectacles in the book, to mark the place, while he turned round to drive some usurious bargain.

Some say that Tom grew a little crackbrained in his old days and that, fancying his end approaching, he had his horse new-shod, saddled and bridled, and buried with his feet uppermost, because he supposed that at the last day the world would be turned upside down; in which case he should find his horse standing ready for mounting, and he was determined at the worst to give his old friend a run for it. This, however, is probably a mere old wives' fable. If he really did take such a precaution, it was totally superfluous; at least so says the authentic old legend, which closes his story in the following manner.

One hot summer afternoon in the dog days, just as a terrible black thunder-gust was coming up, Tom sat in his countinghouse, in his white linen cap and India-silk morning gown. He was on the point of foreclosing a mortgage, by which he would complete the ruin of an unlucky land speculator for whom he had professed the greatest friendship. The poor land jobber begged him to grant a few months' indulgence. Tom had grown testy and irritated and refused another day.

"My family will be ruined and brought upon the parish," said the land jobber.

"Charity begins at home," replied Tom; "I must take care of myself in these hard times."

"You have made so much money out of me," said the speculator.

Tom lost his patience and his piety. "The Devil take me," said he, "if I have made a farthing!"

Just then there were three loud knocks at the street door. He stepped out to see who was there. A black man was holding a black horse, which neighed and stamped with impatience.

"Tom, you're come for," said the black fellow gruffly. Tom shrank back, but too late. He had left his little Bible at the bottom of his coat pocket and his big Bible on the desk, buried under the mortgage he was about to foreclose: never was sinner taken more unawares. The black man whisked him like a child into the saddle, gave the horse the lash, and away he galloped, with Tom on his back, in the midst of the thunderstorm. The clerks stuck their pens behind their ears and stared after him from the windows. Away went Tom Walker, dashing down the street, his white cap bobbing up and down, his morning gown fluttering in the wind, and his steed striking fire out of the pavement at every bound. When the clerks turned to look for the black man he had disappeared.

Tom Walker never returned to foreclose the mortgage. A countryman, who lived on the border of the swamp, reported that in the height of the thunder-gust he had heard a great clattering of hoofs and a howling along the road and, running to the window, caught sight of a figure, such as I have described, on a horse that galloped like mad across the fields, over the hills, and down into the black hemlock swamp toward the old Indian fort, and that shortly after a thunderbolt falling in that direction seemed to set the whole forest in a blaze.

The good people of Boston shook their heads and shrugged their shoulders but had been so much accustomed to witches and goblins and tricks of the Devil, in all kinds of shapes, from the first settlement of the colony, that they were not so much horror-struck as might have been expected. Trustees were appointed to take charge of Tom's effects. There was nothing, however, to administer upon. On searching his coffers, all his bonds and mortgages were found reduced to cinders. In place of gold and silver, his iron chest was filled with chips and shavings; two skeletons lay in his stable instead of his half-starved horses, and the very next day his great house took fire and was burnt to the ground.

Such was the end of Tom Walker and his ill-gotten wealth. Let all griping money brokers lay this story to heart. The truth of it is not to be doubted. The very hole under the oak trees, whence he dug Kidd's money, is to be seen to this day, and the neighboring swamp and old Indian fort are often haunted in stormy nights by a figure on horseback, in morning gown and white cap, which is doubtless the troubled spirit of the usurer. In fact, the story has resolved itself into a proverb and is the origin of that popular saying, so prevalent throughout New England, of "The Devil and Tom Walker."

THE DEVIL IN MANUSCRIPT

Nathaniel Hawthorne

ON A BITTER EVENING OF DECEMBER I arrived by mail in a large town, which was then the residence of an intimate friend, one of those gifted youths who cultivate poetry and the belles-lettres, and call themselves students at law. My first business, after supper, was to visit him at the office of his distinguished instructor. As I have said, it was a bitter night, clear starlight, but cold as Nova Zembla—the shopwindows along the street being frosted, so as almost to hide the lights, while the wheels of coaches thundered equally loud over frozen earth and pavements of stone. There was no snow, either on the ground or the roofs of the houses. The wind blew so violently that I had but to spread my cloak like a mainsail and scud along the street at the rate of ten knots, greatly envied by other navigators, who were beating slowly up, with the gale right in their teeth. One of these I capsized, but was gone on the wings of the wind before he could even vociferate an oath.

After this picture of an inclement night, behold us seated by a great blazing fire, which looked so comfortable and delicious that I felt inclined to lie down and roll among the hot coals. The usual furniture of a lawyer's office was around us—rows of volumes in sheepskin, and a multitude of writs, summonses, and other legal papers, scattered over the desks and tables. But there were certain objects which seemed to intimate that we had little dread of the intrusion of clients. or of the learned counselor himself, who, indeed, was attending court in a distant town. A tall, decanter-shaped bottle stood on the table, between two tumblers, and beside a pile of blotted manuscripts, altogether dissimilar to any law documents recognized in other courts. My friend, whom I shall call Oberon—it was a name of fancy and friendship between him and me—my friend Oberon looked at these papers with a peculiar expression of disquietude.

"I do believe," said he soberly, "or, at least, I could believe, if I chose, that there is a devil in this pile of blotted papers. You have read them and know what I mean—that conception in which I endeavored to embody the character of a fiend, as represented in our traditions and the written records of witchcraft. Oh, I have a horror of what was created in my own brain, and shudder at the manuscripts in which I gave that dark idea a sort of material existence! Would they were out of my sight!"

"And of mine too," thought I.

"You remember," continued Oberon, "how the hellish thing used to suck away the happiness of those who, by a simple concession that seemed almost innocent, subjected themselves to his power. Just so my peace is gone, and all by these accursed manuscripts. Have you felt nothing of the same influence?"

"Nothing," replied I, "unless the spell be hid in a desire to turn novelist, after reading your delightful tales."

"Novelist!" exclaimed Oberon half seriously. "Then, indeed, my devil has his claw on you! You are gone! You cannot even pray for deliverance! But we will be the last and only victims, for this night I mean to burn the manuscripts and commit the fiend to his retribution in the flames."

"Burn your tales!" repeated I, startled at the desperation of the idea.

"Even so," said the author despondingly. "You cannot conceive what an effect the composition of these tales has had on me. I have become ambitious of a bubble and careless of solid reputation. I am surrounding myself with shadows, which bewilder me, by aping the realities of life. They have drawn me aside from the beaten path of the world and led me into a strange sort of solitude—a solitude in the midst of men—where nobody wishes for what I do, nor thinks nor feels as I do. The tales have done all this. When they are ashes, perhaps I shall be as I was before they had existence. Moreover, the sacrifice is less than you may suppose, since nobody will publish them."

"That does make a difference, indeed," said I.

"They have been offered, by letter," continued Oberon, reddening with vexation, "to some seventeen booksellers. It would make you

stare to read their answers; and read them you should, only that I
burnt them as fast as they arrived. One man publishes nothing but
schoolbooks; another has five novels already under examination."

"What a voluminous mass the unpublished literature of America
must be!" cried I.

"Oh, the Alexandrian manuscripts were nothing to it!" said my
friend. "Well, another gentleman is just giving up business, on purpose, I verily believe, to escape publishing my book. Several, however,
would not absolutely decline the agency, on my advancing half the
cost of an edition and giving bonds for the remainder, besides a high
percentage to themselves, whether the book sells or not. Another ad-
vises a subscription."

"The villain!" exclaimed I.

"A fact!" said Oberon. "In short, of all the seventeen booksellers,
only one has vouchsafed even to read my tales; and he—a literary
dabbler himself, I should judge—has the impertinence to criticize
them, proposing what he calls vast improvements, and concluding,
after a general sentence of condemnation, with the definitive assurance
that he will not be concerned on any terms."

"It might not be amiss to pull that fellow's nose," remarked I.

"If the whole 'trade' had one common nose, there would be some
satisfaction in pulling it," answered the author. "But there does seem
to be one honest man among these seventeen unrighteous ones, and
he tells me fairly that no American publisher will meddle with an
American work—seldom if by a known writer, and never if by a new
one—unless at the writer's risk."

"The paltry rogues!" cried I. "Will they live by literature and yet
risk nothing for its sake? But, after all, you might publish on your
own account."

"And so I might," replied Oberon. "But the devil of the business
is this. These people have put me so out of conceit with the tales that
I loathe the very thought of them and actually experience a physical
sickness of the stomach whenever I glance at them on the table. I
tell you there is a demon in them! I anticipate a wild enjoyment in
seeing them in the blaze, such as I should feel in taking vengeance on
an enemy, or destroying something noxious."

I did not very strenuously oppose this determination, being privately of opinion, in spite of my partiality for the author, that his
tales would make a more brilliant appearance in the fire than anywhere else. Before proceeding to execution, we broached the bottle of
champagne, which Oberon had provided for keeping up his spirits
in this doleful business. We swallowed each a tumblerful, in sparkling

commotion; it went bubbling down our throats and brightened my eyes at once, but left my friend sad and heavy as before. He drew the tales toward him, with a mixture of natural affection and natural disgust, like a father taking a deformed infant into his arms.

"Pooh! Pish! Pshaw!" exclaimed he, holding them at arm's length. "It was Gray's idea of Heaven, to lounge on a sofa and read new novels. Now, what more appropriate torture would Dante himself have contrived, for the sinner who perpetrates a bad book, than to be continually turning over the manuscript?"

"It would fail of effect," said I, "because a bad author is always his own great admirer."

"I lack that one characteristic of my tribe—the only desirable one," observed Oberon. "But how many recollections throng upon me as I turn over these leaves! This scene came into my fancy as I walked along a hilly road on a starlight October evening; in the pure and bracing air, I became all soul and felt as if I could climb the sky and run a race along the Milky Way. Here is another tale, in which I wrapt myself during a dark and dreary night ride in the month of March, till the rattling of the wheels and the voices of my companions seemed like faint sounds of a dream, and my visions a bright reality. That scribbled page describes shadows which I summoned to my bedside at midnight: they would not depart when I bade them; the gray dawn came and found me wide awake and feverish, the victim of my own enchantments!"

"There must have been a sort of happiness in all this," said I, smitten with a strange longing to make proof of it.

"There may be happiness in a fever fit," replied the author. "And then the various moods in which I wrote! Sometimes my ideas were like precious stones under the earth, requiring toil to dig them up and care to polish and brighten them, but often a delicious stream of thought would gush out upon the page at once, like water sparkling up suddenly in the desert; and when it had passed I gnawed my pen hopelessly, or blundered on with cold and miserable toil, as if there were a wall of ice between me and my subject."

"Do you now perceive a corresponding difference," inquired I, "between the passages which you wrote so coldly and those fervid flashes of the mind?"

"No," said Oberon, tossing the manuscripts on the table. "I find no traces of the golden pen with which I wrote in characters of fire. My treasure of fairy coin is changed to worthless dross. My picture, painted in what seemed the loveliest hues, presents nothing but a faded and indistinguishable surface. I have been eloquent and poetical and humorous in a dream—and behold! it is all nonsense, now that I am awake."

My friend now threw sticks of wood and dry chips upon the fire and, seeing it blaze like Nebuchadnezzar's furnace, seized the champagne bottle and drank two or three brimming bumpers successively. The heady liquor combined with his agitation to throw him into a species of rage. He laid violent hands on the tales. In one instant more their faults and beauties would alike have vanished in a glowing purgatory. But, all at once, I remembered passages of high imagination, deep pathos, original thoughts and points of such varied excellence that the vastness of the sacrifice struck me most forcibly. I caught his arm.

"Surely, you do not mean to burn them!" I exclaimed.

"Let me alone!" cried Oberon, his eyes flashing fire. "I will burn them! Not a scorched syllable shall escape! Would you have me a damned author? To undergo sneers, taunts, abuse, and cold neglect, and faint praise, bestowed, for pity's sake, against the giver's conscience! A hissing and laughingstock to my own traitorous thoughts! An outlaw from the protection of the grave—one whose ashes every careless foot might spurn, unhonored in life and remembered scornfully in death! Am I to bear all this, when yonder fire will insure me from the whole? No! There go the tales! May my hand wither when it would write another!"

The deed was done. He had thrown the manuscripts into the hottest of the fire, which at first seemed to shrink away, but soon curled around them and made them a part of its own fervent brightness. Oberon stood gazing at the conflagration and shortly began to soliloquize in the wildest strain, as if Fancy resisted and became riotous at the moment when he would have compelled her to ascend that funeral pile. His words described objects which he appeared to discern in the fire, fed by his own precious thoughts; perhaps the thousand visions which the writer's magic had incorporated with these pages became visible to him in the dissolving heat, brightening forth ere they vanished forever, while the smoke, the vivid sheets of flame, the ruddy and whitening coals caught the aspect of a varied scenery.

"They blaze," said he, "as if I had steeped them in the intensest spirit of genius. There I see my lovers clasped in each other's arms. How pure the flame that bursts from their glowing hearts! And yonder the features of a villain writhing in the fire that shall torment him to eternity. My holy men, my pious and angelic women stand like martyrs amid the flames, their mild eyes lifted heavenward. Ring out the bells! A city is on fire. See!—destruction roars through my dark forests, while the lakes boil up in steaming billows, and the mountains are volcanoes, and the sky kindles with a lurid brightness! All elements are but one pervading flame! Ha! The fiend!"

I was somewhat startled by this latter exclamation. The tales were almost consumed but just then threw forth a broad sheet of fire, which flickered as with laughter, making the whole room dance in its brightness, and then roared portentously up the chimney.

"You saw him? You must have seen him!" cried Oberon. "How he glared at me and laughed, in that last sheet of flame, with just the features that I imagined for him! Well! The tales are gone."

The papers were indeed reduced to a heap of black cinders, with a multitude of sparks hurrying confusedly among them, the traces of the pen being now represented by white lines, and the whole mass fluttering to and fro in the draughts of air. The destroyer knelt down to look at them.

"What is more potent than fire!" said he in his gloomiest tone. "Even thought, invisible and incorporeal as it is, cannot escape it. In this little time it has annihilated the creations of long nights and days, which I could no more reproduce, in their first glow and freshness, than cause ashes and whitened bones to rise up and live. There, too, I sacrificed the unborn children of my mind. All that I had accomplished—all that I planned for future years—has perished by one common ruin and left only this heap of embers! The deed has been my fate. And what remains? A weary and aimless life—a long repentance of this hour—and at last an obscure grave, where they will bury and forget me!"

As the author concluded his dolorous moan the extinguished embers arose and settled down and arose again, and finally flew up the chimney, like a demon with sable wings. Just as they disappeared there was a loud and solitary cry in the street below us. "Fire!" Fire! Other voices caught up that terrible word, and it speedily became the shout of a multitude. Oberon started to his feet in fresh excitement.

"A fire on such a night!" cried he. "The wind blows a gale, and wherever it whirls the flames the roofs will flash up like gunpowder. Every pump is frozen up, and boiling water would turn to ice the moment it was flung from the engine. In an hour this wooden town will be one great bonfire! What a glorious scene for my next—— Pshaw!"

The street was now all alive with footsteps and the air full of voices. We heard one engine thundering round a corner and another rattling from a distance over the pavements. The bells of three steeples clanged out at once, spreading the alarm to many a neighboring town and expressing hurry, confusion, and terror, so inimitably that I could almost distinguish in their peal the burden of the universal cry, "Fire! Fire! Fire!"

"What is so eloquent as their iron tongues!" exclaimed Oberon. "My heart leaps and trembles, but not with fear. And that other sound, too—deep and awful as a mighty organ—the roar and thunder of the multitude on the pavement below! Come! We are losing time. I will cry out in the loudest of the uproar and mingle my spirit with the wildest of the confusion and be a bubble on the top of the ferment!"

From the first outcry my forebodings had warned me of the true object and center of alarm. There was nothing now but uproar, above, beneath, and around us; footsteps stumbling pell-mell up the public staircase, eager shouts and heavy thumps at the door, the whiz and dash of water from the engines, and the crash of furniture thrown upon the pavement. At once the truth flashed upon my friend. His frenzy took the hue of joy, and with a wild gesture of exultation he leaped almost to the ceiling of the chamber.

"My tales!" cried Oberon. "The chimney! The roof! The fiend has gone forth by night and startled thousands in fear and wonder from their beds! Here I stand—a triumphant author! Huzza! Huzza! My brain has set the town on fire! Huzza!"

BALAAM FOSTER'S FIDDLE

Chapman J. Milling

BACK in de olden times all de music in dese parts was made by nigger fiddlers or banjo pickers or guitar players. Ever' plantation nuster have two or three real good ones to play for de white folks' dances an' parties. Hit was good pickin' for a man what hadn't been converted— co'se now, fiddlin' never was de thing for a man atter he bawned ag'in—but de fiddler boys would be give' a good dinner an' drinks an' ginally a han'ful of money too. Natchelly, mos' de young bucks want to be fiddlers.

Now dis hyah Balaam was as likely a boy as ever been raise in dis part de country, so I been tole. He six foot tall an' able to do a power o' work. All de 'oomans crazy 'bout him, but he ain' never stick to one un 'em mo'n a week at a time. All he care 'bout was dat fiddle of hisn. He fiddle from mawnin' till night, den fiddle right on atter de las' rooster crow. He could beat anybody else fiddlin', but he want to say satisfy. He say he gwine be de bes' fiddler in de whole worl', let 'lone de country. Ever'body tell him 'taint no nuse to try to git any better, 'cause he done able to outfiddle anybody else what had ever been hear tell of. He already playin' to all de white folks' dances an' totin' silver money in he pocket an' tu'nin' up he nose at de other niggers.

Well, one day he gone down by de creek wid he fiddle in he han' lak he allus use to tote it. He set down top of a stump an' he start studyin'. He say to hisse'f, "I shore wisht I could play dis here fiddle like I wanta play it. Co'se I know I got all dese here other niggers beat, but I want to show 'em some real fiddlin'!"

Wid dat he taken an' scrape a few sof' notes on he fiddle an' say, "Ole fiddle, you do very well now, but I aims to make you natchelly talk one dese days."

De words wa'n't out'n he mout' 'fo' a voice come right out de fiddle an' say, "If you wants me to talk, Balaam, I talkin' now. What you want me to say?"

When he hear dat voice in de fiddle, Balaam mos' drop it out'n he han', he so scared, but he git up 'nough strengt' to answer de voice back. "Ole fiddle," he say, "I'll tell you what I want. I want you to make us 'nough money to buy us freedom. Den you'n' me'll go all over de country an' see all sorts of places an' have all de licker us wants."

"All right," say de fiddle, "but you cain't play good 'nough yet, Balaam. You jes' startin' good. You shore is got to git better dan you is now."

"Why, I 'lowed I could play pretty good now," say Balaam.

"Pretty good ain't to say plum good," say de fiddle.

"What I hafta do to git plum good?" Balaam ax.

"Nuttin' much," say de voice. "All you got to do is to go to de crossroads ever' night for nine nights an' make a cross mark in de middle o' de road. On de las' night you make de mark somebody'll be dar to tell you what to do nex'." Atter dis de fiddle ain't speak no mo'.

Balaam set an' he study, an' de longer he set de mo' he study. Somep'm tell him dat if he follow dat voice out de fiddle he'll be los' in sin, but when he done 'bout 'cide not to go somep'm else 'suade him it ain' no harm nohow. So he set dar a-rasslin' wid dem two no-tion' till dark catch him 'fo' he knowed it. Den he git up an' start for home, still a-studyin'. He study so hard he ain't pay no min' whar he gwine, an' fus' news you know, dar he been in de middle o' de crossroads. He git kinda frighten' when he fin' hisse'f dar, but he taken he fiddle an' he play a chune or two right dar in de middle o' de road, an' when he finish playin' he taken he foot an' mark a cross right whar de two roads meet. Jes' as he make de mark he hear a noise an' when he look up dar been a great big ole rabbit a-settin' side de road in de moonlight an' a-lookin' straight atter him. Balaam ain't like de looks o' dat rabbit, but he make out he ain't scared, so's he retch down an' heave a rock at him. De rock miss de rabbit, an' jes' as Balaam tu'n to leave hit seem like he hear dat rabbit say somep'm 'bout he'd fiddle better Friday atter nex'. Den he gone on home.

De nex' day Balaam ain't no good for work. He jes' set 'roun' an' play chunes on he fiddle, mournful an' scary like. An' dat night he take an' ramble off, an' whar you reckon he win' up? De crossroads, you mought know!

When he git dar Balaam say to hisse'f, "Shorely can't be no harm makin' jes' one mo' cross mark. Maybe I'll go to de big meetin' nex' fall an' dat'll make it all right." So's he gone on an' taken he foot an' make 'nother cross mark right whar he make de one de night befo'. An' jes' as he turn 'roun' to go dar been dat same ole rabbit a-settin' in de moonlight a-laughin' at him. But Balaam a bol' fellow, 'cause he taken an' throw another rock at him jes' like he done de night befo', but it ain't do no good, 'cause he miss him ag'in. An' atter he throw de rock, he ain't sure, but seem like to Balaam dat de rabbit say de same thing as las' night 'bout he fiddlin'.

Dis here business kep' up for six mo' nights, an' Balaam study so much, people think he gittin' mindless. Ever' night he slip out an' head for de crossroads, an' ever' time he git dar he make some 'scuse to go on an' make de cross mark. An' ever' single time he make de mark he see dat same ole rabbit laughin' at him when he tu'n 'roun'.

De las' day Balaam study so much dat he mos' crazy sho' nough. He play he fiddle all day long an' set 'roun' an' look 'way off. De Cap'm sen' for de doctor to fin' out what ail Balaam, but all he do was to gin him a big dose of physic salts. De Cap'm ax him what ail Balaam, an' de doctor tell him ain't nuttin' ail him less'n he hoodooed. So de Cap'm think he all right an' gone on off an' lef' him 'lone.

Well, dat night Balaam slip off ag'in an' he head straight for de crossroads dis time. He walk fas' an' when he git dar he make he cross mark quick, so's he won't have time to change his min'. Atter he make de mark hit didn' look like nuttin' gwine happen, an' Balaam begin to breave easy when he hear somebody call he name. He look up, an' shore 'nough dar been dat same ole rabbit a-settin' right whar he allus set.

"I gwine to git you dis time," Balaam holler, an' wid dat he grab up a rock an' sail it at dat air rabbit hard as he could let her fly. But de rock sail right on th'oo dat rabbit. When he seen dat, Balaam gin a screech an' make a grab at 'nother rock, but he han' was strike to he side an' de rabbit jes' disappear. In he place Balaam see a black cloud full of smoke an' sulphur, an he hear a fiddle comin' from de cloud an' a voice singin':

> *"Munanee, munanee ho!*
> *Munanee, munanee ho!*
> *Munanee, munanee ho!*
> *Big pot o' mush I gwine to git dar."*

Wid dat de cloud part in two an' out step de natchel ole Bugger Man hisse'f, lookin' jes' like people say he look. He had a long tail wid a arrer p'int; he hoofs was clove an' he tote a long, slim, narrer li'l pitchfork. He look to be 'bout six foot tall an' he had on a black robe line' wid red velvet on de inside. He step out an' bow perlite like white folks an' he say:

"Evenin', Mister Foster, sho is a pretty fiddle you got dar. I hears dat you'd like to be able to play a li'l better dan you been a-playin'. Now you jes' lemme hol' yo' fiddle a minute an' I'll show you some rale playin'. I de inventor of de fiddle, you know."

By dis time Balaam so scared he han' he fiddle right over to de Bugger Man. De ole Bugger Man take he fiddle an' bow low an' switch he tail sassy-like an' start in for to play. An' de chunes he didn't git out'n dat fiddle. He make de air natchelly ring like silver bells; he make hit soun' like all de mockin'birds in de whole worl' a-bustin' dey th'oats at de same time. He make hit soun' like cowbells late in de evenin' an' de song of little frogs down by de millpon'. He make dat fiddle sob an' cry. Hit soun' like a 'ooman moanin' for her los' man. Hit soun' like people singin' acrost still water. Den he turnt 'roun' an' play dance chunes an' reels, an' Balaam jes' can't stan' it less'n he stomp an' pat he han'.

When de Bugger Man done playin' it wa'n't nuttin' Balaam wouldn't give to be able to play dat-a-way, an' when de Bugger Man ax him would he 'gree to whatever he say, Balaam say, "Sho I will!" So right den an' dar de Bugger Man make Balaam promise him he'd serve him all he life an' let him have he soul when he die. To bin' de promise, Balaam have to bow down to Satan an' receive de serpent mark on he lef' shoulder. He have to eat a moufful of powder Satan give him an' he have to swaller some of Satan' spit. When he do all dem things de Bugger Man han' him back he fiddle an' disappear right 'fo' he eyes th'oo a hole in de groun' what open up whar he standin'. When he drap outa sight a great smoke come out de hole an' flames belch fo'th an' Balaam smell sulphur an' brimstone.

Balaam so scared by dis time dat he mos' forgit he fiddle, but in a minute he 'member it an' he taken an' try a chune or so. He fin' when he done dat he could play jes' as good as de Bugger Man. Dat make him so happy he git over bein' scared an' he gone on home an' gone to bed. De nex' day he take he fiddle up an' fin' he kin still play jes' as good as de Bugger Man, an' dat make him so proud he glad of he bargain.

It wa'n't long 'fo' ever'body axin' for Balaam to play, an' dey jes' wouldn' be satisfy less'n he come. He reppertation gone all over de country. De ole Cap'm glad 'nough to let him go, 'cause he got so he wa'n't no good nohow for nuttin' 'cep'n fiddlin'. By'mby Balaam had save 'nough money to buy he freedom. He kep' on playin' for ever' dance an' party he hear 'bout. Hit git so he gone fifty an' a hundred mile 'way f'um home to play. He live to be a ole man, but nemmine how ole he been, he play jes' as good as ever.

One day, atter Balaam no tellin' how ole, he call he ole 'ooman an' all he chillun an' gran'chillun 'roun' him an' tell 'em he gwine die. He ain't look sick, an' he say he ain't feel sick, but he sho he time done come. Dey want to sen' for de doctor right away, but Balaam tell 'em it wa'n't no nuse. He say, dough, dat he got somep'm to tell 'em, an' when dey been all 'gether 'roun' he 'splain to 'em 'bout what happen dat night to de crossroads. When he tell em dat, dey all start to cry an' moan an' car' on, but Balaam ax 'em not to do dat-a-way, 'cause it ain' gwine do no good. When dey sorta quiet'n down he tell 'em dat when he die dey mus' lay him out, an' atter he be lay out a clap o' thunder would come, an' when dey hear dat dey mought know he soul had enter Tarment. Atter he tell 'em dat, hit seem like he feel better, an' he git outa de bed an' fetch he fiddle out de trunk an' start to play "Turkey in de Straw."

He play so good dat de mourners couldn't he'p pattin' an' stompin' to save dey souls. When he finish playin' he take de fiddle over to de trunk, lock de lid, an' throw de key in de fire. Den he walk back to de bed, lie down, an' breave he las'.

De mourners all stay quiet for a minute, den dey make sho he gone for true, an' dey put de money on he eye an' sen' for de preacher.

But whilst dey all a-standin' 'roun' lookin' at de co'pse, de fiddle in de trunk commence to play. Hit play de lonesomes' chunes you ever hear, an' ever' note hit play soun' like hit was sayin' "Po' los' soul! Po' los' soul!"

De people in de house couldn' stan' no sicha doin's, an' dey all make a break for de door. Soon's dey git outside de house dey git bolder, an' one de mens grab up a ax an' say he gwine in dar an' bus' open dat trunk an' smash dat fiddle. De res' o' de people back him up an' say for him to go on in, so he spit on he han's an' take holda de ax like he mean business an' gone on back in de house. Time he outa sight de people outside hear a voice comin' out de house 'long wid de music o' de fiddle an' hit soun' like hit say:

> "*Munanee, munanee ho!*
> *Munanee, munanee ho!*
> *Munanee, munanee ho!*
> *Big pot o' mush I gwine to git dar.*"

Jes' as soon as dat song stop dar come a turrible peal o' thunder an' de whole house shake same as de Charleston yearthquake. De man wid de ax come a-flyin' out like a mule done kick 'im. De lamp inside was blowed out an' de whole place smell like smoke. After while some de mens git bol' 'nough to go in an' see what had happen. But soon as dey git inside de ones outside hear 'em holler, "Whar Balaam?"

Wid dat de res' of de mens gone on in an' dey fin' dat, sho 'nough, de co'pse done gone, an' whar he been a-lyin' all de bedclothes was scorch black as de chimbly flue. Atter dey see Balaam' co'pse done gone dey think 'bout de fiddle an' gone over to de trunk, but it wa'n't no nuse o' dat. Dat trunk got a hole burn out de top big as a nail kag, an' hit was all scorch' on de inside, an' dat fiddle was gone for keeps. So dat was de een o' Balaam Foster an' he conjured fiddle.

Tell me nuttin' 'bout no fiddlin'. Dese days dey got fiddles in de chu'ches an' ever'whars else, but us ole people what know 'bout Balaam, us ain't got no nuse for fiddlin'.

SATAN AND SAM SHAY

Robert Arthur

I AM TOLD that sin has somewhat declined since Satan met Sam Shay. I cannot vouch for this, but they say that production has definitely fallen off since that evening when Sam Shay won three wagers from the Devil. And this is the tale of it.

Sam Shay, you'll understand, was a bold rascal with Irish blood in his veins, though Yankee-born and -bred. Six feet he stood, with wide shoulders and a grin and dark hair with a touch of curl to it. Looking at his hands and his brawn, you'd hardly have guessed he'd never done an honest day's labor in his life. But it was true. For Sam was a gambling man, and since he was a boy, matching coppers or playing odd and even with his fellows, every penny passing through his fingers had been the fruit of wagering. And he was now approaching his thirtieth year.

Do not think to his discredit, however, that Sam Shay was a flinty-hearted professional betting only on things that were sure or at odds much tipped in his favor. He bet not mathematically but by intuition, and the betting was as important as the winning. Were you to have given him the money he would not have taken it; there would have been no savor to it. He must win it by his wits to enjoy it, and he could find fun in losing a good wager too.

So it was a sad thing to Sam that the one girl of his heart, Shannon Malloy, should be dead set against gambling. But the late Malloy had squandered all his earnings in just such divertisements as Sam Shay enjoyed, and the Widow Malloy had brought her daughter up most strictly to abjure men who loved the sound of rolling dice, the riffle of the cards, or the quickening of the pulse that comes as the horses turn into the home stretch and stream for the finish line.

In the early days of their acquaintance Shannon Malloy, who was small, with dark eyes that held a glow in their depths, had overlooked Sam's failing, feeling that Sam would mend his ways for love of her. And indeed Sam promised. But he could no more live without betting than he could without eating—less, for he could go a day without food undistressed, but in twenty years no sun had set without his making a wager of some kind, however small, just to keep his hand in.

Frequently, therefore, Sam Shay found himself in disgrace, while Shannon, more in sorrow than in anger, pleaded with him. And each time Sam once again promised to reform, knowing in his heart that once again he would fail. Inevitably, then, there came the time when Shannon, putting aside the veils that love cast upon her vision, saw with sad clarity that Sam Shay was Sam Shay, and naught would alter him. She loved him, but her convictions were as adamant. So she gave him back the ring she had accepted from him when his resolves had been less tarnished.

"I'm sorry, Sam," she had said, this very evening, and her words rang knell-like in Sam's ears now as he strode homeward through the soft evening dusk that lay across the park. "I'm sorry," and her voice had broken. "But today I heard your name spoken. By some men. And they were saying you are a born gambler who could make three bets with Satan and win them all. And if that is true, I can't marry you. Not feeling as I do. Not until you change."

And Sam, knowing that only some force far stronger than himself could turn him from his wagering, took the ring and went with only one backward glance. That glance showed him Shannon Malloy weeping but resolute, and he was as proud of her resolution as disconsolate that she should feel so strongly about his little weakness.

The ring was in his pocket and his fingers touched it sadly as he walked. It was a circlet cold to the touch, a metal zero that summed the total of his chances for having Shannon Malloy to wife. The twilight lay upon the park, and it was queerly hushed, as if something was impending. But, lost in his thoughts, he strode along taking no notice.

It was as he came abreast an ancient oak that the shadow of the tree, athwart the sidewalk, with great unexpectedness solidified into a pillar of blackness church-steeple high, which condensed swiftly into a smallish individual with flowing white locks and a benign countenance.

The individual who had so unconventionally placed himself in Sam's path was clad in garments of sober cut, an old-fashioned cape slung over his shoulders, and a soft dark hat upon his white hair. He smiled with innocent engagingness at Samuel Shay and spoke in a voice both mild and friendly.

"Good evening, Sam," he said, as one might to an acquaintance not seen in a great while. "I'll bet you don't know who I am."

But Sam Shay, his right hand gripping the stout thorn stick he liked to carry about with him, was not to be trapped. He had seen the shadow of an oak tree change into a man, and this, to say the least, was unusual.

"Why," he proclaimed boldly, "I have a hundred dollars in my pocket, and I'll lay it against one that you are Satan."

Satan—for Sam's intuition had not failed him—let an expression of displeasure cross the benign countenance he had assumed for this visit. For he, too, had heard the report Shannon Malloy had quoted to Sam—that he could make three bets with Satan and win them all. And, his curiosity aroused, the Devil had come to test Sam's prowess, for he was fond of gambling, though a bad loser.

But the expression was gone in an instant and the gentle smile resumed its place. The old gentleman reached beneath his cloak and brought out a wallet which bulged pleasingly, although it was of a leather whose appearance Sam did not care for.

"That may be, Sam," Satan replied genially. "And if I am, I owe you a dollar. But I have another hundred here says you can't prove it."

And he waited, well pleased, for this was a wager that had stumped many eminent philosophers in centuries past. But Sam Shay was a man of action, not of words.

"Taken," he agreed at once, and raised his thorn stick above his head. "I'll just bash you a time or two over the pate. If you're an honest citizen I'll take your wallet, and if you're Satan I'll win the wager. For you could not let a mortal man trounce you so and still look yourself in the eye—an accomplishment quite individually yours. So——"

And Sam brought the stick down in a whistling blow.

A sulphurous sheet of flame cracked out from the heart of the oak tree, and the thorn stick was riven into a thousand splinters that hissed away through the air. A strong pain shot up Sam's arm, a tingling, numbing sensation that extended to the shoulder. But, rubbing his wrist, he was well satisfied.

Not so Satan. In his anger the little old gentleman had shot upward until he loomed twelve feet high now, and looked far more terrifying than benign.

"You win, Sam Shay," Satan told him sourly. "But there's a third bet yet to come." Which Sam knew to be true, for on any such occasion as this when the Devil showed himself to a mortal, the unhappy man must win three wagers from him to go free. "And this time we'll increase the stakes. Your soul against the contents of this wallet that you can't win from me again."

Sam did not hesitate. For he must wager, whether he would or not.

"Taken," he answered. "But I must name the bet, since you named the others, and it is my turn now."

Satan it was who hesitated, but right and logic were with Sam, so he nodded.

"Name it, then," he directed, and his voice was like grumbling thunder beyond the sky line.

"Why, as to that," Sam told him with an impudent grin, "I'm betting you do not intend for me to win this wager."

Hardly were the words out of his mouth before Satan, in uncontrolled rage, had shot up to a tremendous height, his black cloak flowing from him like night itself draping over the city. For Sam had caught him neatly. If he responded that he did intend for Sam to win, then Sam perforce must go free. And if he responded that he had not so intended, then Sam won anyway.

Glaring down from his great height, Satan directed an awful gaze upon Sam Shay.

"This is an ill night's work you have done!" he cried in a voice that shook with rage, so that the skyscrapers near by trembled a bit, and the next day's papers carried an item concerning a small earthquake. "Hear me well, Sam Shay! From this moment onward, never shall you win another wager! All the forces of hell will be marshaled to prevent you."

Then, while Sam still gaped upward in dismay, the great figure faded from sight. A vast blast of hot air fanned past Sam, singeing the leaves of the nearest trees. He heard a distant clanging sound, as of a metal gate closing. After that all was quiet as it had been before.

Sam Shay stood in thought for several minutes and then realized he still was fingering the ring Shannon Malloy had returned to him. He laughed in something of relief.

"Glory!" he said aloud. "I've been standing here dreaming, while my mind wandered. If I'm to have nightmares, I'd best have them in bed."

And he hurried homeward, stopping by the way only long enough to buy the next day's racing form.

By morning Sam had half forgotten his queer bemusement of the evening before. But that Shannon had dismissed him and returned his ring he remembered all too well. The bit of gold seemed heavy in his pocket as the weight that lay on his heart, so that he set about choosing his wagers for the day's racing with a gloomy mind.

It was perhaps this gloom that made it harder than was customary for him to make a choice. Usually his intuition made quick decision. But today he labored long and was only half satisfied when he had finished marking down his picks.

Then, having breakfasted, with Shannon Malloy's face coming betwixt him and his coffee, he rode out to the track. Today he desired action, crowds, noise, excitement to take his mind off Shannon's rejection of him. So that the pushing throngs about the mutuel windows, the crowd murmur that rose to a shrill ululation as the horses burst from the barrier, the heart-tightening sensation as they turned into the home stretch, all fitted well into his mood.

And he was feeling better when, his tickets tucked inside his pocket, he stood with the rest and watched the leaders in the first swing round the turn. He was well pleased to note his choice to the fore by half a dozen lengths, when something happened. Perhaps the nag put its hoof into a pocket in the track. Perhaps it broke stride or merely tired. At all events, it faltered, slowed as though the Devil himself had it by the tail—now why had that precise comparison flashed across his mind then? Sam Shay wondered—and was beaten to the finish by a neck.

Sam tore up his tickets and scattered them to the breeze. He was not distressed. There were six races yet to come, and his pockets were well filled with money.

But when in the second his pick threw its jockey rounding the three-quarter pole and in the lead, and when in the third a saddle girth broke just as the jockey was lifting his mount for a winning surge, Sam Shay began to whistle a bit beneath his breath.

It was queer. It was decidedly queer, and he did not like it in the least. And when in the fourth, just as it was in the clear, his choice swerved and cut across the nag behind it, thus being disqualified, Sam's whistle grew more tuneless. He sniffed and sniffed again. Yes, it was there—the faintest whiff of sulphur somewhere about. In a most meditative mood Sam purchased a single two-dollar ticket for the fifth.

The ticket, as he had been unhappily convinced would be the case, proved a poor investment, his horse throwing a shoe at the far turn and pulling up last, limping badly.

Sam's whistle dropped until it was quite inaudible. He made his way toward the paddock and stood close as they led the winded horses out. As his choice passed he sniffed strongly. And this time there was the slightest touch of brimstone mixed with the smell of sulphur.

Walking with a slow pace that did not in any way reflect the churning of his thoughts, Sam Shay returned to the grandstand and in the minutes before the next race was run reflected fast and furiously. Already his pockets, so thickly lined but an hour before, were well-nigh empty. And apprehension was beginning to sit, a tiny cloud, on Sam's brow.

This time he bought no ticket. But he sought out an individual with whom he had had dealings and stood beside him as the race was run. The ponies were streaming around the three-quarter pole and into the stretch, with forty lengths and half-a-dozen horses separating the first nag from the last, when Sam spoke suddenly.

"Ten dollars," he said to his acquaintance, "to a dime that Seven doesn't win."

The bookie gave him an odd glance. For Seven was the trailer, forty lengths behind and losing distance steadily. Any mortal eye could see she couldn't win, and it came to him Sam might be daft.

"Twenty dollars!" said Samuel Shay. "To a five-cent piece!"

They were odds not to be resisted, and the bookie nodded.

"Taken!" he agreed, and the words were scarce out of his mouth before Seven put on a burst of speed. She seemed to rise into the air with the very rapidity of her motion. Her legs churned. And she whisked forward so fast her astonished jockey was but an ace from being blown out of the saddle by the very rush of air. Closing the gap in a manner quite unbelievable, she came up to the leaders and, with a scant yard to the finish, shot ahead to win.

The crowd was too dazed even to roar. The judges gathered at once in frowning conference. But nothing amiss with Seven's equipment could be found—no electric batteries or other illegal contrivances—so at last her number was posted.

Sam Shay paid over the twenty dollars, while his acquaintance goggled at him. He would have asked questions, but Sam was in no mood for conversation. He moved away and sought a seat. There he pondered.

There could no longer be any doubt. His dream of the evening before had been no dream. It was Satan himself he had met face to face in the park, and Satan was having his vengeance for being bested. Sam could not call to mind the name of any other man in history who had outwitted the Devil without ruing it, and it was plain he was not to be the exception.

Wagering was Sam's life and livelihood, as Satan had well known. And if Sam was never to win another bet—— He swallowed hard at the thought. Not only would he have lost Shannon Malloy for naught, but he would even be forced to the indignity of earning his living by the strength of his hands, he who had lived by his wits so pleasantly for so long.

It was a sobering reflection. But for the moment no helpful scheme would come. Just before the warning bell for the last race of the day, however, Sam rose with alacrity. He counted his money. Aside from carfare back to town, he had just fourteen dollars upon him. Seven two-dollar tickets—and in the last there was a field of seven!

Sam chuckled and bought seven tickets to win, one on each of the entries. Then, feeling somewhat set up, he found a position of vantage. "Now," he said beneath his breath, "let's see the Devil himself keep you from having a winning ticket this time, Samuel Shay!" And complacently he watched his seven horses get off to a good start.

The race proceeded normally toward the half, and then to the three quarters, with nothing untoward come about. Sam chuckled some more, for if he cashed a ticket on this race, then Satan had been bested again, and his curse on Sam's wagering broken.

But the chuckle came too soon. As the seven turned into the stretch, into a sky that had been cerulean blue leaped a storm cloud purple and black. From the cloud a bolt of lightning sped downward, in a blinding flash, to strike among the branches of an ancient elm which stood beside the grandstand near the finish line. A horrid thunder-clap deafened the throng. The elm tottered. Then it toppled and fell across the track, so that the seven jockeys were just able to pull up their mounts in time to avoid plunging into it.

And as sudden as it had come, the storm cloud was gone.

But obviously there could be no winner of the last race. The per-plexed and shaken stewards hurriedly declared it no race and an-nounced that all bets would be refunded. Sam received his money back —but that was not winning. And with the bills thrust into his coat he gloomily returned to his lodgings to devote more thought to this mat-ter. For it was plain the Devil had meant what he had said—Sam would never win another wager. And with all the myriad hosts of Hell arrayed against him, Sam did not see what he could do about it.

But the Shays were never a quitter stock. Though Beelzebub and all his myrmidons opposed him, Sam was of no mind to turn to honest labor without giving the Devil a run for his money. So in the days that followed, Sam, with dogged resolution, did not cease his efforts to make a wager he could win. And his endeavors were a source of some concern in Hell.

It was on an afternoon two weeks perhaps after the fateful meeting between Satan and Sam Shay that the Devil recalled the matter to his mind and pressed a button summoning his chief lieutenant to make report. Whisking from his private laboratory, where he was engaged in a delicate experiment leading toward the creation of a brand-new and improved form of sin, his head assistant covered seven million miles in no time at all and deposited himself in Satan's presence, still scorching from the speed at which he had come.

The Devil, seated behind a desk of basalt, frowned upon him.

"I wish," he stated, "to know if my orders concerning the mortal y-clept Sam Shay have been carried out."

"To the letter, Infernal Highness," his lieutenant replied with a slight air of reserve.

"He has not won a wager since I pronounced my curse upon him?"

"Not of the most inconsequential kind."

"He is thoroughly miserable?"

"Completely so."

"He is in such despair he might even commit suicide, and so place himself in our hands?"

The other was silent. Satan's voice took on sharpness.

"He is *not* in despair?"

"He is in a very low frame of mind indeed," his chief assistant replied with reluctance. "But there is no notion of suicide in his mind. He is defiant. And troublesome in the extreme, I must add."

"Troublesome?" The three-billion-bulb chandelier overhead rattled. "How can a mere mortal be troublesome to the hosts of Hell? Kindly explain yourself."

The tips of his lieutenant's batwings quivered with inward nervousness, and absently he plucked a loose scale from his chest. But summoning his resolution, he answered.

"He is a persistent mortal, this Sam Shay," he replied humbly. "Although your infernal curse has been passed upon him, he refuses to be convinced he cannot evade it. He is constantly scheming to get around the fiat by means of trickery and verbal quibbling. And I have had to assign a good many of my best and most resourceful workers to keep a twenty-four-hour watch on Sam Shay to see he does not succeed. Let me explain.

"Last week, having already tried some hundreds of wagers of various kinds, he offered to bet an acquaintance it would not rain before noon. The wager was the merest quibble of a bet, for it then lacked but ten seconds of the hour, the sun was shining in a cloudless sky, and, in addition, the Weather Bureau had actually predicted storm.

"Sam Shay, however, got his gamble accepted by promising to spend double his winnings, if he won, on strong drink for his companion. A completely specious wager if ever one was made. Nevertheless, had it not rained before the hour of noon, technically he would have been the winner of a bet, and so the letter of your hellish curse would have been violated.

"So, upon the notice of merest seconds, I had to call two hundred and eighty workers away from urgent duty in Proselytizing, to borrow on an instant's notice another hundred from Punishment, to take a score of my best laboratory technicians off Research, and rush them all to the spot. Between them they managed to divert a storm that was raging over Ohio and scheduled to cause a flood estimated to produce for us a job lot of a hundred and eighty souls, whisking it to cover New England within the time limit.

"But the affair caused widespread comment, threw us off schedule, and has disrupted my entire force, due to the necessity of keeping a large emergency squad upon twenty-four-hour duty in constant readiness for any other such calls. And there have been dozens of them. Simply dozens!"

A drop of sweat rolled down the unhappy demon's brow, dissolving in steam.

"That's only a sample," he said earnestly. "This Sam Shay has scores of such tricks up his sleeves. Only yesterday he was attempting to win a wager at the race track, and his efforts kept us busy the entire afternoon. In the fifth race he made such a complicated series of bets as to the relative positions in which the various horses would finish that my most trusted aide completely lost track of them. He had to call on me personally at the last moment, and since one of the wagers was that the race itself wouldn't be finished, the only solution I could hit upon in time was to have all the horses finish in a dead heat, save for the one Sam Shay had bet upon to win.

"This one, in order to confound the fellow, I was forced to remove entirely from the race and set down in Australia, so that none of Shay's various stipulations concerning it could come true. But the talk caused by a seven-horse dead heat, together with the complete disappearance of one of the beasts and its jockey, caused a considerable stir.

"Taken in conjunction with the storm I had to arrange, and a number of similar matters, it has started a religious revival. People are flocking into the churches, undoing some of our best work. So, Your Infernal Highness, if only we could overlook one or two of Sam Shay's more difficult wagers, it would make things much easier to——"

The crash of Satan's hoofs upon the adamantine tiling cut him short.

"Never! I have put my curse upon this Shay! It must be carried out to the letter. Tend to it!"

"Yes, Prince of Evil," his head assistant squeaked and, being a prudent demon, hurled himself away and across the seven million miles of space to his laboratory so swiftly that he struck with such force at the other end he was lame for a month. And never again did he dare mention the matter.

But of all this Sam Shay had no inkling. He was immersed in his own problems. Having failed in every wager he had made, however difficult to lose, he was in a depressed state of mind.

His resources were coming to an end. There were but a few dollars left in his pockets and none in his bank account. Shannon Malloy refused to see him. He had not won a wager since the night he had met the Devil, and he was so low in his mind that several times he had caught himself glancing through the "Help Wanted" sections of the papers.

Upon this particular day he was so sunk in despair that it was the middle of the afternoon, and he had not once tried the Devil's mettle to see if this time he could slip a winning wager past the demonic forces on watchful guard all about him. It was a day cut and tailored to his mood. The sky was lowering gray, and rain whipped down out of the north as if each drop had personal anger against the earth upon which it struck. And Sam Shay sat in his room, staring out at the storm, as close to despair as it had ever been his misfortune to come.

At last he bestirred himself; it was not in the blood of a Shay to sit thus, forever wrapped in gray gloom. He found his hat and ulster and with heavy step made his way out and down the street to a cozy bar and grill where perhaps a cheery companion might lighten his mood.

Ensconced in a corner where a fireplace glowed he found Tim Malloy, who was by way of being Shannon's brother, a round, merry little man who was the merrier because a mug of dark stood upon the table before him. Tim Malloy greeted him with words of cheer, and Sam sat himself down, answering as nearly in kind as he might. He ordered himself a mug of dark, too, and made inquiry concerning Shannon.

"Why, as to that," Tim Malloy said, draining off half his mug, "sometimes of a night I hear her crying behind her locked door. And" —he drained off the rest of his dark—"she never did that before she gave you back your ring, Sam."

"Have another," Sam invited, feeling suddenly somewhat heartened. "Then mayhap she might take back the ring if I asked her, you think?" he asked, hope in his tone.

Tim Malloy accepted the dark, but after dipping into it shook his head, a mustache of foam on his lip.

"Never while you're a betting man, Sam, and that'll be forever," he said, "unless some wondrous force stronger than she is makes her do it. Not though she's unhappy the rest of her life from sending you away."

Sam sighed.

"Would it make any difference if she knew I lost all the wagers I make now?" he asked.

"Not so much as a pin point of difference," Tim Malloy answered. "Not so much as a pin point. To change the subject, how long will it keep raining, would you say?"

"All day, I suppose," Sam said, in a gloom again. "And all night, too, I've no doubt. Though I could stop it raining in five minutes if I'd a mind to."

"Could you so?" Tim Malloy said, interested. "Let's see how it goes, Sam. Just for curiosity's sake."

Sam Shay shrugged.

"Bet me a dollar it'll stop raining within five minutes," he said. "And I'll bet the same it'll not. But since it'll be costing me a dollar to show, you must promise to spend it back again treating me."

"Fair's fair," Tim Malloy answered prompt. "And I promise. Then, Sam, I bet you a dollar it'll stop raining inside five minutes."

Lackadaisically Sam accepted, and they laid their wagers out upon the table. And sure enough, within the five minutes the storm clouds overhead abruptly whisked away. The blue sky appeared; the sun shone, and it was as if the storm had never been.

"Now that's a curious thing, Sam," Tim Malloy said, eyes wide, as he ordered up more dark. "And if you could do that any time you wished, your fortune would be made."

"Oh, I can do it." Sam sighed, disinterested. "Fair to storm and storm to fair; I need but wager on it to make it come the opposite of my bet. For that matter, any event I make a gamble on will come out the opposite, be it what it may. It's a curse laid upon me, Tim."

"Is it now?" said Tim Malloy, and his eyes grew wider. "And by whom would the curse be laid, Sam Shay?"

Sam leaned forward and whispered in his ear, and Tim Malloy's eyes bade fair to start from their sockets.

"Draw in a deep breath," Sam said, nodding. "Sniff hard, Tim. You'll see."

Tim Malloy sniffed long and deep, and awe crept upon his features.

"Sulphur!" he whispered. "Sulphur and brimstone!"

Sam but nodded and went on drinking his dark. Tim Malloy, though, stretched out a hand and put it upon his arm.

"Sam," he said, voice hoarse, "you have never heard that there's people willing to pay good money to insure the weather'll be as they want it upon a certain day? Have you never heard of insuring against storms, Sam, and against accidents, sickness, twins, and such misfortunes? And insuring isn't really betting. It's but a business—a legitimate, money-making business."

Sam stopped drinking his dark. He put his mug upon the table with a bang, and upon his face there came a look.

"So it is," he said, struck by the sudden thought. "So it is!"

"Sam," Tim Malloy said, emotion in his tone, "let us take but a single example. This Sunday coming the Loyal Sons of St. Patrick parade. Suppose, then, the Loyal Sons said to you, 'Sam, we want to insure it does not storm this Sunday coming. Here's twenty dollars insurance money against rain. If it storms, now, you must pay us five hundred, but if it's fair, you keep the twenty.'

"And then suppose, Sam, you came to me and, 'Tim,' you'd say, 'I want to make a bet. And the bet is one dollar against another dollar that this Sunday coming it will rain.' Whereupon I'd say to you, 'Sam,

I accept the wager. One dollar to one dollar that it does not rain this Sunday coming.'

"And as you are doomed to lose your gamble, it does not rain; you keep the twenty dollars paid you by the Loyal Sons, and your profit, Sam, your fair profit on a straightforward business deal which no one could call gambling, would be——"

"Nineteen dollars!" Sam said, much moved. "Nineteen dollars profit, Tim, and no wager involved. And you say there are many people wanting such insurance?"

"Thousands of them," said Tim Malloy. "Thousands upon thousands of them. And there's no reason why you shouldn't insure them against anything they wish—seeing as you're backed, one might say, by all the resources of a tremendous big firm."

Sam Shay stood up, and in his eyes there was a light.

"Tim," he said in a voice that rang, "here is twenty dollars. Rent me an office and have a sign painted saying 'Samuel Shay, Insurance.' The biggest sign that can be managed. And here, Tim, is a dollar. That dollar I bet you Shannon will not say 'yes' to me a moment hence when I call upon her. Do you take the wager?"

"I take it, Sam," agreed Tim Malloy, but already Sam was striding out and in scarce a minute was standing in the Malloy living room, large and masterful, while Shannon, who had tried to hold the door shut against him, stared at him with blazing eyes.

"Sam Shay," she cried hotly, "I won't see you!"

"You cannot help seeing me," Sam replied with tenderness, "for I am standing here before you."

"Then I won't look at you!" cried Shannon, and shut her eyes.

"In that case you must take the consequences," said Sam and, stepping forward, kissed her so that Shannon's eyes flew open again.

"Sam Shay," she exclaimed, "I——"

"I'll bet a dollar," Sam interrupted her, "you're going to say you hate me."

It was indeed what Shannon had been about to say, but now some perverse demon seemed to seize her tongue.

"I'm not!" she denied. "I was going to say I love you." And, having said it, she stared at Sam as if she could not believe her ears.

"Then, Shannon darling," Sam Shay asked, "will you take back my ring and marry me? And I'll bet another dollar you're going to say no."

And "no" it was that Shannon tried to say. But once again it was as if a contrary devil had her tongue.

"Indeed I'm not," she declared, to her own consternation. "For I say yes, and I will."

With which Sam swept her into his arms and kissed her again, so soundly she had no more time to wonder at the way her tongue had twisted. Indeed, she was forced to believe it was some strange power in Sam himself that had drawn the words from her. And on this point Sam wisely refrained from ever correcting her.

Thus they were married, and at this moment Sam Shay's insurance business is prospering beyond belief. Money is flowing in from all sides, and, being a prudent man, Sam has arranged his affairs in excellent order. He has wagered with Tim Malloy, his junior partner, that he and Shannon will not live in good health to be ninety-nine each, while Tim has wagered they will. Sam has likewise bet that he and Shannon will be desperately unhappy, Tim gambling to the contrary. Finally Sam has gambled that they will not have ten fine, strapping children, six boys and four girls, and Tim has placed his money that they will.

So sin continues to decline as Sam's business grows, and Sam himself sleeps soundly of nights. And if there is sometimes the faintest smell of brimstone and sulphur about the house, as though from much coming and going of harassed demons, no one in the household minds it, not even Dion, youngest of the ten young Shays.

THE DEVIL AND DANIEL WEBSTER

Stephen Vincent Benét

IT'S A STORY they tell in the border country, where Massachusetts joins Vermont and New Hampshire.

Yes, Dan'l Webster's dead—or, at least, they buried him. But every time there's a thunderstorm around Marshfield, they say you can hear his rolling voice in the hollows of the sky. And they say that if you go to his grave and speak loud and clear, "Dan'l Webster—Dan'l Webster!" the ground'll begin to shiver and the trees begin to shake. And after a while you'll hear a deep voice saying, "Neighbor, how stands the Union?" Then you better answer the Union stands as she stood, rock-bottomed and copper-sheathed, one and indivisible, or he's liable to rear right out of the ground. At least, that's what I was told when I was a youngster.

You see, for a while, he was the biggest man in the country. He never got to be President, but he was the biggest man. There were thousands that trusted in him right next to God Almighty, and they told stories about him and all the things that belonged to him that were like the stories of patriarchs and such. They said, when he stood up to speak, stars and stripes came right out in the sky, and once he spoke against a river and made it sink into the ground. They said, when he walked the woods with his fishing rod, Killall, the trout would jump out of the streams right into his pockets, for they knew it was no use putting up a fight against him; and, when he argued a case, he could turn on the harps of the blessed and the shaking of the earth underground. That was the kind of man he was, and his big farm up at Marshfield was suitable to him. The chickens he raised were all white meat down through the drumsticks; the cows were tended like children, and the big ram he called Goliath had horns with a curl like a morning-glory vine and could butt through an iron door. But Dan'l wasn't one of your gentlemen farmers; he knew all the ways of the land, and he'd be up by candlelight to see that the chores got done. A man with a mouth like a mastiff, a brow like a mountain, and eyes like burning anthracite—that was Dan'l Webster in his prime. And the biggest case he argued never got written down in the books, for he argued it against the Devil, nip and tuck and no holds barred. And this is the way I used to hear it told.

There was a man named Jabez Stone, lived at Cross Corners, New Hampshire. He wasn't a bad man to start with, but he was an unlucky man. If he planted corn, he got borers; if he planted potatoes, he got blight. He had good-enough land, but it didn't prosper him; he had a decent wife and children, but the more children he had, the less there was to feed them. If stones cropped up in his neighbor's field, boulders boiled up in his; if he had a horse with the spavins, he'd trade it for one with the staggers and give something extra. There's some folks bound to be like that, apparently. But one day Jabez Stone got sick of the whole business.

He'd been plowing that morning and he'd just broke the plowshare on a rock that he could have sworn hadn't been there yesterday. And, as he stood looking at the plowshare, the off horse began to cough— that ropy kind of cough that means sickness and horse doctors. There were two children down with the measles; his wife was ailing, and he had a whitlow on his thumb. It was about the last straw for Jabez Stone. "I vow," he said, and he looked around him kind of desperate —"I vow it's enough to make a man want to sell his soul to the Devil! And I would, too, for two cents!"

Then he felt a kind of queerness come over him at having said what he'd said; though, naturally, being a New Hampshireman, he wouldn't take it back. But, all the same, when it got to be evening and, as far as he could see, no notice had been taken, he felt relieved in his mind, for he was a religious man. But notice is always taken, sooner or later, just like the Good Book says. And, sure enough, next day, about suppertime, a soft-spoken, dark-dressed stranger drove up in a handsome buggy and asked for Jabez Stone.

Well, Jabez told his family it was a lawyer, come to see him about a legacy. But he knew who it was. He didn't like the looks of the stranger, nor the way he smiled with his teeth. They were white teeth, and plentiful—some say they were filed to a point, but I wouldn't vouch for that. And he didn't like it when the dog took one look at the stranger and ran away howling, with his tail between his legs. But having passed his word, more or less, he stuck to it, and they went out behind the barn and made their bargain. Jabez Stone had to prick his finger to sign, and the stranger lent him a silver pin. The wound healed clean, but it left a little white scar.

II

After that, all of a sudden, things began to pick up and prosper for Jabez Stone. His cows got fat and his horses sleek; his crops were the envy of the neighborhood, and lightning might strike all over the valley, but it wouldn't strike his barn. Pretty soon, he was one of the prosperous people of the county; they asked him to stand for selectman, and he stood for it; there began to be talk of running him for state senate. All in all, you might say the Stone family was as happy and contented as cats in a dairy. And so they were, except for Jabez Stone.

He'd been contented enough, the first few years. It's a great thing when bad luck turns; it drives most other things out of your head. True, every now and then, especially in rainy weather, the little white scar on his finger would give him a twinge. And once a year, punctual as clockwork, the stranger with the handsome buggy would come driving by. But the sixth year, the stranger lighted, and, after that, his peace was over for Jabez Stone.

The stranger came up through the lower field, switching his boots with a cane—they were handsome black boots, but Jabez Stone never liked the look of them, particularly the toes. And, after he'd passed the time of day, he said, "Well, Mr. Stone, you're a hummer! It's a very pretty property you've got here, Mr. Stone."

"Well, some might favor it and others might not," said Jabez Stone, for he was a New Hampshireman.

"Oh, no need to decry your industry!" said the stranger, very easy, showing his teeth in a smile. "After all, we know what's been done, and it's been according to contract and specifications. So when—ahem —the mortgage falls due next year, you shouldn't have any regrets."

"Speaking of that mortgage, mister," said Jabez Stone, and he looked around for help to the earth and the sky, "I'm beginning to have one or two doubts about it."

"Doubts?" said the stranger, not quite so pleasantly.

"Why, yes," said Jabez Stone. "This being the U.S.A. and me always having been a religious man." He cleared his throat and got bolder. "Yes sir," he said, "I'm beginning to have considerable doubts as to that mortgage holding in court."

"There's courts and courts," said the stranger, clicking his teeth. "Still, we might as well have a look at the original document." And he hauled out a big black pocketbook, full of papers. "Sherwin, Slater, Stevens, Stone," he muttered. " 'I, Jabez Stone, for a term of seven years——' Oh, it's quite in order, I think."

But Jabez Stone wasn't listening, for he saw something else flutter out of the black pocketbook. It was something that looked like a moth, but it wasn't a moth. And as Jabez Stone stared at it, it seemed to speak to him in a small sort of piping voice, terrible small and thin, but terrible human.

"Neighbor Stone!" it squeaked. "Neighbor Stone! Help me! For God's sake, help me!"

But before Jabez Stone could stir a hand or foot, the stranger whipped out a big bandanna handkerchief, caught the creature in it, just like a butterfly, and started tying up the ends of the bandanna.

"Sorry for the interruption," he said. "As I was saying——"

But Jabez Stone was shaking all over like a scared horse.

"That's Miser Stevens' voice!" he said, in a croak. "And you've got him in your handkerchief!"

The stranger looked a little embarrassed.

"Yes, I really should have transferred him to the collecting box," he said with a simper, "but there were some rather unusual specimens there and I didn't want them crowded. Well, well, these little contretemps will occur."

"I don't know what you mean by contertan," said Jabez Stone, "but that was Miser Stevens' voice! And he ain't dead! You can't tell me he is! He was just as spry and mean as a woodchuck, Tuesday!"

"In the midst of life——" said the stranger, kind of pious. "Listen!" Then a bell began to toll in the valley and Jabez Stone listened, with the sweat running down his face. For he knew it was tolled for Miser Stevens and that he was dead.

"These long-standing accounts," said the stranger with a sigh; "one really hates to close them. But business is business."

He still had the bandanna in his hand, and Jabez Stone felt sick as he saw the cloth struggle and flutter.

"Are they all as small as that?" he asked hoarsely.

"Small?" said the stranger. "Oh, I see what you mean. Why, they vary." He measured Jabez Stone with his eyes, and his teeth showed. "Don't worry, Mr. Stone," he said. "You'll go with a very good grade. I wouldn't trust you outside the collecting box. Now, a man like Dan'l Webster, of course—well, we'd have to build a special box for him, and even at that, I imagine the wingspread would astonish you. He'd certainly be a prize. I wish we could see our way clear to him. But, in your case, as I was saying——"

"Put that handkerchief away!" said Jabez Stone, and he began to beg and to pray. But the best he could get at the end was a three years' extension, with conditions.

But till you make a bargain like that, you've got no idea of how fast four years can run. By the last months of those years, Jabez Stone's known all over the state and there's talk of running him for governor —and it's dust and ashes in his mouth. For every day, when he gets up, he thinks, "There's one more night gone," and every night when he lies down, he thinks of the black pocketbook and the soul of Miser Stevens, and it makes him sick at heart. Till, finally, he can't bear it any longer, and, in the last days of the last year, he hitches up his horse and drives off to seek Dan'l Webster. For Dan'l was born in New Hampshire, only a few miles from Cross Corners, and it's well known that he has a particular soft spot for old neighbors.

III

It was early in the morning when he got to Marshfield, but Dan'l was up already, talking Latin to the farm hands and wrestling with the ram, Goliath, and trying out a new trotter and working up speeches to make against John C. Calhoun. But when he heard a New Hampshireman had come to see him, he dropped everything else he was doing, for that was Dan'l's way. He gave Jabez Stone a breakfast that five men couldn't eat, went into the living history of every man and woman in Cross Corners, and finally asked him how he could serve him.

Jabez Stone allowed that it was a kind of mortgage case.

"Well, I haven't pleaded a mortgage case in a long time, and I don't generally plead now, except before the Supreme Court," said Dan'l, "but if I can, I'll help you."

"Then I've got hope for the first time in ten years," said Jabez Stone, and told him the details.

Dan'l walked up and down as he listened, hands behind his back, now and then asking a question, now and then plunging his eyes at the floor, as if they'd bore through it like gimlets. When Jabez Stone had finished, Dan'l puffed out his cheeks and blew. Then he turned to Jabez Stone and a smile broke over his face like the sunrise over Monadnock.

"You've certainly given yourself the Devil's own row to hoe, Neighbor Stone," he said, "but I'll take your case."

"You'll take it?" said Jabez Stone, hardly daring to believe.

"Yes," said Dan'l Webster. "I've got about seventy-five other things to do and the Missouri Compromise to straighten out, but I'll take your case. For if two New Hampshiremen aren't a match for the Devil, we might as well give the country back to the Indians."

Then he shook Jabez Stone by the hand and said, "Did you come down here in a hurry?"

"Well, I admit I made time," said Jabez Stone.

"You'll go back faster," said Dan'l Webster, and he told 'em to hitch up Constitution and Constellation to the carriage. They were matched grays with one white forefoot, and they stepped like greased lightning.

Well, I won't describe how excited and pleased the whole Stone family was to have the great Dan'l Webster for a guest, when they finally got there. Jabez Stone had lost his hat on the way, blown off when they overtook a wind, but he didn't take much account of that. But after supper he sent the family off to bed, for he had most particular business with Mr. Webster. Mrs. Stone wanted them to sit in the front parlor, but Dan'l Webster knew front parlors and said he preferred the kitchen. So it was there they sat, waiting for the stranger, with a jug on the table between them and a bright fire on the hearth —the stranger being scheduled to show up on the stroke of midnight, according to specification.

Well, most men wouldn't have asked for better company than Dan'l Webster and a jug. But with every tick of the clock Jabez Stone got sadder and sadder. His eyes roved round, and though he sampled the jug you could see he couldn't taste it. Finally, on the stroke of eleven-thirty he reached over and grabbed Dan'l Webster by the arm.

"Mr. Webster, Mr. Webster!" he said, and his voice was shaking with fear and a desperate courage. "For God's sake, Mr. Webster, harness your horses and get away from this place while you can!"

"You've brought me a long way, neighbor, to tell me you don't like my company," said Dan'l Webster, quite peaceable, pulling at the jug.

"Miserable wretch that I am!" groaned Jabez Stone. "I've brought you a devilish way, and now I see my folly. Let him take me if he wills. I don't hanker after it, I must say, but I can stand it. But you're the Union's stay and New Hampshire's pride! He mustn't get you, Mr. Webster! He mustn't get you!"

Dan'l Webster looked at the distracted man, all gray and shaking in the firelight, and laid a hand on his shoulder.

"I'm obliged to you, Neighbor Stone," he said gently. "It's kindly thought of. But there's a jug on the table and a case in hand. And I never left a jug or a case half finished in my life."

And just at that moment there was a sharp rap on the door.

"Ah," said Dan'l Webster, very coolly, "I thought your clock was a trifle slow, Neighbor Stone." He stepped to the door and opened it. "Come in!" he said.

The stranger came in—very dark and tall he looked in the firelight. He was carrying a box under his arm—a black, japanned box with little air holes in the lid. At the sight of the box, Jabez Stone gave a low cry and shrank into a corner of the room.

"Mr. Webster, I presume," said the stranger, very polite, but with his eyes glowing like a fox's deep in the woods.

"Attorney of record for Jabez Stone," said Dan'l Webster, but his eyes were glowing too. "Might I ask your name?"

"I've gone by a good many," said the stranger carelessly. "Perhaps Scratch will do for the evening. I'm often called that in these regions."

Then he sat down at the table and poured himself a drink from the jug. The liquor was cold in the jug, but it came steaming into the glass.

"And now," said the stranger, smiling and showing his teeth, "I shall call upon you, as a law-abiding citizen, to assist me in taking possession of my property."

Well, with that the argument began—and it went hot and heavy. At first, Jabez Stone had a flicker of hope, but when he saw Dan'l Webster being forced back at point after point, he just sat scrunched in his corner, with his eyes on that japanned box. For there wasn't any doubt as to the deed or the signature—that was the worst of it. Dan'l Webster twisted and turned and thumped his fist on the table, but he couldn't get away from that. He offered to compromise the case; the stranger wouldn't hear of it. He pointed out the property had increased in value, and state senators ought to be worth more; the stranger stuck to the letter of the law. He was a great lawyer, Dan'l Webster, but we know who's the King of Lawyers, as the Good Book tells us, and it seemed as if, for the first time, Dan'l Webster had met his match.

Finally, the stranger yawned a little. "Your spirited efforts on behalf of your client do you credit, Mr. Webster," he said, "but if you have no more arguments to adduce, I'm rather pressed for time——" And Jabez Stone shuddered.

Dan'l Webster's brow looked dark as a thundercloud. "Pressed or not, you shall not have this man!" he thundered. "Mr. Stone is an American citizen, and no American citizen may be forced into the service of a foreign prince. We fought England for that in '12 and we'll fight all Hell for it again!"

"Foreign?" said the stranger. "And who calls me a foreigner?"

"Well, I never yet heard of the Dev—of your claiming American citizenship," said Dan'l Webster with surprise.

"And who with better right?" said the stranger, with one of his terrible smiles. "When the first wrong was done to the first Indian, I was there. When the first slaver put out for the Congo, I stood on her deck. Am I not in your books and stories and beliefs, from the first settlements on? Am I not spoken of, still, in every church in New England? 'Tis true the North claims me for a Southerner, and the South for a Northerner, but I am neither. I am merely an honest American like yourself—and of the best descent—for, to tell the truth, Mr. Webster, though I don't like to boast of it, my name is older in this country than yours."

"Aha!" said Dan'l Webster, with the veins standing out in his forehead. "Then I stand on the Constitution! I demand a trial for my client!"

"The case is hardly one for an ordinary court," said the stranger, his eyes flickering. "And, indeed, the lateness of the hour——"

"Let it be any court you choose, so it is an American judge and an American jury!" said Dan'l Webster in his pride. "Let it be the quick or the dead; I'll abide the issue!"

"You have said it," said the stranger, and pointed his finger at the door. And with that, and all of a sudden, there was a rushing of wind outside and a noise of footsteps. They came, clear and distinct, through the night. And yet, they were not like the footsteps of living men.

"In God's name, who comes by so late?" cried Jabez Stone, in an ague of fear.

"The jury Mr. Webster demands," said the stranger, sipping at his boiling glass. "You must pardon the rough appearance of one or two; they will have come a long way."

IV

And with that the fire burned blue and the door blew open and twelve men entered, one by one.

If Jabez Stone had been sick with terror before, he was blind with terror now. For there was Walter Butler, the loyalist, who spread fire and horror through the Mohawk Valley in the times of the Revolution; and there was Simon Girty, the renegade, who saw white men burned at the stake and whooped with the Indians to see them burn. His eyes were green, like a catamount's, and the stains on his hunting shirt did not come from the blood of the deer. King Philip was there, wild and proud as he had been in life, with the great gash in his head that gave him his death wound, and cruel Governor Dale, who broke men on the wheel. There was Morton of Merry Mount, who so vexed the Plymouth Colony, with his flushed, loose, handsome face and his hate of the godly. There was Teach, the bloody pirate, with his black beard curling on his breast. The Reverend John Smeet, with his strangler's hands and his Geneva gown, walked as daintily as he had to the gallows. The red print of the rope was still around his neck, but he carried a perfumed handkerchief in one hand. One and all, they came into the room with the fires of Hell still upon them, and the stranger named their names and their deeds as they came, till the tale of twelve was told. Yet the stranger had told the truth—they had all played a part in America.

"Are you satisfied with the jury, Mr. Webster?" said the stranger mockingly, when they had taken their places.

The sweat stood upon Dan'l Webster's brow, but his voice was clear.

"Quite satisfied," he said. "Though I miss General Arnold from the company."

"Benedict Arnold is engaged upon other business," said the stranger, with a glower. "Ah, you asked for a justice, I believe."

He pointed his finger once more, and a tall man, soberly clad in Puritan garb, with the burning gaze of the fanatic, stalked into the room and took his judge's place.

"Justice Hathorne is a jurist of experience," said the stranger. "He presided at certain witch trials once held in Salem. There were others who repented of the business later, but not he."

"Repent of such notable wonders and undertakings?" said the stern old justice. "Nay, hang them—hang them all!" And he muttered to himself in a way that struck ice into the soul of Jabez Stone.

Then the trial began, and, as you might expect, it didn't look anyways good for the defense. And Jabez Stone didn't make much of a witness in his own behalf. He took one look at Simon Girty and screeched, and they had to put him back in his corner in a kind of swoon.

It didn't halt the trial, though; the trial went on, as trials do. Dan'l Webster had faced some hard juries and hanging judges in his time, but this was the hardest he'd ever faced, and he knew it. They sat there with a kind of glitter in their eyes, and the stranger's smooth voice went on and on. Every time he'd raise an objection, it'd be "Objection sustained," but whenever Dan'l objected, it'd be "Objection denied." Well, you couldn't expect fair play from a fellow like this Mr. Scratch.

It got to Dan'l in the end, and he began to heat, like iron in the forge. When he got up to speak he was going to flay that stranger with every trick known to the law, and the judge and jury too. He didn't care if it was contempt of court or what would happen to him for it. He didn't care any more what happened to Jabez Stone. He just got madder and madder, thinking of what he'd say. And yet, curiously enough, the more he thought about it, the less he was able to arrange his speech in his mind.

Till, finally, it was time for him to get up on his feet, and he did so, all ready to bust out with lightnings and denunciations. But before he started he looked over the judge and jury for a moment, such being his custom. And he noticed the glitter in their eyes was twice as strong as before and they all leaned forward. Like hounds just before they get the fox, they looked, and the blue mist of evil in the room thickened as he watched them. Then he saw what he'd been about to do, and he wiped his forehead, as a man might who's just escaped falling into a pit in the dark.

For it was him they'd come for, not only Jabez Stone. He read it in the glitter of their eyes and in the way the stranger hid his mouth with one hand. And if he fought them with their own weapons, he'd fall into their power; he knew that, though he couldn't have told you how. It was his own anger and horror that burned in their eyes; and he'd have to wipe that out or the case was lost. He stood there for a moment, his black eyes burning like anthracite. And then he began to speak.

He started off in a low voice, though you could hear every word.

They say he could call on the harps of the blessed when he chose. And this was just as simple and easy as a man could talk. But he didn't start out by condemning or reviling. He was talking about the things that make a country a country, and a man a man.

And he began with the simple things that everybody's known and felt—the freshness of a fine morning when you're young, and the taste of food when you're hungry, and the new day that's every day when you're a child. He took them up and he turned them in his hands. They were good things for any man. But without freedom, they sickened. And when he talked of those enslaved, and the sorrows of slavery, his voice got like a big bell. He talked of the early days of America and the men who had made those days. It wasn't a spread-eagle speech, but he made you see it. He admitted all the wrong that had ever been done. But he showed how, out of the wrong and the right, the suffering and the starvations, something new had come. And everybody had played a part in it, even the traitors.

Then he turned to Jabez Stone and showed him as he was—an ordinary man who'd had hard luck and wanted to change it. And, because he'd wanted to change it, now he was going to be punished for all eternity. And yet there was good in Jabez Stone, and he showed that good. He was hard and mean, in some ways, but he was a man. There was sadness in being a man, but it was a proud thing too. And he showed what the pride of it was till you couldn't help feeling it. Yes, even in Hell, if a man was a man, you'd know it. And he wasn't pleading for any one person any more, though his voice rang like an organ. He was telling the story and the failures and the endless journey of mankind. They got tricked and trapped and bamboozled, but it was a great journey. And no demon that was ever foaled could know the inwardness of it—it took a man to do that.

V

The fire began to die on the hearth and the wind before morning to blow. The light was getting gray in the room when Dan'l Webster finished. And his words came back at the end to New Hampshire ground, and the one spot of land that each man loves and clings to. He painted a picture of that, and to each one of that jury he spoke of things long forgotten. For his voice could search the heart, and that was his gift and his strength. And to one, his voice was like the forest and its secrecy, and to another like the sea and the storms of the sea; and one heard the cry of his lost nation in it, and another saw a little harmless scene he hadn't remembered for years. But each saw something. And when Dan'l Webster finished he didn't know whether or not he'd saved Jabez Stone. But he knew he'd done a miracle. For the glitter was gone from the eyes of the judge and jury, and, for the moment, they were men again, and knew they were men.

"The defense rests," said Dan'l Webster, and stood there like a mountain. His ears were still ringing with his speech, and he didn't hear anything else till he heard Judge Hathorne say, "The jury will retire to consider its verdict."

Walter Butler rose in his place and his face had a dark, gay pride on it.

"The jury has considered its verdict," he said, and looked the stranger full in the eye. "We find for the defendant, Jabez Stone."

With that, the smile left the stranger's face, but Walter Butler did not flinch.

"Perhaps 'tis not strictly in accordance with the evidence," he said, "but even the damned may salute the eloquence of Mr. Webster."

With that, the long crow of a rooster split the gray morning sky, and judge and jury were gone from the room like a puff of smoke and as if they had never been there. The stranger turned to Dan'l Webster, smiling wryly. "Major Butler was always a bold man," he said. "I had not thought him quite so bold. Nevertheless, my congratulations, as between two gentlemen."

"I'll have that paper first, if you please," said Dan'l Webster, and he took it and tore it into four pieces. It was queerly warm to the touch. "And now," he said, "I'll have you!" and his hand came down like a bear trap on the stranger's arm. For he knew that once you bested anybody like Mr. Scratch in fair fight, his power on you was gone. And he could see that Mr. Scratch knew it too.

The stranger twisted and wriggled, but he couldn't get out of that grip. "Come, come, Mr. Webster," he said, smiling palely. "This sort of thing is ridic—ouch!—is ridiculous. If you're worried about the costs of the case, naturally, I'd be glad to pay——"

"And so you shall!" said Dan'l Webster, shaking him till his teeth rattled. "For you'll sit right down at that table and draw up a document, promising never to bother Jabez Stone nor his heirs or assigns nor any other New Hampshireman till doomsday! For any hades we want to raise in this state, we can raise ourselves, without assistance from strangers."

"Ouch!" said the stranger. "Ouch! Well, they never did run very big to the barrel, but—ouch!—I agree!"

So he sat down and drew up the document. But Dan'l Webster kept his hand on his coat collar all the time.

"And, now, may I go?" said the stranger, quite humble, when Dan'l'd seen the document was in proper and legal form.

"Go?" said Dan'l, giving him another shake. "I'm still trying to figure out what I'll do with you. For you've settled the costs of the case, but you haven't settled with me. I think I'll take you back to Marshfield," he said, kind of reflective. "I've got a ram there named Goliath that can butt through an iron door. I'd kind of like to turn you loose in his field and see what he'd do."

Well, with that the stranger began to beg and to plead. And he begged and he pled so humble that finally Dan'l, who was naturally kindhearted, agreed to let him go. The stranger seemed terrible grateful for that and said, just to show they were friends, he'd tell Dan'l's fortune before leaving. So Dan'l agreed to that, though he didn't take much stock in fortunetellers ordinarily.

But, naturally, the stranger was a little different. Well, he pried and he peered at the lines in Dan'l's hands. And he told him one thing and another that was quite remarkable. But they were all in the past.

"Yes, all that's true, and it happened," said Dan'l Webster. "But what's to come in the future?"

The stranger grinned, kind of happily, and shook his head. "The future's not as you think it," he said. "It's dark. You have a great ambition, Mr. Webster."

"I have," said Dan'l firmly, for everybody knew he wanted to be President.

"It seems almost within your grasp," said the stranger, "but you will not attain it. Lesser men will be made President and you will be passed over."

"And, if I am, I'll still be Daniel Webster," said Dan'l. "Say on."

"You have two strong sons," said the stranger, shaking his head. "You look to found a line. But each will die in war and neither reach greatness."

"Live or die, they are still my sons," said Dan'l Webster. "Say on."

"You have made great speeches," said the stranger. "You will make more."

"Ah," said Dan'l Webster.

"But the last great speech you make will turn many of your own against you," said the stranger. "They will call you Ichabod; they will call you by other names. Even in New England some will say you have turned your coat and sold your country, and their voices will be loud against you till you die."

"So it is an honest speech, it does not matter what men say," said

Dan'l Webster. Then he looked at the stranger and their glances locked.

"One question," he said. "I have fought for the Union all my life. Will I see that fight won against those who would tear it apart?"

"Not while you live," said the stranger, grimly, "but it will be won. And after you are dead, there are thousands who will fight for your cause, because of words that you spoke."

"Why, then, you long-barreled, slab-sided, lantern-jawed, fortune-telling note shaver," said Dan'l Webster, with a great roar of laughter, "be off with you to your own place before I put my mark on you! For, by the thirteen original colonies, I'd go to the Pit itself to save the Union!"

And with that he drew back his foot for a kick that would have stunned a horse. It was only the tip of his shoe that caught the stranger, but he went flying out of the door with his collection box under his arm.

"And now," said Dan'l Webster, seeing Jabez Stone beginning to rouse from his swoon, "let's see what's left in the jug, for it's dry work talking all night. I hope there's pie for breakfast, Neighbor Stone."

But they say that whenever the Devil comes near Marshfield, even now, he gives it a wide berth. And he hasn't been seen in the state of New Hampshire from that day to this. I'm not talking about Massachusetts or Vermont.